George Stephenson
The Engineer and His Letters

George Stephenson: painted by Lucas

W. O. Skeat BSc FKC CEng FIMechE

George Stephenson
The Engineer and His Letters

The Institution of Mechanical Engineers
London

First published 1973

ISBN 0 85298 150 3

Published by The Institution of Mechanical Engineers

Designed by Derek Morrison
and printed by photolitho in Great Britain by
BAS Printers Ltd, Wallop, Hampshire.
Bound by G. and J. Kitcat Ltd, London, England

Made and printed in Great Britain

Contents

Acknowledgments

The author acknowledges, with gratitude, the help he has received from numerous museums, local authorities, Institutions, Societies, and individuals in the compilation of this book. In particular, he wishes to record his indebtedness to the following:

The Library staffs of the Institution of Mechanical Engineers, the Institution of Civil Engineers, the Stephenson Locomotive Society, the Royal Borough of Kensington and Chelsea, the Boroughs of Chesterfield, Darlington, Newcastle upon Tyne, and Stockton-on-Tees; and the Newcastle Literary and Philosophical Society;

The Liverpool City Record Office (Local History Department); the Lancashire County Record Office; the Northumberland Record Office; the County High School, Killingworth; the Curator of Historical Relics, British Railways Board; British Railways Archivist's staffs, in London and in York; the Science Museum, South Kensington; the Birmingham Museum of Science and Industry; and Tapton House School.

Particular acknowledgment is made to the following individuals, some of whom are connected with the foregoing organizations, and all of whom gave valuable assistance: John Scholes Esq. (British Railways); Brigadier C. C. Parkman, C.B.E., F.I.C.E.; Adin Hull Esq., C.I.Mech.E.; W. K. Moss Esq., F.I.W.E.; Lt-Col. T. M. Simmons, also B. Ironmonger Esq., J. S. Canham Esq., and Miss Annette Crane (Science Museum); E. C. Hamilton-Russell Esq.; Michael R. E. Swanwick Esq., M.B.E.; L. G. Charlton Esq. (Newcastle); W. Pearson Esq., B.Sc., (Tapton House School); Professor W. A. Taplin, DSc., F.I.Mech.E.; R. T. Everett Esq., B.E.M., S. G. Morrison Esq., and E. F. Potter Esq. (I.Mech.E. Staff); Professor Jack Simmons (University of Leicester); K. L. Forster Esq., F.I.C.E. (Harrogate); Charles Lee Esq., M.Inst.T. (London); H. V. Borley Esq. (London); and W. Thorman Esq. (Stockton-on-Tees).

The author consulted biographical works on the Stephensons by Samuel Smiles, W. R. Parsonage, L. J. C. Rolt, and Michael Robbins, and works by Cecil J. Allen on 'The Great Eastern Railway', (Ian Allan, Ltd), Rixon Bucknall on 'Our Railway History' (George Allen and Unwin, Ltd.), and R. H. Parsons on the Centenary History of the Institution of Mechanical Engineers. For further information on authorities consulted please refer to page 268.

List of Illustrations

Foreword

by A. J. Boston,

PRESIDENT, THE STEPHENSON LOCOMOTIVE SOCIETY

One would imagine that after the many writings about George Stephenson there was little of note that was new to record. How wrong is that impression is brought home to the reader of this book.

Reading the correspondence in the context of events confirms in my mind the opinion already formed of his greatness and pioneering spirit, but also revealed is his tenacity of purpose, his transparent honesty, and his ability to rise above the humiliation that he suffered at the hands of those who took advantage of his lack of education.

His inventive brain led him from the stationary engine to the locomotive steam engine and, to prove his faith in the latter machine, to become his own civil engineer in the building of railways. He was trained in none of these things, but his inquisitive mind and his intuitive genius drove him forward to become the world's benefactor in steam locomotive and railway development, a benign revolution in itself. New standards of speed were set that made neighbours of strangers. It can be said that George Stephenson did as much to consolidate the British Empire as did the soldiers and sailors before him.

His unbounded enthusiasm for his projects is expressed in his letter to his son Robert in Colombia in February 1827. He writes with pride of his achievements on the Liverpool line, the Stockton & Darlington Railway, the Welsh line (Nantlle Railway), his involvement with the Canterbury line, and his experimental engine with horizontal cylinders driving on to the same crankshaft. He chided Robert that if he did not come home soon there would be nothing left to invent!

William Skeat, in his own painstaking research and compilation, has added further proof—if any were needed—of the profound effect George Stephenson had upon the industrial and social history of Great Britain and the world.

Preface

The purpose of this book is to present George Stephenson to readers through his letters, and at the same time to supply a connecting narrative giving, so far as is possible, the 'background' against which they were written. The background is intended to be always subservient to the letters, which can be relied upon to speak for themselves.

George Stephenson's life has been recounted by many biographers, so only a brief outline need be given here, simply to fix his place in Time and to note the chief stages in his career. He was born on 9 June 1781 at Wylam, Northumberland, the second son of a labourer in the local collieries. He worked as a young boy on farms for wages of a few pence a day, but when twelve years old he was taken on at the Black Callerton pit, later assisting his father who was employed as fireman on the steam-driven winding engines. The family had to move about a good deal, in order to 'follow the work' as old seams became worked out and new ones were exploited.

Stephenson's early life – especially the twenty years from 1796 to 1816 – coincided with a period of increasing awareness, in the mining world, of the advantages of steam as a prime mover, compared with horses; he himself found an absorbing attraction in the stationary winding engines, and gained a most notable mastery over all details of their working and maintenance. With his growing skill in this direction, and the desire to improve his position, he became more and more aware of the tremendous handicap which his lack of schooling had put upon him; between the ages of eighteen and twenty, therefore, he strove to overcome this drawback by attending night-school, where he learned reading, writing, and arithmetic.

In 1802 he married Fanny Henderson; their son Robert was born a year later. In 1804 he moved to Killingworth, where he was employed as a brakesman at the West Moor Colliery of the 'Grand Allies' (the Earl of Strathmore, Sir Thomas Liddell, and Stuart Wortley). This was an important move, because these employers were later to become much impressed with his talents, and gave him a good deal of liberty to work at other collieries, where he became renowned as an engine 'doctor'.

However, in 1806 his wife died. In his distress and restlessness, he engaged a housekeeper to look after Robert, and took himself to Montrose, Scotland, where he supervised the working of some Boulton and Watt engines in a textile factory. Returning to Killingworth – on foot – a year later, he was re-employed by the Grand Allies at West Moor, and developed still further his outstanding skill in the running and repairing of steam plant. By 1812 he had been made an engine-wright and was put in charge of all the machinery in the collieries of the Grand Allies. Gradually his connection with his employers became more and more free until the £100 a year which he received from them was in the nature of a 'retainer'. He then became an engineer on his own account and built numbers of stationary engines.

In 1813 Stephenson was requested to take charge of the construction of one of the earliest steam locomotives, after the pioneering efforts of Trevithick and Hedley. His machine, the 'Blücher', was completed in July 1814, and demonstrated the principle established by Hedley that a locomotive with smooth wheels could draw a load on smooth rails.

From that time onwards Stephenson gradually became the country's most renowned advocate of steam traction. However, before steam power

Fig 1. Colliers' cottages at Long Benton, Northumberland. (Courtesy: Northumberland County Record Office)

Fig. 2. George Stephenson throwing the hammer. (From Illustrated London News, *4 June 1881)*

could be applied to railways, great improvements were needed to adapt the primitive track to take the concentrated weight of the locomotives, which in their early days were unsprung.

The colliery wagonways in the first quarter of the nineteenth century were built for the haulage, by horses or by ropes, of four-wheeled wagons which carried at the most about 3 tons of coal, the tare being about 1 to $1\frac{1}{4}$ tons; axle loadings were therefore around the 2-ton mark. The Wylam wagonway comprised oak rails supported by sleepers spaced at 3 ft. centres. To protect the oak rails a hardwood strip (beechwood) was fixed to their upper surfaces; this was renewable and took the wear. In other collieries short cast-iron plates were laid in lengths of about 3 ft. Clearly, such tracks would not have taken the steam locomotives, weighing anything from 4 to 6 tons, without damage. Stephenson gave much attention to possible improvements in cast-iron rails and in 1816 took out a patent jointly with William Losh, for a new form of rail and chair, the rails having half-lap joints, and the seating within the chairs for the rails being rounded so that any settlement or tilting of the sleepers was not transferred to the rails. Another joint patent of Losh and Stephenson was the application of 'steam springs' (cylinders below the boiler, supplied with boiler water or, later, with live steam) to reduce the shocks caused to the track by the unsprung locomotives of the period.

In 1818 a scheme was launched in Stockton-on-Tees to cut a canal from Auckland to the river, to facilitate the conveyance of coal to ships

Fig 3. George Stephenson's cottage at Wylam, in May 1971. (Photo: L. G. Charlton)

(then the only practicable way to transport it to the South of England). A rival scheme was promoted by a new company, with which the influential Quaker, Edward Pease, was associated, to construct a railway. There were prolonged discussions and disagreements between expert advisers, but eventually a railway was decided upon, and by 1820 a survey was begun; and in April 1821 an Act of Parliament authorized the construction of the Stockton and Darlington Railway. In 1820 Stephenson married his second wife, Elizabeth Hindmarsh.

Before the month of April 1821 was out, Pease had invited Stephenson to carry out a fresh survey, and to supervise the construction of the Stockton and Darlington line. This was Stephenson's great chance and he knew it. He invited Pease to visit Killingworth to see his locomotives at work; and Pease was much impressed. Although horse traction had been envisaged for the new railway, an amending Act in 1823 authorized the use of locomotives.

Foreseeing not only the completion of the Stockton and Darlington line, but the construction of other railways, Stephenson went into partnership with Pease, and with Michael Longridge, of Bedlington Iron Works, Morpeth, for the establishment of a locomotive-building works in Newcastle upon Tyne, Robert Stephenson also being a partner. The firm was thus in being and was able to supply the locomotives which were required for the operation of the Stockton and Darlington Railway from

Fig 4. Replica of a memorial tablet of which the original was affixed to Stephenson's cottage at Wylam, Northumberland, by the Institution of Mechanical Engineers, 8 June 1929.

its inception. The Railway was opened on 27 September 1825, the first public railway in the world. It was, however, largely a mineral line, passenger traffic being of much less importance.

During his years as an engine-wright Stephenson's duties were by no means confined to surface installations. He often had to go down the pits, frequently in highly dangerous conditions; and the appalling loss of life in fire-damp explosions had led him to the invention of the miner's safety lamp, which was always known as the 'Geordy' in recognition of his invention. At this time the Government was offering a reward of £2,000 to anyone who could devise an effective safety-lamp for miners; as a result, one of the foremost scientists of the time, Sir Humphry Davy, produced his own design, and claimed (and received) the reward. But Stephenson was able to show that his lamp had priority of invention; his friends caused a fund to be opened for public contributions to provide a separate award to Stephenson, and a sum of £1,000 was duly presented to him.

While the construction of the Stockton and Darlington Railway was advancing, Stephenson was invited in May 1824 to re-survey the proposed railway between Liverpool and Manchester, the line of which had been first laid out by William James. From that time until the line had been opened and had been running successfully in 1830 Stephenson experienced the most hectic years of his life. The opposition to the

Liverpool and Manchester Bill was intense; Stephenson was ridiculed and humiliated in the witness box by Parliamentary lawyers, and even after a fresh Bill had been passed in 1826, the Directors of the Company were divided on whether to use locomotives or to adopt stationary engines and rope haulage. Further, the construction of the Liverpool and Manchester Railway, the biggest civil engineering project ever carried out in Britain up to that time, bristled with difficulties and dangers, some of which had never been solved previously. Some of Stephenson's darkest hours must have been spent during this period, when many of his keenest supporters began to doubt the wisdom of using steam locomotives, and when his Directors decided to call in consultants, who advised in favour of stationary engines.

Stephenson's true greatness and heroic determination were never more in evidence than at that time. He based his resolute adherence to steam locomotion upon his inner certain knowledge that it was the best form of motive power; and even though many of his Directors, like other influential people who had become associated with him, found themselves in disagreement with him, he won them round by his absolute confidence in the steam locomotive as the only practicable power unit for railways. The fact that he was right and his opponents – many of them the most illustrious professional engineers of the time – were wrong, did not endear him to them.

The motive power question was solved by the holding of the Rainhill locomotive trials in 1829, one of the most important events in the social history of Britain. The 'Rocket' was so obviously the best machine that Stephenson's reputation was established unshakeably from that time. The success of the Liverpool and Manchester Railway, opened in the following year, marked the most decisive turning point in railway history; from that time Stephenson was besieged with requests for the surveying of newly projected lines and was invited to the Continent to advise on rail transport in various countries; he had already organized the survey for the Canterbury and Whitstable Railway, which was in fact opened before the Liverpool and Manchester line; and this was followed by the Leicester and Swannington Railway, during the construction of which, by his son Robert, Stephenson became convinced that valuable coal seams were undeveloped in that area. He was now so secure financially that he could take considerable risks in promoting coal-mining operations at Snibston; this became one of his most rewarding enterprises, and induced him to move his house from Liverpool to Alton Grange, near Ashby-de-la-Zouch. Here he lived for several years until his final removal to Tapton House, Chesterfield, which became his home until his death in 1848.

In his latter years Stephenson had the good sense – and the money – to withdraw gradually from the increasing activity of the railway scene, though he carried out some very important surveys, and took an intense interest in many proposed lines, in particular the Newcastle and Berwick Railway. To see a direct route through Newcastle, uniting London and Edinburgh was one of his fondest hopes, which was realized only after his death. He kept aloof from the 'railway mania' of 1845, though he could have multiplied his wealth many times through it.

In his last years he took an especial interest in the education of young engineers, and supported movements for the foundation of mechanics' institutes which were beginning to be needed, largely through the industrial effects of railways. But in that direction the great monument to which he gave unquestioned impetus was the Institution of Mechanical Engineers, established in 1847.

Previously, there had been only two recognized categories of engineers – civil and military. The Institution of Civil Engineers began in the first quarter of the nineteenth century; it was left to George Stephenson, near the end of his life, to give the hall-mark of his name to the first of the new and more specialized Institutions that were to follow. As with his championship of railways (and in particular of the steam locomotive), with their enormous and unforeseeable social influences, so in the world of technical education, with its incalculable value to the nations, George Stephenson's contribution, through the growth and the power of the Institution, was princely and enduring.

1

Early Letters, 1816–25, and their Background

In attempting to present George Stephenson, through his letters, to a reader living in the late twentieth century, it is important to realize that letter-writing was, to him, always a difficult, rather uncongenial, business although he made increasing use of it as his career developed and his work expanded. How he would have revelled in a telephone! Because he was unable to read or write until he was nearing his twentieth year, we find that there is almost nothing in his hand that can be traced to him in his twenties, though there is his laboured signature in the parish register at Newburn Church, Northumberland, where he married his first wife, Francis (Fanny) Henderson, on 28 November 1802.

At that time, Stephenson was working as a brakesman at the Dolly Pit, Black Callerton, his duty being to control the winding engine, known locally as a 'whim', which drew up the baskets ('corves') of coal to the surface and also took the miners to and from the workings. In those days, although many whims were still operated by horses, steam power was becoming well established at the pits, not only for winding engines but also for the pumping plant which kept the underground passages from becoming water-logged.

The steam plant had always excited Stephenson's most intense interest from the time when, as a boy of eight, he succeeded in getting work at the pits, at better wages than he had ever received for helping on farms as a little lad. One of his great assets was his insatiable curiosity about natural phenomena, to which was allied an inflexible determination to achieve mastery of his job; these characteristics were among the guiding forces throughout his life.

A brakesman's job carried with it a considerable responsibility, for the lives of his workmates literally depended on the skill with which the winding gear was put into action or stopped. Good judgment in working the engine was accordingly recognized by colliery owners, and was reflected in a brakesman's pay (17s 6d to £1 a week in those days) which was definitely above the average.

Stephenson developed his skill in his work on colliery engines to such purpose that he was noticed by one of the leading engine-wrights in the

Fig 5. Interior of Newburn Church, Northumberland, where George Stephenson was married. (From Illustrated London News, *4 June 1881)*

district, Robert Hawthorn; Hawthorn's confidence in Stephenson's ability was such that he eventually recommended him for the position of brakesman at an improved wage, at Willington Quay, some 6 miles downriver from Newcastle. At Willington Quay the ships, which had brought coal from Newcastle to London, used to discharge the ballast with which they had been loaded for the return voyage; a great heap of ballast thus accumulated, and Hawthorn installed a notable engine to draw the ballast, when it had been loaded into wagons, to the top of what became a formidable mound, known as Ballast Hill. Stephenson and his wife accordingly moved to Willington Quay shortly after their marriage; their only son Robert was born there in October 1803. To augment his income, Stephenson used to mend clocks (a most important article in a miner's home), and make shoes for the men and their families.

However, after a year, Stephenson moved to West Moor, Killingworth, where he obtained a job as a brakesman in a pit belonging to the 'Grand Allies'; this was to be the beginning of an important connection for him. The Grand Allies were Sir Thomas Liddell, afterwards Lord Ravensworth, The Earl of Strathmore, and Mr. Stuart Wortley, afterwards Lord Wharncliffe; they had become the most powerful group of colliery owners in the country, and it was fortunate for Stephenson that he was employed by them, as they became increasingly impressed with his achievements as time went on, and eventually allowed him very considerable freedom to carry out other work, so long as he kept their engines in good working order.

The tragic death of Stephenson's wife in 1806, a few months after the birth of their daughter, who died in infancy, left him in a very unsettled state of mind; his restlessness was no doubt the cause of his taking a job at a Montrose spinning mill where he took charge of the working of a Boulton and Watt engine, recently erected there. It does not seem that he ever intended to work permanently across the Border. However, he showed his ingenuity by devising a boxed-in sump for the boiler feed-pump, by which all sand and grit were prevented from entering, with great improvement in the life of the pump-barrel and the bucket and clack leathers.

Returning to England with savings from his Montrose job amounting to £28, Stephenson's first actions were to help his family. His father, blinded in a boiler accident, and unable to work, had run up debts which Stephenson promptly paid, and thereafter he provided for his parents, and placed Robert, then four years old, in the care of his unmarried sister Eleanor who thereafter kept house for them both for several years. Because of the Napoleonic Wars, he was faced with a call-up for military service, which he strongly wished to avoid; with the help of a borrowed sum of money (£6) he was, however, able to buy his way out of the militia by finding a substitute. Uncertain as to what his best course should be, he seriously thought of emigration; his sister Ann had already gone to America with her husband, and it may well be that only the inability to raise the money for the passage prevented Stephenson from doing likewise.

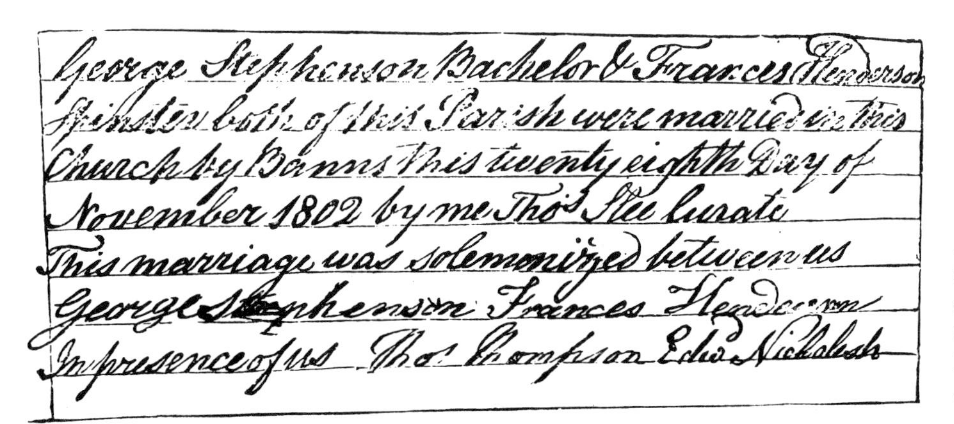
George Stephenson Bachelor & Frances Henderson
Spinster both of this Parish were married in this
Church by Banns this twenty eighth Day of
November 1802 by me Thos Stee Curate
This marriage was solemnized between us
George Stephenson Frances Henderson
In presence of us Thos Thompson Edw Nicholesh

Fig 6. Facsimile of George Stephenson's marriage certificate. (From Illustrated London News, *4 June 1881)*

But with the bogey of military service banished, Stephenson turned again to the familiar territory of Killingworth, and was re-employed by the Grand Allies as a brakesman; one imagines that they were glad to have him back, for he had by then become a highly skilled man with a considerable knowledge of steam engines.

In 1808, with two other brakesmen, Stephenson was allowed by the Grand Allies to enter into a small contract with them, under which, in addition to their braking duties, they purchased the stores (oil and tallow), divided the work between them, and received an agreed rate of pay. There was thus every inducement to make the contract pay and to root out any causes of wasteful working. Stephenson was a man of far too high integrity to be a party to skimped work or dishonest dealings, so the contract was satisfying to the Grand Allies as well as to Stephenson and his fellow-workmen. Seeing that undue wear was taking place on the winding ropes, the lives of which were only about one-third of those at adjacent pits, Stephenson sought the cause, and obtained permission to re-align pulleys and gearing, thus reducing the wear on the ropes to a normal amount.

In 1810 the Grand Allies sank a new pit, which was named the Killingworth High Pit and installed a pumping engine working on the Newcomen principle to pump water out of the workings. The engine was, to all outward appearances, a failure; even after many months of attempts to obtain satisfactory service, with the help and advice of skilled engine-wrights, the pit remained 'drowned out'. Stephenson became intrigued by this state of affairs—his curiosity impelled him to make visits to the site, and eventually one of the pit sinkers asked him his opinion of the failure. He offered to get the engine working and have the pit pumped dry in a week, and gave an impression of such confidence that the 'head viewer' (then the equivalent of chief engineer) was told, and decided to let Stephenson try his hand.

Considering that he was scarcely thirty years of age, and only held the position of brakesman, and that the skilled engine-wrights who had themselves failed would be highly critical if he, too, could not succeed, Stephenson was certainly risking his whole reputation when he agreed to take this chance.

What he did, and how he succeeded, has been recounted in all the Stephenson biographies; it is mentioned here because it marked a definite stage in his career, for from that time his engineering reputation was made. In 1812 he was promoted to be engine-wright at Killingworth High Pit, his pay being £100 a year, and while holding this post he was placed in charge of all the colliery machinery of the Grand Allies.

Stephenson's work was first and foremost that of a highly skilled mechanical craftsman, and his environment was essentially the coal-mining industry and its machinery, whether on the surface or underground. He very frequently had to go down the mines on maintenance or repair jobs, and he had as intimate a knowledge of the working condi-

Fig 7. George Stephenson and his wife going home on their wedding day. (*From* Illustrated London News, *4 June 1881*)

tions as the miners themselves. It was, therefore, not surprising that he was deeply affected by the terrible loss of life which occurred, particularly as a result of firedamp explosions. Some mines were very dangerous in that respect, and serious explosions occurred at West Moor in 1806, when 10 miners were killed, and again in 1809, when 12 perished. Stephenson was working at the pit mouth at the time when the former disaster occurred. In a more terrible explosion, at Felling, in 1812, 90 men and boys died, either by burning or by suffocation; again, at the same pit in 1813, 22 persons were killed from a similar accident.

The need for a safety lamp thus became a matter of the utmost urgency. Stephenson felt impelled to discover whether a lamp could be devised which could be used safely in gaseous mines, and carried out a large number of experiments to this end. To the layman, and even to experienced miners, some of these tests appeared highly dangerous, but in Stephenson's character there was blended a large measure of natural caution and a high degree of confidence in his own powers of observation and deduction. His safety lamp was based on what he had himself noticed—that when a lighted candle was burning in air charged with carburetted hydrogen gas, the combustion took place round the base, not the top, of the candle's flame. He concluded that, given a sufficient velocity to the draught of air passing to the flame, the dangerous inflammable gas would not ignite.

On 21 October 1815, Stephenson's first design for a safety lamp was tested at Killingworth, under conditions so dangerous that those whom he asked to witness the test hung back. The test was successful: the lamp did not cause an explosion—it went out. It also tended to go out unless it was held very steadily, so Stephenson quickly brought out an improved design, tested on 4 November 1815; and on 20 November a third design was completed, having circular holes instead of tubes in the cover; and with this, Stephenson was satisfied. The speed with which each design was superseded by an improved pattern is noteworthy.

Quite independently of Stephenson, Sir Humphry Davy, with the assistance of Michael Faraday, was working at the same time upon the same problem, but with all the advantages of education and of standing, as a leading scientist, which in Stephenson had been lacking. Davy had been invited by the Society in Sunderland for Preventing Accidents in Coal Mines (formed in 1813), to consider how mine explosions might be prevented. He produced his design for a safety lamp on 9 November 1815; it was basically similar to Stephenson's, except that wire gauze was used instead of a perforated cover. Davy's invention was undoubtedly an original effort, and his eminence as a scientist secured for it considerable publicity. As a result, grateful colliery owners and lessees combined to present Davy with a premium of £2,000. Then the controversy began, as to the originality of the invention; Stephenson had by then become a well-known and respected figure in the Northumberland coal-mines; and certain colliery owners, indignant that Davy alone should reap the reward, called meetings at which Stephenson's merits for originality were strongly argued. A sort of consolation prize of £100 was accordingly offered to Stephenson, but his supporters regarded such a sum as totally inadequate; led by Charles Brandling, a colliery owner, of Gosforth, and by William Losh, the senior partner in the firm of Losh, Wilson and Bell, of Walker Ironworks, Newcastle, efforts were made to secure a suitable reward for Stephenson. It is worth remembering that by this time Stephenson had advanced considerably in his career, and had the construction of successful stationary engines and steam locomotives to his credit. Charles Brandling organized a meeting, to present the merits of Stephenson's lamp, and persuaded him to write a press statement on the subject. This notice,* produced with much difficulty by Stephenson,

* Report on the Claims of Mr. George Stephenson relative to his Invention of his Safety Lamp. By the Committee appointed at a Meeting holden in Newcastle on this 1st of November 1817. With an Appendix containing the Evidence.

Fig 8. Portrait reputed to be of George Stephenson, in oils, at the age of 28.

with his son Robert as scribe (Robert was then 13 years old), was edited by Charles Brandling, for publication as a pamphlet; it is of interest as being one of the earliest of all the Stephenson documents, and it certainly deserves a place in the present work.

Killingworth, 13 March, 1817

Sir, I observe you have thought proper to insert in the last number of the Philosophical Magazine your opinion that my attempts at safety Tubes and apertures were borrowed from what I had heard of Sir Humphrey Davys' researches. You cannot have read the Statement I considered myself called upon to lay before the public, or you would not have questioned my veracity without producing the Evidence that induced you to do so. If the Fire damp was admitted to the flame of a Lamp through a small tube, that it would be consumed by combustion, and that explosion would not pass, and communicate with the external Gas, was the Idea I had embraced, as the principle upon which a safety Lamp might be constructed, and which I stated to several persons long before Sir Humphrey Davy came into this part of the Country, the plan of such a Lamp was seen by several, and the Lamp itself was in the hands of the manufacturers

Fig 9. George Stephenson experimenting with his safety lamp in a mine. (From Illustrated London News, *4 June 1881)*

during the Time he was here, at which period it is not pretended he had formed any correct idea upon which he intended to act. With any *subsequent* private communication between him and Mr. Hodgson, I was not acquainted, nor can it in the slightest degree affect my claim. That I pursued the principle thus discovered and applied, and constructed a Lamp with three Tubes and one with small perforations without knowing that Sir Humphrey had adopted the same Idea and without receiving any hint of his experiments is what I solemnly assert. To my Statement (which may be procured at Mr. Baldwins) you are bound to give credit unless by the evidence of facts and dates you are able to disprove it. If you are in possession of any, I call upon you to lay them before the public, if not, as editor of a journal, professing to be independent, I trust you will acknowledge that *you* have hastily committed an act of great injustice.

George Stevenson

As a result of the drive to ensure due recognition for Stephenson, the sum of £1,000 was collected; a silver tankard was purchased and inscribed and, with the balance of the £1,000, was presented to him at a public dinner in the Assembly Rooms, Newcastle, on 12 January 1818, the chairman being Charles Brandling.

There is also, in the safe keeping of the Institution of Mechanical Engineers, a letter, dated 23 December 1816, from Stephenson to Robert

Brandling (brother of Charles Brandling) in which he describes his efforts to perfect the safety lamp. (*See Centenary History of I Mech E, page 248.*)

During the dispute between the Davy and the Stephenson adherents, Stephenson maintained a dignified detachment from the controversy (in marked contrast to Davy) and there is no doubt that he thereby increased his stature very considerably. By this time he had become a well-known figure in mining and engineering circles in the North of England.

In tracing the history of the 'Geordy' (i.e. Stephenson's) safety lamp, which became widely used in Northumberland and Durham, it has been necessary to go forward some years, leaving out other extremely important matters in which Stephenson had become involved. We must now return to the main thread of his life's work; but in fact, Stephenson had a highly complex career, occupying himself with many different projects concurrently, and it is sometimes difficult to appreciate fully how many matters were receiving his attention at any given time.

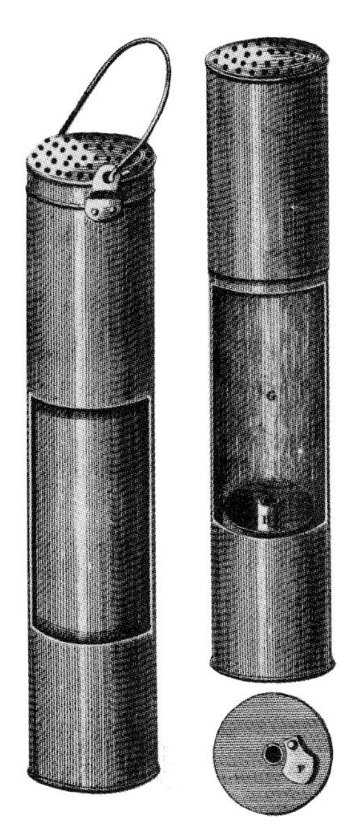

Fig 10. Miner's safety lamp made by George Stephenson.

Opportunities for widening his activities were much increased by the liberal attitude of the Grand Allies, whose payment to him of £100 a year for looking after their engines gradually took on the character of a retaining fee for his services.

During the period 1810–11, when Stephenson was engineman at Killingworth, ideas for the replacement of horses by steam locomotives began to circulate increasingly; Trevithick's pioneering effort of February 1804, at Penydarran, marked the dawn of steam traction in Britain, and was all the more important in that it showed the possibility of steam locomotives with smooth tyres running on smooth rails. But widespread doubts about the practicability of smooth tyres on smooth rails, at least where the power required might have damaged the track, remained for many years, and were evidenced in 1812 when Charles Brandling ordered a locomotive which had been devised in 1811 for a system of rack-rail propulsion by John Blenkinsop, who was acting as Agent for Brandling at collieries owned by the latter in the Leeds area. This rack locomotive was constructed by Matthew Murray, partner in the Leeds engineering firm of Fenton, Murray, and Wood and was ready for trial runs in June 1812, the Middleton tramway being relaid with rack rails for this purpose. In 1813 a similar locomotive was sent to the Tyneside area, and was tried on the Kenton and Coxlodge tramway, not far from the centre of Stephenson's main activities.

As an alternative to rack rails, William Chapman, of Durham, devised a system involving a chain laid between the rails, for use with a steam locomotive which hauled itself and its train along the chain, the engine being on two bogies, to distribute the weight better on the primitive track.

Another important development was taking place at the same time at

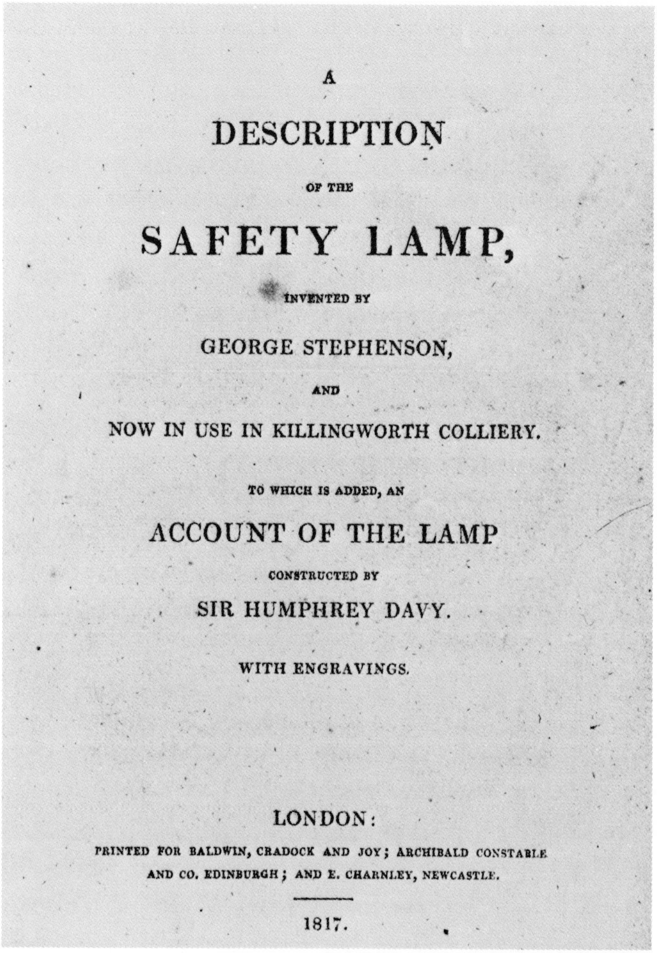

A
DESCRIPTION
OF THE
SAFETY LAMP,
INVENTED BY
GEORGE STEPHENSON,
AND
NOW IN USE IN KILLINGWORTH COLLIERY.
TO WHICH IS ADDED, AN
ACCOUNT OF THE LAMP
CONSTRUCTED BY
SIR HUMPHREY DAVY.
WITH ENGRAVINGS.

LONDON:
PRINTED FOR BALDWIN, CRADOCK AND JOY; ARCHIBALD CONSTABLE AND CO. EDINBURGH; AND E. CHARNLEY, NEWCASTLE.
1817.

Fig 11. Facsimile of title-page of George Stephenson's description of his safety lamp.

Wylam where William Hedley, the viewer of Christopher Blackett's colliery, carried out experiments on a four-wheeled truck (each of the wheels being rotated by a separate crank) to ascertain what power might be applied to smooth wheels on the smooth cast iron rails or plate-way with which the Wylam track had just been relaid. In 1813 Hedley built his celebrated locomotives 'Puffing Billy' and 'Wylam Dilly'; with these famous and successful pioneers, Hedley found that the rack could be abandoned, though he kept to a geared drive somewhat like the Blenkinsop and Murray locomotive. This engine, like Chapman's, was mounted on four wheels, soon afterwards altered to eight, to reduce possible damage to the track. Later still, it was rebuilt with four wheels. The driving gear resembled that of the beam engines which were widely used in collieries at the time.

Stephenson, in a speech recorded in the Minutes of the inaugural meeting, on 27 January 1847, of the Institution of Mechanical Engineers, told the members that they must all bear in mind he himself had no one to assist him and when he went to Parliament with his little tin model of his locomotive engine and stated to the committee that he would make an engine to go 10 or 15 miles an hour he was at that time taken by some to be a foreigner and others thought him mad. Before he erected any locomotive engine he had erected several engines underground in the mines.

There can be no doubt that Stephenson, now in his early thirties, was taking an intense interest in these developments, and must by then have become imbued with his unshakable confidence in the steam locomotive as the future motive power for land transport. He must have observed closely the efforts of Blenkinsop, Chapman, and Hedley, and when he was presented with the opportunity of a lifetime, by one of the Grand Allies, Sir Thomas Liddell, who requested him to construct a steam locomotive for Killingworth Colliery, he was ready for this challenge. Fortunately for Stephenson the Grand Allies were progressive in their attitude towards improvements in the operation of their collieries, and they had shown themselves to be much impressed by his great abilities; but another guiding influence towards the substitution of steam power for horses was the country-wide effect of the long drawn-out war with

Fig 12. Model locomotive, said to have been the first ever constructed by George Stephenson. (From The Locomotive, *1905,* 11, *p. 44)*

Napoleon. Large numbers of horses were required for the cavalry regiments, and vast amounts of fodder were needed to sustain them; in consequence the prices of both horses and fodder rose to such an extent that colliery owners, with haulage problems as one of their main worries, were at once interested in alternative motive power.

Stephenson's first locomotive was named 'My Lord' after Lord Ravensworth (the titled name of Sir Thomas Liddell) but it soon acquired the name 'Blücher', after Wellington's ally at the Battle of Waterloo. It is most regrettable that no drawings of it have survived, but J. G. H. Warren gives a description of it, and an illustration of its geared drive was included in the famous *Treatise on Rail Roads* (1825) by Nicholas Wood (1795–1865), a lifelong friend of Stephenson, who in later life became head viewer at Killingworth. Warren states that the locomotive had two cylinders, 8 in. diameter by 20 in. stroke, with a boiler 8 ft. long and 34 in. in diameter, having a flue of 20 in. diameter passing through it. As in Blenkinsop's engine, the cylinders were placed axially along the centre line of the boiler.

On 27 July 1814, the locomotive was given a trial run on a portion of the Killingworth tracks which had been laid with the edge rail (edge rails taking the wheels as in present-day practice, in contrast to the plate rails, shaped like angle-irons, which had a flat surface to take flangeless wheels, with the raised portion acting as a guide). The load hauled during the trial run was eight loaded wagons, weighing altogether 30 tons; the speed was 4 m.p.h. The gradient was about 1 in 450. Nicholas Wood's description of the locomotive mentions the great noise caused by the gearing and the jerkiness of the propulsion, especially as the gear-teeth became worn.

Fig 13. Model to illustrate Hedley's experiment on adhesion of smooth tyres on smooth rails. (*Photo: Science Museum, London*)

To obviate this became desirable, and Mr. Stephenson, in conjunction with Mr. Dodds (then viewer at Killingworth) took out a patent for a method of communicating the power of the engine directly to the wheels without the aid of these cog-wheels. The patent was dated 28 February 1815, and consisted of the application of a pin upon one of the spokes of the wheel that supported the engine . . . the lower end of the connecting rod being attached to it by what is termed a ball and socket joint; and other end of the connecting rod being attached to the cross-beam, worked up and down by the piston.

The patent specification goes on to state that, to keep the crank-pins at right-angles to one another, use could be made of a cranked axle, on which each of the wheels was fixed, with a connecting (i.e. coupling) rod between them to keep them always at the same angle relative to one another; or else an endless chain could be used, passing over a toothed wheel on each axle. This is the first record of the application of cranked axles to locomotives; it was, however, superseded by coupling rods outside the wheels, because of the difficulty, in those days, of producing sufficiently sound forgings for the cranked axles.

There is some evidence to show that Stephenson's earliest locomotives had six wheels, but in the course of time they were designed to run on four wheels, as improvements to the track were introduced. This brings us to a new stage in Stephenson's career.

During the period around 1813–14 Stephenson went into practice as an engineer in partnership with Ralph Dodds and Robert Weatherburn, the latter having been a fellow-brakesman with him at West Moor Pit. He maintained, however, his connection with the Grand Allies, and supervised the engineering works at Newbottle and Hetton collieries and at a pit owned by Lord Stewart.

As Stephenson became more and more convinced of the potentialities of the steam locomotive, he realized with increasing concern that satisfactory progress would never be made until better track was available. In his search for such improvements he came into contact with William Losh, senior partner of Messrs. Losh, Wilson, and Bell, of the Walker Ironworks, Newcastle. Losh, says Warren, was 'a cultivated and ingenious man' who was quick to realize Stephenson's talents, and who became one of his allies in the safety-lamp controversy. Stephenson was invited by Losh to devote two days a week of his time to the Walker Ironworks, for which he was to receive £100 a year. It is remarkable that the Grand Allies (on 30 September 1816) gave their sanction to this proposal, without reducing the fee he received from them.

Stephenson, in collaboration with Losh, improved the fixing and jointing of the short cast-iron rails then in use (the usual length was 3 to 4 ft.). Half-lap joints superseded the butt-ended joints, and a new type of stone-block sleeper was patented; this prevented the slight canting or settling of the blocks, in service, which used to affect the height of the rail. Another ingenious product of their collaboration was the 'steam spring' for locomotives: interposed between the boiler (with the driving gear) and the axles were small cylinders fixed by flanges to the underside of the boiler, their upper ends being open to the boiler water; these cylinders were provided with pistons and packing, and with flanges at their bottom ends, by which they were fixed to the engine-frames. Thus was secured a cushioning effect, with much benefit to the track at a period when locomotives were unsprung. In addition, Losh and Stephenson patented a new form of malleable iron wheel, to replace cast iron wheels which, in those days of rough and uneven tracks, were liable to fracture.

The ramifications of Stephenson's activities during these years of consolidation of his astonishing career—none the less remarkable because his name quickly became known throughout the world—are emphasized when

Fig 14. Picture, possibly by George Stephenson, showing early locomotive with chain drive. (Photo: Science Museum, London)

Fig 15. Painting of the 'Steam Elephant' locomotive. (Original now in George Stephenson County High School, Killingworth, Northumberland)

one realizes that during a sustained period of concentration on the development of locomotives, permanent way, and his safety lamp, and the continuation of his earlier work on the installation and maintenance of stationary steam plant at collieries, he was one of the earliest in the application of steam power to underground haulage. He devised and installed numerous underground engines which gave much economic benefit to the owners by greatly increased output. Pits, which had been abandoned because of gaseous concentrations or difficult haulage conditions, could, with the aid of Stephenson's safety lamp and his application of steam power, be made profitable. The ventilation problem was solved by carrying the flues right up to the surface, to which they passed through boreholes lined with bricks; this admittedly introduced a fire risk if the flues became too hot when they passed through coal strata. Three such underground engines were put to work at Killingworth by Stephenson and were nicknamed 'Geordie', 'Jimmy', and 'Bobby' after George Stephenson and his brothers. In a letter to his old friend Joseph Cabery, who had worked on one of the winding engines at the Jimmy Pit, Killingworth, but had since migrated to a Cheshire colliery, Stephenson wrote:

My Dear Friend,

I am afraid you will think I have quite forgot you. But if you knew what a troublesome time I have had particularly this last week you would really excuse me—

The soot in the Geordy Flues caught fire beside the damper and set the Coal on fire nearly all the way to the Jemmy. We got it under last night—

I have talked a good deal to Mr. Johnson about Thomas Wages I hope Sir Thos will not Behave so mean as you mention in Your Letter—I think he ought to be paid to the full. I hope your Sawney has made a good start—I think if you can possibly finish the Lifting Engine it will be better—I hope they will lay meanness aside—

I will provide work for you and Thomas when you return—I intend setting you both with my Brother Robt to assist in erecting the Large Engine at Tyne Main Colliery—it will very likely be 15 or 16 Months in finishing—Burraton Engine is started and works very well—I am sorry to inform you I have become a Soldier—We send a Dozen every day to Mr. Brandling's to learn exercise—& I do assure you we can handle the sword pretty well—Mr. Wood makes & excellent soldier—But I hope we shall never be called to action as I think if any of us be wounded it will be on the Back.

We have about 3 hours drill every day & then plenty to eat & drink at Gosforth house—The Reformed have also been learing (sic) these exercise—I do assure you they have alarmed the Gents in our country especially our worthy masters—Lord Strathmore's Cavalry having marched through Winlaton lately, the day following the Reformers of that place marched their Cavalry through in imitation of their Noble Lords—It consisted of 72 Asses with hardy Nailers for their Riders—I think upon the whole the Reformers are now diminishing in numbers—We are afraid your books have been miss-carried as it is a Month since they were sent from here accompanied by a letter from your Wife with directions as you requested—Your family are all well & send Their Kind Love to you—Give my Kind respects to Mr. Ashurst—Mr. Jones—

I remain Your
Well Wisher
Geo. Stephenson

Killingworth Colly.)
Decm 21st 1819)

Fig 16. Sundial fixed above door of George Stephenson's cottage at Killingworth. (From Illustrated London News, *4 June 1881, in possession of British Railways Archives, York)*

To this letter a post-script has been added by Robert, as follows:

Dr Thomas,

I am glad to hear you are so much recovered and I would be glad to see you at Killingworth again to spend a few hours with me—My father has almost wrought me to Death in the Flues but he himself has been two or three times dropt with the choak damp but I took care not to go so far as that—But where I was I think I would not have been long in making a joint of Meat Ready—

I remain Your
Affectionate Companion
R. Stephenson

(Addressed to: Mr. Jo[s] Cabry Engineer.
Mr. Jo[s] Davis
Publican
Nesston—
Cheshire—)

In 1817 Stephenson constructed a locomotive at the request of the Duke of Portland; it was based on his Killingworth design, and was sent to the Duke's tramway in Scotland, which ran from Troon to Kilmarnock, but was not much used there as the track was apparently too light. In the following year Stephenson received a visit from Robert Stevenson, a notable civil engineer, of Edinburgh, who reported* that

some of the most striking improvements in the system of railways are the patent inventions of Mr. Stephenson, of Newcastle, particularly his Locomotive Engine.

Robert Stevenson, incidentally, was the grandfather of the essayist and novelist, Robert Louis Stevenson.

Charles E. Lee, the distinguished railway historian, has recorded† how, on 5 October 1818, testing was carried out on an ingenious combination of gravity and stationary steam engines for the Coxlodge Railway, and Samuel Smiles has stated that the dynamometer used for these tests was of Stephenson's own construction. Friction was found to be constant at all velocities. In the same month Stephenson began resistance tests on cast-iron edge rails 3 ft. 9½ in. long, of the type which he had developed in collaboration with Losh; the flat bearing surface was 2½ in. broad. But the need for something superior to cast iron, with its liability to fracture, was becoming evident; wrought iron was the obvious alternative, and Lee has noted that by 1820 John Birkinshaw, an engineer at the Bedlington Ironworks, Northumberland, had produced wrought-iron rails which were laid at Killingworth. The Bedlington Ironworks were owned by Michael Longridge (1785–1858), soon to become a most important figure in the life of Stephenson.

Robert Bald, a celebrated Scottish mining engineer, at about the same time visited the Killingworth collieries, which were becoming recognized as a model of the improvement which could be effected by steam power in mining. At the request of Dr. David Brewster, editor of the *Edinburgh*

* See Warren's *A Century of Locomotive Building*, p. 29.
† *Trans. Newcomen Soc.*, *1947–49*, vol. XXVI, pp. 199–299, 'Tyneside Tramroads of Northumberland'.

Encyclopaedia, Bald wrote an article entitled 'Mine' in which he gave an account of his meeting with Stephenson. Bald later became a Corresponding Member of the Institution of Civil Engineers, which had been founded in that year.

Charles E. Lee has also recorded how the owners of a colliery at Hetton, Co. Durham, having noted the successful working of Stephenson's locomotive at Killingworth, asked him to construct a similar railway for their colliery, which Stephenson did, with the assistance of his talented brother Robert. The line was five miles long, and eventually there were five Stephenson engines in use on it; George Stephenson was allowed by the Grand Allies to hold the appointment of part-time engineer to the Hetton Colliery Company, without any reduction of the salary he received for the Killingworth post.

Another of Stephenson's visitors in 1819 was Simon Goodrich, whose great interest in all kinds of steam engines is reflected in his papers; he recorded in his Journal (preserved at the Science Museum) the chief dimensions of the 'movable steam engine' and gave details of its performance.

While these significant developments were taking place, changes were occurring, too, in Stephenson's home life. His sister Eleanor, who had for many years been his housekeeper and who had looked after young Robert with affection and kindness, was married in 1819 to Stephen Liddell. In the same year Robert's schooling ended, and he was apprenticed to Nicholas Wood, by now head viewer at Killingworth. Stephenson must therefore have felt the need to re-marry; accordingly he turned to Elizabeth Hindmarsh, whom he had courted in the days before his first marriage; at that time she had declined him, but had remained unmarried. She now accepted him, and the wedding took place in March 1820. Stephenson brought his wife to his West Moor cottage, which he had improved and extended so that it had become a comfortable house; it is still in existence.

Stephenson had for some years been building locomotives for various collieries, and evidently received so many inquiries that the production of a brochure about them was justified. He writes as follows to one Joseph Harrison:

Killingworth Colliery
Jany 28th 1821

To Mr. Joseph Harrison,
Dear Sir,

I thought I could not do better than send you a pamphlet which you may forward to the Gentleman. As there is not a full explanation of your question in it I add the following, viz,

1st The Engine will either draw or propel, but I prefer the former
2nd Six Newcastle Bolls of Coals will serve an Eight Horse Engine
3rd It will work on a plain road but not to advantage
4th One Engine of the above power will cost £500 (complete)
5th It will travel 3 to 6 miles per Hour with 40 Tons of Goods on a level road, & from 10 to 12 hour pr Miles with a light load, Wood may be used in place of Coals if the latter is scarce or Costly.

I am dear Sir
Your truly
G. Stephenson

Stephenson did not forget his old friend Joseph Cabry, now in 'exile' (as it appeared to Stephenson) at a colliery in Cheshire, and despite the approaching time of his second marriage he found time to write, giving one or two hints that he hoped would encourage Cabry's return to Northumberland. Here is the letter (the alternative spellings, 'Cabry' and 'Cabery' seem to have been used indiscriminately):

Killingworth Colly. Mar. 2d 1820

Dr Sir,

I received your's of the 24th Feby—And I think you have had your trouble with these Cheshire Gents—I am astonished to hear of Mr. Ashurst finding fault with you for accompanying Mr. Storey down the Pit—Mr. Johnson wrote to me a few days ago with your Letter inclosed and a £5 note also for the interest of your money which I sent to your wife who is very uneasy for you two Gentlemen—Mr. Johnson desires me to inform you we are coming in a fortnight or three weeks—It is very likely your Wife will pay you a Visit—I have got orders for two more Engines for Newbottle Colliery: one on the Waggon way and the other down the pit—We are putting up one at Burraton and we are getting on with that large Engine also. So I think you may have an idea how my time will be spent—Thompson has behaved very badly to Joseph—he said he had no work for him as soon as he got plenty of water—I had him 3 weeks at Chester Engine assisting Robert in making the Joints—I have him now at Walker making Soda for Mr. Losh & Co.—Henry at his old job—he is also very attentive at School and gets forward very well—He is now a very good arithmetician and is at present learning Measuration in which he makes good progress—Your wife and family are all well—If time does not allow me to accompany Mr. Johnson to Ness. you will please let me know your intentions about coming Back —as I either intend you to go to Burraton or Tyne Main—The South Shields Colliery proprietors failed a few months ago. But the (Colliery) is now taken by the Brandlings and is now currently working—Mr. King is viewer there and Mr. Hill has got his situation at Kenton Mr. Stiker is at Walker now which was King berth awhile ago you know—King is getting much out of favour—So there has been almost a revolution amongst the Viewers—Mr. Johnson is now at Berwick and desires me to inform you we are much satisfied with your

proceedings—Give my kind respects to Mr Storey & Mr Jones
I remain Yours
Respectably
Geo- Stephenson

(Envelope addressed to Mr Jos Cabry Engineer
Mr Jones
Ness Colliery, Nr Park Gate
Cheshire)

The stage was now set for the impact of events of the utmost importance in Stephenson's life. During the coming months he was destined to meet persons who were to have a great and lasting effect on his career; while various influences were conspiring to produce favourable conditions for the establishment of railways. At that time, canals were being constructed in many parts of the country, and appeared to have a bright future ahead of them. But the enormous rise in the production of manufactured goods, textiles, etc., at this stage of the Industrial Revolution was beginning to create a demand for bulk transport which the canals would never have been able to meet, with their capacities limited by restricted widths and slow navigational speeds. Another factor (already mentioned) was the effect of the Napoleonic wars on the availability of horses and fodder. The coal and iron industries of the North East were thus in an especially good position to gain by a form of transport which could outpace the canals. Nevertheless the canals had a great following; they formed a recognized and well-established facility, and for their extensions and improvements the services of some of the most distinguished civil engineers in the country were secured.

Consequently, when the need became urgent for dealing with the increasing tonnage of minerals to be transported from collieries in the Darlington area to Stockton-on-Tees for shipment, there was no unanimity on the form of transport to be adopted when a public meeting to settle the matter was held in Darlington on 13 November 1818. (Darlington people favoured a railway; Stockton people a canal. Canal schemes for linking Darlington with Stockton had been proposed nearly forty years before; the last survey for a canal had been carried out by Rennie in 1813.) However, the upshot of the meeting was a majority decision in favour of a railway, and an experienced engineer, George Overton, was engaged to survey the line. By March 1819 all was ready for application to be made for Parliamentary powers to proceed with construction. However the Bill failed to pass. A second survey, to obviate landowners' objections, was finished by August 1820, too late to be effective during that session, but it received the Royal Assent on 19 April 1821.

On that very day, before the news of the passing of the Bill could have reached Darlington, the momentous meeting took place between Stephenson and Edward Pease, the influential Darlington Quaker, well known in banking circles and the chief of the promoters of the railway; its importance can hardly be exaggerated, for it was destined to give Stephenson his grand opportunity to spread his wings beyond the limits of colliery tramways, and take charge of the making of a full-scale railway. Nicholas Wood, who was acquainted with Pease, accompanied Stephenson on this historic occasion, when Pease, obviously impressed by Stephenson, invited him to re-survey the line and to supervise its construction. News of the passing of the Bill reached Pease the next day, and he immediately wrote to Stephenson, confirming the agreement reached between them at their interview; Stephenson's reply is of historic interest:

Killingworth Colliery
April 28th, 1821

Edward Pease Esq.,
Sir,

I have been favoured with your letter of the 20 Inst & am glad to learn that the Bill has passed for the Darlington Rail Way.

I am much obliged by the favourable sentiments you express towards me: & shall be happy if I can be of service in carrying into execution your plans.

From the nature of my engagement here and in the neighbourhood, I could not devote the whole of my time to your Rail Way, but I am willing to undertake the survey & mark out the best line of Way within the limits prescribed by the Act of Parliament and also, to assist the Committee with plans & estimates, and in letting to the different Contractors such work as they might judge it advisable to do by Contract and also to superintend the execution of the Work. And I am induced to recommend the whole being done by Contract under the superintendence of competent persons appointed by the Committee.

Were I to contract for the whole line of Road it would be necessary for me to do so at an advanced price upon the Sub Contractors, and it would also be necessary for the Committee to have some persons to superintend my undertaking. This would be attended by an extra expence, and the Committee would derive no advantage to compensate for it.

If you wish it, I will wait upon you at Darlington at an early opportunity when I can enter into more particulars as to remuneration &c &c

I remain yours
respectfully
Geo. Stephenson

Many years afterwards, Nicholas Wood related that, on their way to Edward Pease, they made a point of going over the whole of the projected line on foot. There is no unanimity among historians as to whether it was Pease or Stephenson who took the initiative in bringing about this momentous meeting, but we can now turn to Stephenson himself for, years afterwards, he dictated some of his reminiscences on the genesis of the Stockton and Darlington Railway; these are of great interest as a record of what he regarded as the important steps in the establishment of the Company. They were in the possession of E. C. Hamilton-Russell, Esq., of Corbridge, who has deposited them with the Northumberland County Record Office and has kindly agreed to their publication. The memorandum is given below:

A SHORT ACCOUNT OF THE COMMENCEMENT OF THE STOCKTON & DARLINGTON RAILWAY

About the beginning of the year an act of Parliament was obtained for making a tram-road from Stockton to West Auckland passing near Darlington, the distance might be about 24 miles.

A tram road has derived its name from a horse tramping or walking with a load after him.* The castings or a flat plate with a flange turned up on one side to keep the wheels of the carriage in their path, and the length of the plate varying from 2½ feet to 4 feet long. This is a description of the plan of the road for which an Act was got. The name of the Engineer who prepared the plans for Parliament is J. Oferton (Overton) who was brought from Wales for that purpose.—Maynell Esqr of Yarm was the Chairman of the Company. Edw[d] Pease & Jon[a] Backhouse of Darlington were two of the leading Directors—Leonard Raisbeck of Stockton & Francis Mewburn of Darlington were the Solicitors for the Bill. After the Bill had been obtained some doubts arose amongst the Directors whether they were right in having a tram-road, it being the opinion of many people in the country that a Railway was preferable. At this time a considerable improvement had been made in the rails by Mr. George Stephenson of Killingworth for which a patent had been taken out by Mr. W[m] Losh & himself; the patent rail was very extensively used on which the Locomotive engines were then working very successfully at Killingworth & had been doing so for several years.

Mr. Stephenson having succeeded so well with his Locomotive engine on the Killingworth, Springwell & Hetton railways which had been constructed under his care, he was advised by many of his friends to apply to the Stockton and Darlington Company to be appointed their engineer for the construction of the line for Locomotive engines—Mr. Stephenson having obtained several letters of recommendation from his friends, & accompanied by Mr. Nicholas Wood started from Newcastle to Stockton by Coach with the intention of seeing Mr. Raisbeck to whom he had letters of recommendation upon arriving at Stockton in the evening & finding Mr. Raisbeck was not at home they then proceeded to walk to Darlington after dark in a very stormy night of snow and arrived at

* This derivation is, alas, incorrect. Tram is a Scandinavian word, giving the sense of a log or beam; hence the shaft of a small truck or wagon, and later acquiring the meaning of the vehicle itself. The etymology is complex and difficult. It is not related to 'tramp'.

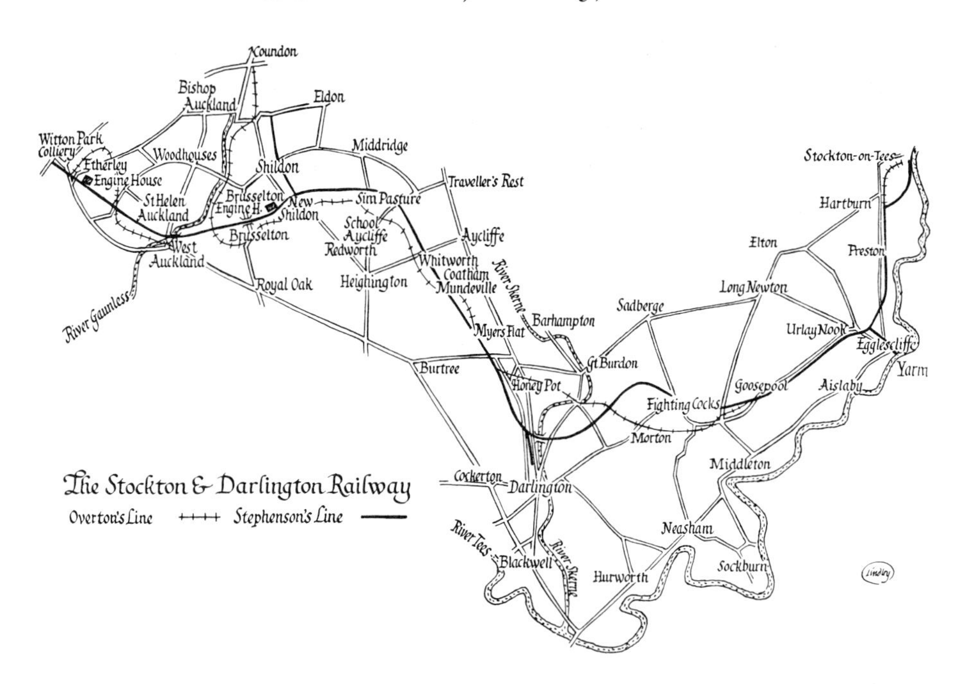

Fig 17. The Stockton and Darlington Railway. (From George and Robert Stephenson, *by L. T. C. Rolt)*

that Town at a very late hour and took up their quarters at a small Inn opposite the Church—The next morning they called upon Mr. Edward Pease & Mr. Jon[a] Backhouse. Mr. Stephenson having given his letter of recommendation to these gentlemen, a short conversation took place, in which Mr. Stephenson explained the powers of his Locomotive engine & recommending the substitution of a railroad in the place of a tramroad. After having heard Mr. Stephenson's statement, Messrs. Pease & Backhouse said a deputation from the Darlington Co. should be sent to Killingworth to inspect the engines: shortly after a deputation was sent from the Co. and returned to Darlington with a favourable report of their powers and in a few days after their return an application was made to Mr. Stephenson to become their engineer & inform them what remuneration he would expect—his reply was £300 per year including travelling expenses. As soon as this arrangement was made Mr. Stephenson was requested to re-survey the line & make such improvements as he thought desirable—the survey was made and several alterations recommended & a new Act of Parliament applied for which was obtained & Mr. Stephenson remained the Company's engineer until the line was finished to Stockton. Both Locomotive engines & horses were employed upon the line at the opening; however it was soon found that the latter could not compete with the former & of course the horses were disused. The speed of the engines might then vary from 5 to 10 miles per hour

These observations are the outline of the commencement of the Stockton & Darlington railway. Edward Pease appeared to be the most firm amongst the directors in carrying out the scheme. The success that followed the opening of the line was the cause of the commencement of the Liverpool & Manchester Railway & after its opening at high velocities led to the general construction of railways all over the civilized World.

The invitation to Stephenson to proceed with the Stockton and Darlington re-survey marked the end of Overton's connection with the project; Overton had only envisaged horse-drawn traffic, but Stephenson's conviction that locomotives ought to be used must have impressed Pease profoundly. On 22 May 1821 Stephenson again called on Pease, and from 23 to 25 May he went carefully over the route again. While the next general meeting of the Railway Company was pending (it took place in July) Stephenson was losing no time in making his preparations. He was already considering what type of rails would be needed. By that time Stephenson had become much impressed with Birkinshaw's wrought ('malleable') iron rails which were now being produced at Bedlington in 15 ft. lengths. Robert Stevenson, the civil engineer, whom Stephenson had met in 1817, was still connected in an advisory capacity with the Stockton and Darlington Railway (he was to have surveyed it jointly with Rennie before Rennie withdrew and the survey passed to Overton) and received a letter from George Stephenson as early as 28 June 1821 on the subject of rails. The letter throws a powerful light on Stephenson's character, and indicates his zeal for securing the best material and equipment available for the railway, even though he himself stood to gain financially by the use of the short cast-iron rails which he had devised with William Losh some five years previously. Losh was understandably exasperated by Stephenson's recommendation of Birkinshaw's rails; the collaboration between the two men consequently ended, and Stephenson's contacts with Michael Longridge's Bedlington Ironworks began. The letter, written from Killingworth,* reads:

Sir,—With this you will receive three copies of a specification of a patent malleable iron rail invented by John Birkinshaw of Bedlington, near Morpeth.

The hints were got from your Report on Railways, which you were so kind as to send me by Mr. Cookson some time ago. Your reference to Tindal Fell Railway led the inventor to make some experiments on malleable iron bars, the result of which convinced him of the superiority of the malleable over the cast iron—so much so, that he took out a patent.

Those rails are so much liked in this neighbourhood, that I think in a short time they will do away with the cast iron railways.

They make a fine line for our engines, as there are so few joints compared with the other.

I have lately started on a new locomotive engine, with some improvements on the others which you saw. It has far surpassed my expectations. I am confident a railway on which my engines can work is far superior to a canal. On a long and favourable railway I would stent my engines to travel 60 miles per day with from 40 to 60 tons of goods.

* See Warren, *A Century of Locomotive Building*, p. 45.

They would work nearly fourfold cheaper than horses where coals are not very costly.

I merely make these observations, as I know you have been at more trouble than any man I know of in searching into the utility of railways, and I return you my sincere thanks for your favour by Mr. Cookson.

If you should be in this neighbourhood, I hope you will not pass Killingworth Colliery, as I should be extremely glad if you could spend a day or two with me.

I am sir,
Yours most respectfully,
G. Stephenson

A letter officially appointing Stephenson to proceed with the re-survey of the line was sent by Pease on 28 July 1821. The survey was to begin 'as soon as the crops are off the ground', and the railway was to be 'a great public way, and to remain as long as any coal in the district remains'. Stephenson's reply, dated 2 August 1821 was as follows:

After carefully examining your favour, I find it impossible to form an accurate idea of what such a survey would cost, as not only the old line must be gone over, but all the other deviating parts, which will be equal to a double survey, and, indeed it must be done in a very different manner from your former one, so as to enable me to make a correct measurement of all the cuts and batteries on the whole line. It would, I think, occupy me at least five weeks. My charge shall include all necessary assistance for the accomplishment of the survey, estimates of the expense of cuts and batteries on the different projected lines, together with all remarks, reports, &c., of the same. Also the comparative cost of malleable iron and cast-iron rails, winning and preparing the blocks of stone, and all materials wanted to complete the line. I could not do this for less than £140, allowing me to be moderately paid. I assure you, in completing the undertaking, I will act with that economy which would influence me if the whole of the work was my own.

A remarkable man visited Killingworth during the summer of 1821—William James, who deserves more recognition than he has generally received for his enthusiastic advocacy of steam locomotives for railways, and for his unbounded admiration of Stephenson. A man ten years older than Stephenson, he was a lawyer who was also concerned, as a land agent, with large estates; as a mine-owner, too, he was naturally interested in the transport of minerals. His great natural talents and his good education enabled him to convince others of the advantages of railways, and he became involved in a number of schemes for their promotion and construction, being capable of carrying out surveys himself. His enthusiasm for railways, however, led him to become involved in too many projects at a time and eventually he got into financial difficulties, which misfortune was accompanied by a breakdown in his health. But during the period 1820–23 he travelled about the country proposing with a burning zeal the construction of various railways, some schemes being exceedingly ambitious. In the course of his journeyings he became aware of the evils and the inadequacies of the canal monopoly between Liverpool and Manchester and saw the enormous advantages which a railway could bring. He was introduced to a Liverpool merchant named Joseph Sandars who had become so strongly critical of the canal's delays, that he decided to commission James to carry out a survey for a railway between Liverpool and Manchester; earlier surveys for a horse tramway had come to nothing. James and Stephenson were destined to become closely associated during 1820–22; in September 1821 James entered into an agreement with Stephenson and Losh to sell their patented locomotives in return for a greater share of the profits. With James's extensive travelling, his numerous contacts, and his boundless enthusiasm for the steam locomotive—and for Stephenson—this must have appeared a promising arrangement. In 1821 James journeyed to Northumberland to see locomotives built by Stephenson, Hedley, and Chapman; of this tour, he wrote to Edward Pease:

The Locomotive engine of Mr. Stephenson is superior beyond all comparison to all the other engines I have ever seen—Next to the immortal Watt I consider Mr. Stephenson's Merit in the invention of this Engine.

Pease, on receiving this letter, must have felt well reinforced in his opinion that in Stephenson he had got the best man possible for his railway.

The excellent impression made by Stephenson upon those responsible for colliery transport was becoming known far from the North East, as the following letter (a copy kindly supplied by the Northumberland County Record Office) will show:

Pelaw House,
Monday morning,
20th August, 1821

Dear William,

I have deferred writing to you ever since I received your last letter of the 7th inst. until I could give you some information as to the time of my being over at the Haigh Colliery and likewise as to the Engines Machines &c. &c. Mr. Holly requested you to mention to me. The last and best Locomotive Engine Mr. George Stephenson built is certainly a most wonderful piece of machinery; he calls it only an 8 horse power, but it goes full 5 miles an hour up an ascent of $\frac{1}{8}$ of an inch to a yard with 20 Chaldron Wagons of Coals each wagon of 53 cwts or $2\frac{1}{2}$ tons, which is upwards of 50 tons weights—5 miles an hour—exclusive of the weight of the wagons themselves; this is upon a railroad of Wrot Iron of about 27 lbs to a yard which is now only costing 2d. per lb. (one side). The Engine will cost not more, I apprehend, than about £400, and only burns about 6 Botts of Coals in the 24 hours.

He is a most ingenious clever man and I have had an opportunity latterly to be a good deal with him, and last Saturday we spent the whole day together at the Killingworth Colliery, where he lives. I am not certain whether or not you know him, but I think it is very likely you may; he is going into Warwickshire on either tomorrow or Wednesday morning & intends going by the Telegraph Coach to Leeds & then take the express Coach on by Sheffield, to

Fig 18. Hetton Colliery Locomotive built in 1822 by George Stephenson and Nicholas Wood; in service till 1908. (Photo: British Railways Board)

the place he is going to visit. His business is upon a long Railway of about 100 miles & Engines to suit it. Now this Engine & Railway is exactly what Mr. Holy wants upon a smaller scale—if you had an Engine capable to take 100 of your 5 cwt wagons would be = to 25 tons at a time, would be sufficient for your purposes; but I think a better plan than a travelling Engine might be adopted at your place, viz., a fixed Engine with an endless rope to bring the wagons forward as they come to bank, or at 20 at a time as might be considered best; in this case as the weight of the Engine would not be required upon the Road thus the strength of the Rails wanted would only be needed of small dimensions, viz., for instance, 12 or 15 lbs to the yard;—this you see would come in very low;— I am not acquainted with the exact distance between the Main Engine & the Sheffield Soap House, but I do not conceive it is much beyond $\frac{1}{2}$ a mile, and I think it would be upon an ascent all the way from the Pit, which would exactly suit for a pulling Engine, and thus the empty corves would return by the returning end of the rope,—or, indeed, be the rise and fall as it may, a fixed Engine, if the distance is not too great, might be made to suit.—I have mentioned all this to George & given him directions to send to you to meet him on his return at the Tontine Inn; you can then introduce him to the rest of the partners as you see right. I intend to set off for the Haigh on Wednesday morning next, and will most likely be either at Lofthouse or Kettlethorp on Saturday & Sunday,—at the Pits on the Haigh on Monday to finish the Surveys & Plans. I gave him (viz. George Stephenson) directions to write to me at Kettlethorp from Warwickshire when he had fixed about returning home, (his absence I considered would be about 10 or 12 days,) & that if your Company should think it right I would come over to Sheffield & give him a meeting upon the spot. This I think would be an excellent opportunity to get his opinion, and I am persuaded you cannot possibly do better,—you would then be satisfied from the best of advice what would be the best mode to pursue not only in bringing the coals from the New Winning but from the Sheffield Deep Pits,—I mean to stop him a day or two as he passes the Haigh.—If you are not much engaged I would be glad if you could slip over on Monday morning, (viz., this day week,) and meet me at the Haigh by Fisher's Morning Coach, then we could after finishing the business there settle how to meet George on your concerns,—I will be obliged to you to drop me a line in a parcel by one of the Coaches to either Lofthouse or Kettlethorp by Friday or Saturday informing me how you are likely to be engaged, and if I may expect you.

Also what Mr. Holey and the other Partners may determine upon. As I expect you will receive this letter tomorrow previous to the Express Coach coming up to the Tontine there could be no harm in your just calling at the Tontine & enquire if there is a passenger going South of the name of Mr. George Stephenson from Newcastle, an Engineer, & do the same both Wednesday & Thursday next, and also Friday next. You might then fix with him about his return, and then you could tell me what had been determined upon when we meet.

I am quite aware that Mr. Holey, as well as Mr. Dunn, Mr. Willson, would like to see him upon the points mentioned above.—I hope you are getting well forward in your sinking, but the state you give me of the water in the two Pits seems very odd; I wish there may not be some trouble or other confusion between the same.—Your powers, however, I hope will be sufficiently great.—What do you think of the feeders lifted in the Hetton Pit being 1400 Gallons a minute 30 fathoms deep.

I am, Dear Sir,
Yours most truly,
(Signed) Wm. Stobart

(Addressed to William Jeffcock)

We also find Stephenson in correspondence with William James about a railway projected in Gloucestershire at this time:

To: Wm. James Esqre.,
West Bromwich,
Nr. Birmingham.
From: G. Stephenson.

My dear Sir,

I hope you will look closely after Baylis in the surveying of the new line as it is possible he may be disposed to deceive you in laying down the section. Before I could advise the use of an Engine on the Cheltenham Railroad, you must give me the weight of the Rail p. yd.—whether the line descends with or without the loaded waggons also inside breadth of the Railroad, weight of waggons and goods working on the said Line whether the Line is uniform in descent from end to end. We have no Engines to spare in case the above Railroad should be found suitable for them. We are expecting to Commence making 3 Locomotive Engines in a fortnight's time for a neighbouring Colliery. If the Cheltenham way was found suitable we might commence making one for you at the same time but I am afraid it will not. I should be unwilling to recommend an Engine on any Line unless I was confident of it giving satisfaction. The plan and specification will be sent off in a day or two.

I am Dear Sir
Yours sincerely,
G. Stephenson

Killingworth Colls.
Oct. 7th 1821

The exchanges of letters between Stephenson and James were frequent at this period; five weeks later, Stephenson writes:

To: Wm. James Esqr.
West Bromwich
Birmingham.
From: G. Stephenson.

Dear Sir,

I am so much confined with new business coming on me almost every day that I have scarcely had time to answer your Qrs. 1st. I would not recommend my Engines to travel with more than 30 tons including the weight of the waggons which may weigh from ¾ to 1 tun each and move at the rate of from 3 to 4 mls. p. hour with the loaded waggons on such a Line as you describe (viz. 2/16 of an inch ascent p. yd.) and return with the empty waggons at from 8 to 10 miles p. hour. 2nd. With respect to the permanent Engine you should have mentioned the quantity of goods to be discharged p. day, but supposing you want 100 tuns p. hour drawn up this would require an Engine of 40 horses power which would not cost less when complete than £2,500 including house and every other material belonging the same. It would require a 7 inch Rope to draw up 8 waggons each containing 3 tuns of goods such a Rope would cost £200 and might wear from 2 to 3 years. The Rollers fixed ready in their stands would cost £112 which with the Rope is not included in the price of the Engine. 3rd. The undulating Line sketched out in your Letter is certainly a practicable but very objectionable one as to much pains cannot be taken to make a Railway uniform. When any thing is well done it is seldom found fault with afterwards and in the end is always found cheapest. 4th. Wood framing is cheaper than embankments in many situations but when the earth is not far to lead I would always recommend embankments when the Line is intended to continue for generations. 5th. I could not recommend the use of an Engine in making the Road as the Rails could never be kept in order. The best method is to lay down the Rails as the men advance and have light carriages to hold about a tun each of earth—these carriages to be drawn either by men or asses—by this method the men could work thro' the winter when horses and carts could not. Your method of destroying the smoke I dare say would have some effect but I have some objections to it on account of its complexity. I am sure you will agree with me in thinking that the simplification of machinery always adds to its beauty. But however I shall embrace the first opportunity in making some experiments on your plan, yet I do not think any annoying effects may be apprehended from the smoke as coak may be used when passing over gentlemen's seats and towns.

I am Dear Sir,
Yours very truly,
G. Stephenson

Killing^th Colly.
Nov. 12th 1821.

The 'undulating line' refers to a proposal which gained some currency about that time, for railways to be given gradients at strategic points so that starting would be assisted by gravity and retardation would be likewise increased. This idea was quite alien to Stephenson's ideal of level track whenever practicable. It is interesting to observe that the 'undulating' principle was built into the Central London Railway (now the Central Line of London Transport) in 1900.

Stephenson's brief comment on the beauty of simplicity in machinery is most revealing; certainly it was a guiding principle in the locomotive designs for which he and Robert were responsible.

On 14 October 1821, Stephenson was ready to begin the re-survey of the Stockton and Darlington Railway. His son Robert assisted him, entering the figures while Stephenson took the sights. They found that a saving of four miles was possible, in comparison with Overton's line, and easier gradients were practicable. The survey was completed by 31 October: the weather had been kind.

The original Act for the railway had not envisaged steam power, but with Stephenson's successful use of locomotives in collieries at Killingworth and elsewhere, it was not surprising that he should advocate their use on the Stockton and Darlington line. In a letter to William James in December 1821, Stephenson wrote:

I fully expect to get the engine introduced on the Darlington Railway;

and when the Act of 1823 was being drafted he succeeded in getting a clause inserted

That it shall and may be lawful to and for the said Company of proprietors or any person or persons authorized or permitted by them, from and after the passing of this Act, to make and erect such and so many loco-motive or moveable engines, as the said company or proprietors shall from time to time think proper and expedient, and to use and employ the same in or upon the said railways or tramroads or any of them, by the said Act and this Act, directed or authorized to be made, for the purpose of facilitating the transport, conveyance and carriage of goods, merchandise and other articles and things upon and along the same roads, and for the conveyance of passengers upon and along the same roads.

Thus the passenger-carrying function was built into the railway from the start, on Stephenson's initiative.

On 18 January 1822, Stephenson submitted his report, with details of his re-survey of the line, and was appointed Engineer to the Company at a salary of £660 a year. A letter which he wrote to William James soon afterwards is appended; it shows his keen observations on human nature and his characteristic caution when stating the capabilities of his locomotives:

Dear Sir,—I have had a visit from your neighbour Mr. Thos. Brewin and Lord Dudley's Engineer. I being at Darlington the other day, and on my leaving that place I got into the same coach, the above Gents. were in for N. Castle. We had not gone far till they found I belonged to the neighbourhood they were going to. They asked me if I knew one G. Stephenson. I answered I did. They then enquired very closely after his character. I kept myself unknown till we got near N. Castle. I soon found their knowledge of railways was very limited, it would take a volume to hold all our conversation on Railways Locomotive Engines and Stephenson before I was known to them, however in the end we got very kind and I showed them our Engines and Railways which they candidly confessed were superior to anything they ever saw and far exceeded their expectations. I gave Brewin an account of what our Engines would do on various ascents and descents of which the following is a copy similar to what you wanted.

The following is calculated for a load of 12 loaded waggons each containing 3 tons exclusive of the weight of the waggons which may each weigh from 20 to 25 cwt.

When level at from 4 to 8 miles per hour.
When 1/16 ascent per yd. at from $3\frac{1}{2}$ to 6 miles per hour.
,, 2/16 ,, ,, ,, ,, 3 to 5 ,, ,, ,,
,, 3/16 ,, ,, ,, ,, 3 to 4 ,, ,, ,,
,, 4/16 ,, ,, ,, ,, $2\frac{1}{2}$ to 3 ,, ,, ,,
,, 1/16 descent per yd. at from 5 to 9 miles per hour.
,, 2/16 ,, ,, ,, ,, 6 to 10 ,, ,, ,,
,, 3/16 ,, ,, ,, ,, 6 to 10 ,, ,, ,,
,, 4/16 ,, ,, ,, ,, 6 to 10 ,, ,, ,,

I would not recommend my Locomotive Engines to travel on a line that ascends or descends more than 3/16 when there is a load both ways, but if the load was always passing on a descending line the Engines would return with the empty waggons up an ascent of $\frac{1}{2}$ inch per yard, or in a short distance from 5/8 to 6/8 ascent per yard. The above is within the limits at which my Engines will work, but it is my wish to state it below its powers. I dare say the statement I gave Mr. James before may be higher than this, but they are capable of performing whatever I have stated. If your railway should be constructed agreeable to the present Act, one horse will travel with from $2\frac{1}{2}$ to 3 tons, if the new line be adopted one horse will travel with from 4 to $4\frac{1}{2}$ tons. I would advise you to lay your Rails of such a strength that they may suit either horses or engines, it would not add much to the first cost, and would ultimately be a benefit were engines never to be used. The weight of Rails as 'Darlington Specification'.

I am, Sir,
Yours truly,
G. Stephenson

Killingworth Coll.
Feb. 16th 1822.

It will have become clear that by this time Stephenson was giving as much attention to the permanent way as to the engines which were to run on it. Looking ahead, his conviction that railways would become a widespread national transport system also told him that something much better than colliery tracks would be needed. He had already declared himself definitely in favour of wrought iron rails in 15 ft. lengths, as against short cast-iron rails. Every detail came under his scrutiny, backed by an unrivalled practical experience. The design of the stone blocks which supported the track was improved, also the methods of fastening the rails to them, as well as the rail joints. He was also careful to consider economic aspects such as local availability of materials and labour, and was alive to the provision of proper working conditions wherever possible. Here he is writing to John Dixon (one of the two resident engineers appointed to work under him on the Stockton and Darlington Railway, the other being Thomas Storey):

Dear John,

I have had the Quarrymen giving me the full Account of their Labouring charge at Brusselton which amounts to £33–15$^{s.}$–9$^{d.}$ I agreed for him to be paid the above sum including what he has already received & the stones he has already won to be given to him over and above—He is to commence on his bargain to win the Blocks at 5$^{d.}$ each to make a sufficient road into the quarry and also to make himself a Shop and all conveniences he may want without giving us any further trouble—I am glad to hear Sir Phillip has given liberty to go on with the quarries. I hope he has also given liberty to go on with the Cuttings & embankments which is the next thing we must proceed with. You might ride up to the quarries and see how they are getting on and settle with them if you have time—I have sent a person to Stockton to commence making pins for the blocks I have given him a letter to Wilkinson to give him access to the Blocks already in hand—We should have a Store house built immediately for the men to work in, when wet weather for boxing Blocks and making pins—but we probably might get an old house to answer our purpose at present—Perhaps Mr. Pease could accompany us to Stockton the day after the cuttings are let to give his opinion in the above—

I have had several people here looking after the embankments. I think they will be let very low.

I am Dear Sir
your's Sincerely
G. Stephenson

Killingworth Colliery)
April 29th 1822)

The formal way in which Stephenson usually ended his letters—and generally began them—makes a contrast with much of the transatlantic business correspondence of today. Stephenson favoured the division of the constructional work among a number of comparatively small sub-contractors; and this arrangement became usual in future railway construction until men of the calibre of Brassey and Peto showed themselves capable of building entire railways. Wilkinson appears to have been one of the sub-contractors on the Stockton and Darlington line.

It must have been gall and wormwood indeed for Stephenson when, against his recommendation, a portion of the Stockton and Darlington line was laid with cast-iron rails 'to satisfy the interests of other persons', as Warren tactfully puts it. Losh's feelings against Stephenson were by now so bitter that he did not even supply the cast-iron rails for the 'portion'; they came from the Neath Abbey Ironworks, South Wales.

On 23 May 1822 the first rail of the Stockton and Darlington line was laid; on 13 July Stephenson, in a statement to the Company, reported that 22 miles of the line had been completed. The length of the main portion, from the collieries to Stockton, was 25 miles. The line was mostly laid to easy gradients, except where it crossed ridges of hills at Brusselton and Etherley, where stationary engines were to be installed for rope haulage. While the use of steam locomotives was envisaged in the Act of 1823, this was only a permissive measure, and it was then intended that the line, being a public way, should cater for private carriers using horses. Stone blocks thus continued to be used (being better for horse traffic), though transverse sleepers would have been better for ensuring that the rails did not get out of gauge.

A perennial feature of Stephenson's career is the sheer impossibility of dividing it into neat parcels. While he was heavily involved in the Stockton and Darlington Railway construction he was taking a deep interest in the proposals for a railway between Liverpool and Manchester and was, as we have seen, in contact with William James who had, at the request of Joseph Sandars and the other promoters of the line, been commissioned to survey it. This project was a far more formidable task than the Stockton and Darlington Railway; the distance was greater, the physical difficulties more daunting; and above all there was implacable opposition from the landowners who, not being colliery or quarry owners, did not see any advantage to be gained by having a railway and were determined to thwart the proposal. Their agents used every form of harassment against the surveying parties, who were even, at times, in danger of their lives. It is interesting to learn that George Stephenson had agreed to his son Robert, then not yet nineteen years old, becoming one of James's team of surveyors; this early baptism of fire must have been valuable experience to Robert when he himself took charge of the far greater survey of the London and Birmingham Railway.

Stephenson clearly felt the absence of his brilliant son, then assisting William James, for he wrote as follows to James on the subject:

To: Wm. James Esqr.
at Green Dragon Inn
Nr. Prescot
Lancashire.
From: Geo. Stephenson.
Dear Sir,

Wm. Moody not getting off on the 17th as was expected but set off on the 18th, if this should reach you before you see him you will find him at the Sarasen's Head Liverpool as requested. I am very much in want of Robert, you will send him off as soon as possible as I want him to go to Knaresburgh and also to do business on the Darlington Railway as I do not know how soon Steel may leave.

I am Dr. Sir
Yours Truly
Geo. Stephenson

Killingth Colly.
Sepr. 17th 1822

P.S. Your letter has just come to hand. I will have everything considered necessary when you arrive here.

G.S.

William James's survey of the Liverpool and Manchester line was finished on 4 October 1822, and on 15 November he sent a letter to Stephenson, to tell him that this stage of the work was completed and to give the main features of the line. He also asked Stephenson what loads his locomotives could haul, and Stephenson furnished the information in a 'Certificate of Engine Power on Railroad', as follows:

LIVERPOOL & MANCHESTER INTENDED RAIL-ROAD

I have examined the Section of the intended Line of Railroad and presuming the same to be correct, which I have no reason to doubt, I do certify that the following Burthens may be conveyed by the Locomotive Engines and carriages on a Railway properly constructed.

40 Tons 32 Miles in Eight Hours
*30 Tons 32 Miles in Six & half Hours
20 Tons 32 Miles in Five Hours
10 Tons 32 Miles in Two and Half Hours.

and that the same rate of conveyance may be preserved over Everton Hill, and I have *no doubt* the Engines may be made to do considerably *more* than I have mentioned here, particularly as Mr. James states that the Levels may be greatly reduced, tho at some expence in Earth work. As witness my hand the 28th day of October 1822.

(signed) Geo. Stephenson

* This line has been added in pencil in what appears to be William James's handwriting. This document bears a number of pencilled notes and rough calculations in James's hand.

In the following year, James carried out a survey for the Canterbury and Whitstable Railway, and it was on his plans for the line that the successful application for the Parlimentary powers was based.

William James's railway enthusiasms, which were without doubt an important factor in the promotion of lines in England, offer a remarkable contrast to the cautious, reserved ways of Stephenson. Here is an example, written at the conclusion of James's survey of the Liverpool and Manchester Railway:

To: Wm James Esqr.
Horse and Jockey Inn,
Newton,
Nr. Warrington,
Lancashire.
From: Geo. Stephenson.
My Dear Sir,

You try my conscience very I assure you I am quite inclined to do you all the good I possibly can, but you will excuse me saying more than I think I can perform. I hope you have had a safe and pleasant journey home. I have no doubt but I shall please you and the Company with the Engines in the end.

I am Dear Sir,
Yours Truly
Geo. Stephenson

Killingth Colly.
Nov. 4th 1822

Stephenson had always been insistent upon obtaining for his son a good education, feeling deeply his own shortcomings especially now that he was becoming a well-known and important figure in the North of England. It was perhaps through his meeting with Robert Bald in 1818 that his thoughts turned to Edinburgh University for Robert's higher education. At the age of nineteen, Robert Stephenson accordingly became a student there, where he took Natural Philosophy, Chemistry, and Natural History.

On 18 November 1822 Stephenson wrote to a Mr. Charnley, asking him to let the bearer

have 1 or 2 of the pamphlets from Killingworth Coll^{y} relating to the controversy over the Safety Lamp, my son being In Edinburgh and attending the lectures of Dr. Hope on Chemistry who is very desirous to hear the particulars about the Lamp.

The lamp controversy had not yet been extinguished.

One happy result of Robert's student days was a close friendship with George Parker Bidder, then a fellow-student who had earlier achieved

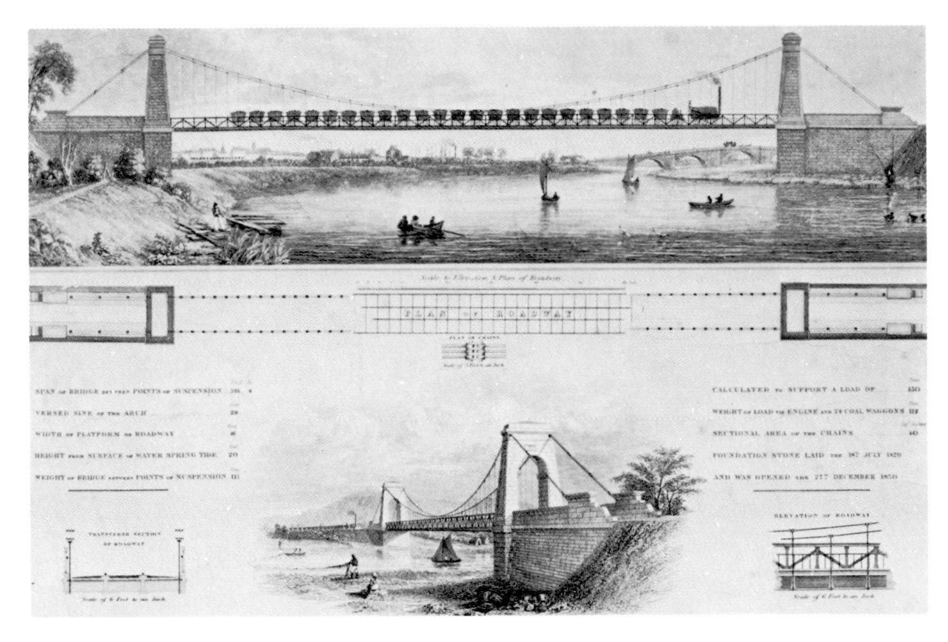

Fig 19. Reproduction of engraving, 'The Stockton and Darlington Railway Suspension Bridge'. (By kind permission of the Borough Libraries and Curator, Public Library, Darlington)

celebrity as 'the Calculating Boy'. Bidder soon became well acquainted with both the Stephensons; in later life he was elected President of the Institution of Civil Engineers. Robert Stephenson also took with him to Edinburgh a number of letters of introduction to engineers and literary men. But his days at the University were very brief; in the Spring of 1823 he was called back by his father who by now had additional irons in the fire. Robert, however, did succeed in bringing home a prize for mathematics.

While Robert was pursuing his studies at Edinburgh University, George Stephenson made two lengthy visits to London, on Parliamentary business concerning the 1823 Act of the Stockton and Darlington Railway. A note of his expenses has survived:

1823 *Feb. 10–14th March*: To travelling expenses on journey to, from, and in London	£22– 0– 0
26 days at £3–3–0 a day	81–18– 0
From *8th April to 13th May*—to travelling expenses to, from, and in London	33– 0– 0
30 days at £3–3–0 a day	94–10– 0
	£231– 8– 0
Received on acct. from Mr. Mewburn £20 } Ditto Mr. Dixon £40 }	60– 0– 0
	171– 8– 0

Stephenson's iron constitution enabled him to achieve almost superhuman feats of endurance, even in the most rigorous conditions, and it is indeed seldom that any hint of illness comes into his letters. However, a fever laid him low towards the end of 1822, when he wrote as follows to William James, at the same time revealing his irritation at the Stockton and Darlington directors' consultations with the Scottish civil engineer Robert Stevenson (spelt 'Stephenson' here) on the line for the railway:

To: Wm. James Esqr.
Horse & Jockey Inn,
Newton,
Nr. Warrington.
From: Geo. Stephenson.
Dear Sir,

I have been dangerously ill for many days but is now recovering. I got a severe cold by travelling and sitting so long with my wet close on which threw me into a fever. I was quite unable to answer your letters. I think you are right in making two estimates. I am not falling off in the poor of my Engines but Sir I want to run safe both for your credit and my own I assure you it is my wish to do you all the good I can and hope your intention's me the same to me. With respect to Mr. Stephenson of Edinburgh giving such a rash opinion on our Railroad and Engines is because the knowledge of machinery has not yet entered head at least I have not seen any marks of it when in his company and if not now its unlikely ever will. I have heard him make some remarks on Railways which I hardly could have expected from a child he has collected news like other book makers and setting it of for his own if we are just rising from darkness I hope we means we are the first, and if so it is likely our North country neighbours will have to grope there by the refracted rays from our light. I have the pleasure to inform you I have made great progress in the scheme for the new Engine and also a considerable saving of friction in the construction of the waggon it would have been of considerable advantage to the Darlington Railway if I had considered it sooner. If you get through Parliament my views shall be open to you being called off in a hurry prevents me saying anything more at present. I am ventering out from my room.

I am Sir with great respect,
Geo. Stephenson

Killingth Colly.
Nov. 25th 1822

Foreshadowing the 1823 Act of the Stockton and Darlington Railway, with its vital clause authorizing operation of the line by steam locomotives, Stephenson wrote to William James:

To: Wm. James Esqr.
at Jos Sanders's Esqr.
Liverpool.
From: Geo. Stephenson.
Dear Sir,

I would be obliged to you if you could return the Darlington Railway Act of parliament with your alterations and remarks upon it as I hope by this time you have got everything therein properly arranged as the Darlington people wishes to see it. I hope you are prospering in your projects. I expect I shall see you in London on the meeting of parliament when we shall have some time to enlarge upon Railways—My wife joins with best respects to you.

I am Dear Sir
Yours Truly
Geo. Stephenson

Killingth Colly.
Dec. 18th 1822

Four weeks later, Stephenson sent William James (who was then seeking to promote a railway from Stratford-on-Avon to Moreton-in-the-Marsh) the following letter, reporting progress on the Stockton and Darlington Railway and comparing some of its features with those which James had in mind:

To: Wm. James Esqr.
at Joseph Sander's Esqr.
Liverpool.
From: Geo. Stephenson.
Dear Sir,

I have just arrived from Darlington, where I have been for some time past or I should have answered yours sooner, we are getting on with our work exceedingly well; the earth work will be done at less than my estimate, it is going on at from 4d to 6d pr Cubic Yard; we have 20 feet deep, at 4d going on and paying the men very well; and on another place going on at 6d and running near a mile to the delivery, at this place the men have been making 30s. p. week. I allowed in my estimate 2^{s} a pair for the blocks delivered on the spot where wanted—13£ p. ton for the Malleable Iron (English re-manufactured) 9£ p. ton for the cast iron chairs delivered at Stockton, but I think we got them for about 8£. I allow 10^{s} p. ton to delivering them on the different parts of the Railway.

Your fencing is much like mine, which I think will do we expect wall fencing to come as cheap as quicks, which is much better as the quicks are so long before they become a fence, I have allowed 3s. p. running yard for ballasting. I think I gave you all the particulars of my estimate. As I am not acquainted with the nature of your sand stone I cannot give my opinion, on the working of it; but I am inclined to think your estimate will do.

The Hetton Standing Engines is doing exceedingly well they will deliver

300000 Tons p. annum; and by laying a double Railway on the bank, they would deliver twice that number.

I have a new scheme for waggons since I wrote you which will travel with less friction: I regret much that I had not thought of it sooner as I am too far forward with the Stockton and Darlington Railway on my former plans to use it there—I was thinking to inform the Stratford on Avon Railway Company of it as it could be used there, as I suppose they have not yet got their castings; but I should not divulge it unless they would pay me well for it if I had been the Engineer I would have adopted it without any remuneration; it diminishes the friction considerably in passing curves: it will be a great advantage to the Engines; it will make no difference with your estimate, only it must be thought of at the commencing of the Works. I set off for London on the 4 February when I expect to see you.

I am Dear Sir
Yours Truly
Geo. Stephenson

Killingth Colliery
Jan. 16, 1823

The momentous circumstance which brought Robert Stephenson back to his father in 1823 was no less than George Stephenson's plan to establish a locomotive-building business in Newcastle. At that time Michael Longridge's works at Bedlington was not able to roll suitable plates for locomotive boilers (although the firm did later enter into the locomotive construction field); Stephenson's entry in 1821 into partnership with the firm of John and Isaac Burrell, ironfounders, of Newcastle, showed the trend of his interests, though no proof has remained that they constructed locomotives. But Stephenson was looking ahead to the completion of railways then only being surveyed or under construction, and to their requirements for locomotives. The historic meeting at which this plan for a locomotive works was put into effect took place on 23 June 1823, when the firm of Robert Stephenson & Co., Newcastle, was established, the original partners being George and Robert Stephenson, Edward Pease, and Michael Longridge. The history of the company has been chronicled with loving care and in painstaking detail by Warren in his great history of the firm, prepared for its centenary in 1923; suffice it here to say that the original capital amounted to £4,000, Pease contributing £1,600 and the other partners £800 each. The company lost no time in purchasing a site, in the angle between South Street and Forth Street, and the works were known by the name of the latter street. The firm was in business for the manufacture of locomotives and stationary steam engines, and for railway material such as wheels and axles. They also went in for the production of iron castings, and this led to George Stephenson's

Fig 20. 'Grasshopper' stationary steam engine constructed by Robert Stephenson and Company, Newcastle upon Tyne, June 1823; now in the Museum of Science and Industry, Birmingham (other examples of steam-driven plant are in the foreground).

withdrawal from partnership with the Burrells, though at a later date the Burrells' firm was merged with Robert Stephenson & Co.

Stephenson's intensely practical nature is exemplified in a letter addressed to an acquaintance in South Wales, about this time; it is worth reading because it is in the language of one engineer talking to another:

To: Mr. Philip Maddison
Old Church Colliery
Nr. Swansea.

My dear Sir,

I duly received yours of November 4th, I am glad you think you can manage the Engine, the Yoke with the side rods form the connecting rods which will unite with the crank pin exactly under the centre of the cylinder.

There is two Yokes one on the top of the piston rod and the other is under the bottom of the cylinder it is like a sayers frame you must not put any wood on the top of the pillar the cylinder bottom is cast sufficiently wide to stretch across the space left in the pillar which you may see by the plan, if you measure the plan by the scale you will find the distance of any part, there is no need of a wall on the back frame—but if stone is cheaper than wood you may put a wall in its place but you would still want a piece of timber on the top of the wall and that piece of timber should reach to the shaft, if you ever intend to work a set of pumps otherwise it would not be kept fast there is no joint in any part of the connecting rod but only at the top and bottom, you will find the distance from the top of the cranks axle frame to the top of the cylinder pillars by measuring of the scale, if you take your compasses and extend it between the cylinder bottom and the crank frame and then lay it on to the scale it will give you the quantity of feet. It will answer very well to have the bottom of the cylinder level with the top of the pitt. I believe you will find the pillar measure about 17 feet high only take care to work by the scale and you will keep right I am afraid the work you have for a holing machine would not defray its expences however I will talk to Mr. Wood about one. I think by looking at your sketch you understand the Engine.

I am, Dear Philip,
Yours sincerely,
Geo. Stephenson

Killingth Colly.
Nov. 10th 1822.

Stephenson's mind was now moving towards the idea of being in a position to survey and construct future railways and to supply their locomotives and rolling stock. For the surveying and constructional side of railways the same partners who had established the Forth Street Works formed another company known as George Stephenson and Son; whether George Stephenson ever imagined that he could secure a monopoly in the business of building and equipping railways is not known, but it seems clear that he was hoping for a substantial slice of the cake. The bestowal of his son's name on the locomotive-building firm is interesting, and indicates the respect in which Robert was held by the other partners, though he was not yet twenty years old when the firm was founded. L. T. C. Rolt, however, in his biography of the Stephensons, has suggested a somewhat sinister explanation, namely, that Stephenson was using his son to bring about achievements and successes for the accomplishment of which he himself, with his lack of schooling and his rough upbringing, was not so well qualified.

In September 1823 George and Robert Stephenson went on an extensive tour, visiting London and Bristol, then crossing to Dublin and later going by road to Cork, and spending several days in Shropshire on the return journey. The business of the tour concerned boilers and stationary engines, the supply of which had for several years been a notable field of activity for Stephenson; no doubt the obtaining of orders for the new Forth Street Works was in his mind. It is interesting to see, in the Birmingham Museum of Science and Industry, one of the first stationary engines made by the firm; it is dated June 1823.

It was just before this tour began that William James was beginning to get into financial difficulties; his enthusiasm for railways remained undiminished, but now he was also laid low with ill health; the circumstances were sufficiently serious to result in a decision by the promoters of the Liverpool and Manchester Railway to replace him by George Stephenson who was requested forthwith to re-survey the line. Nevertheless, James remained a great protagonist in the cause for railways, wherein his zeal and his practical activities have not been widely enough recognized, especially in regard to the Liverpool and Manchester Railway. That scheme, by far the largest project of its kind to that date, was moreover envisaged as a passenger-carrying railway, whereas the conveyance of passengers was regarded only as an incidental source of revenue in the early stages of the Stockton and Darlington Railway.

By the start of 1824 the Forth Street Works at Newcastle upon Tyne were in active operation. Stephenson had moved house from West Moor to a new address in Eldon Place, Newcastle, which was to be his home, and that of his son Robert, until the changed circumstances (due to James's bankruptcy and illness) brought him right into the Liverpool scene, and he accordingly moved house there. James had (as we have seen) carried out a preliminary survey in 1821 from Liverpool to Manchester; his second, more detailed, survey was conducted a year later; work on the promotion of the company followed, and the first prospectus was dated 29 October 1824. Early in 1825 formal application for the powers to construct the line was made, and the Committee stage was reached on 21 March in that year.

It is remarkable how much promotional work on railways was done in the period 1820–30, yet only a small proportion of these lines got to the stage of actual construction. Many of these proposed lines were for horse-drawn traffic only; but it is likely that progressive people were keeping a keen watch on current developments, especially on the Stockton and Darlington Railway. During the period 1823–5 Stephenson was constantly on the move between Liverpool, Newcastle upon Tyne, and Darlington, quite apart from other journeys to other locations of proposed railways, as his advice was frequently in demand. John Dixon had become his right-hand man on the Stockton and Darlington line, and many letters on its construction were sent to him by Stephenson when he was not able to be on the site. Much of Stephenson's considerable correspondence with Michael Longridge dates from this period.

On 6 January 1824, Stephenson wrote from Eldon Place, Newcastle, to John Dixon:

Dear John,

If you advance Blakelock $\frac{1}{2}$(?d.) per yard, he must endeavour to keep the way in good order providing you deliver the ballast on the side of the way, as it cannot be expected that he can lead it from the Gravel bed—I have not heard from Edward Pease whether it meets his approbation for Mr. Grace and Sir

John Swinburns Steward to meet him at Rushyford on Friday to examine Trotters Ground—I shall very likely accompany them when I expect to see you —I am in haste

Yours sincerely
Geo. Stephenson

Eldon Place,
Newcastle
January 6th 1824

It seems likely that during 1824 when construction of the Stockton and Darlington Railway was well advanced, Stephenson was anxious to press on towards the final stages, so as to give himself more time for the great Liverpool and Manchester scheme. So he writes to John Dixon about a notable bridge on the Stockton and Darlington line, the completion of which he was anxious to expedite. It is of interest that he himself had designed the bridge, partly of wrought-iron and partly of cast-iron; it had been constructed by the Burrell brothers, of Newcastle, for erection across the River Gaunless; the remains of this bridge have been preserved, and are now to be seen in the Railway Museum at York, and there is a model of it in the Science Museum.

It has been claimed that this was the first iron railway bridge ever made. There were no rivets; the girders fitted into sockets in the tubular pillars. The length was 50 ft., comprising four $12\frac{1}{2}$ ft. spans. Two curved bars formed each girder; they were of wrought-iron and fitted into cast-iron bosses. Cast-iron vertical posts held each curved bar in place; they were extended upwards to act as supports for the longitudinal timbers bearing the track. At their ends, the girders rested on five pairs of inclined pillars of cast iron, cross-braced and joined at their tops by cast-iron beams. Projecting cantilevers springing from the beams carried the side platforms. On 1 May 1824, Stephenson wrote to Dixon:

Dear John,

I should like to have been with you on Monday or Tuesday but I find I cannot on Account of Mr. Lambert wishing my attendance at their Collieries the most of the week I did not see Mr. Benhomi on my return home from Darlington but will write to him to accompany me on Monday week and I shall have all my plans prepared to show him.

You will get everything ready for the Bridge that you see will be needful. I think it would be much better for the Company to provide all materials of course you can be getting the Line prepared and I think we had better have Free Stone for the whole facing of the Main Pillars and what Limestone may be wanted for the inside of the Pillars must be all of good size—cannot you get forward in cutting up the Elm Trees I do not think the bark will be of any value.

A Plan of a Pile Engine accompanies this the wood work for which you will get prepared immediately—I think you will perfectly understand the drawing it is intended to have a loose leg so as to drive the Piles at any Angle let it be made well as we shall have a great deal of use for it at Stockton.

I am glad to hear such good accounts from Fighting Cocks it will be almost as good as one of the Mexican gold mines I hope we shall get a little more hold of it. I think you should be looking round to try if you can be getting any large larch for the Piling as the Elm Trees will not cut into so many piles as we shall want.

I will forward the waggon wheels as fast as possible. I have received the Plan from Robert that you wrote for.

I am Dear John
Thy Sincere Friend
Geo. Stephenson

Eldon Place
May 1st 1824

In the foregoing letter, 'Mr. Benhomi' is a reference to Ignatius Bonomi, an architect engaged by the Stockton and Darlington Railway, who thus became, as Rolt has pointed out, the first railway architect in the world. Bonomi was responsible for the design of the River Skerne Bridge at Darlington and at Stephenson's request, he supervised its construction, as Stephenson had to be in Liverpool on railway business. There is evidence of a desire to make the station buildings of substantial construction, as well as attractive appearance. 'Fighting Cocks' referred to a point between Stockton and Darlington, where the road to Yarm diverges. The reference to Mexican gold-mines foreshadows the effect of Thomas Richardson's entry upon the scene (p. 68).

The letter, confirming Stephenson's agreement that Ignatius Bonomi should supervise the construction of the bridge which he designed, has survived. It reads:

Dear Sir,

I have this day received your very friendly letter. I have engaged with the Liverpool people to lay out their intended line of Railroad from this place to Manchester, of course I cannot attend to the erection of the Darlington Bridge, so closely as I would wish, and I assure you it will be quite agreeable to me for you or your assistants to undertake the superintendence of it.

I am Dear Sir
Your sincerely
Geo. Stephenson

Liverpool
June 16th 1824

There is a historic interest about this letter, for it shows that Stephenson had now been appointed by the Directors of the Liverpool and Manchester Railway to re-survey the line, because William James's broken health and parlous financial state had obliged him to withdraw. There is a pathetic letter from James's sister, Mrs. Elizabeth Mudie, on the situation in which James found himself, which has been quoted by C. F. Dendy Marshall.*

Stephenson saw, in the surveying and construction of the line, a number of good opportunities for promising young men to learn the business, and he accordingly wrote to his friend Joseph Cabry, who was still working in Cheshire, suggesting that his son, Thomas Cabry, might with advantage take up this employment:

Liverpool June 30th 1824

Dear Sir,

I expected to have had an opportunity of writing to you sooner, inviting you to visit me here as I find it scarcely possible to get over to see you. Could you come over on Sunday morning next when we could have some talk together —If you could spare Joseph I think it might do him a great service to accompany my young me(n) in this Survey, he could manage the Index Stave, but more about it when I see you. Your son Thomas has the appearance of being a very clever man, and I shall take care to see him put forward. I am in great haste— Address) At Mr. Phelps No. 8 East Side Castle Street Liverpool.

Yours very Truly
Geo. Stephenson

(Addressed to: Joseph Cabry—
Neston Colliery—
near Park Gate—
Cheshire—)

Both of Joseph Cabry's sons were afterwards employed by Stephenson on the Canterbury and Whitstable Railway.

Another letter to John Dixon was sent by Stephenson on 9 June 1824:

Newcastle June 9th 1824

Dear John,

A Turn Rail will be delivered to Pickersgill to-morrow—as soon as it arrives you will forward it to the Bottom of Brusselton Incline, it is to turn the Stone Waggons on to the main line—I am getting other two made, as one will be wanted for Darlington in a short time.

I hope you have let the Bridge and are getting on with dressing the stones—

* *Centenary History of the Liverpool and Manchester Railway* Locomotive Publishing Company, 1930, p. 70.

The Engine Houses are all let to a Mason near Chester-le-Street a man of good character—

I shall be obliged to set off for Liverpool on Friday morning, as I am so teased by the proprietors of the intended Railway and also by the Birmingham people to visit them—it will likely be a fortnight or 3 weeks before I can see you again—I will send over the person that I spoke to you about respecting the Piling—at the same time I think you had better have the person from Yarm to stop constantly on the spot as one man can only visit you occasionally—And I would advise at the same time to get as much of Storey's time, to the Bridge as you can. I think he will endeavour to have it properly done, and his Ideas on Bridges show him to have abilities for such work.

My expenses to & from London say £20 will you have the goodness to lay before the Committee, and likewise Roberts Expences—you will recollect a great (? part) of the above was paid out of our own pockets.

I will send our man over on Monday to meet you and Mr. Storey—he has little to say for himself but in the end you will find him a useful man—Pray do push the Bridge forward with all possible speed. Any thing you may want from Forth Street in my absence drop a line to Thos Nicholson the clerk in our office—

I am Dear John
Yours Truly
Geo. Stephenson

Stephenson was anxious to give all possible guidance to Dixon, for he wrote again, only two days later, on the same matter:

Dear John,

The Bearer Mr. Fife is the person I mentioned to you about looking after the Bridge and Piling. You will show him what you have done about making the Ram if you can introduce him to the Yarm man they will consult together about the piling if he can not see you in this visit he may in the next if Mr. Fife can continue to visit you I think there will be no need of any other.

I am Dear John
Thy Sincere Friend
Geo. Stephenson

June 11th 1824
Newcastle

But there were constant calls away from the Stockton and Darlington constructional work which Stephenson had to answer in order to keep the goodwill of the promoters of other lines. Thus on 28 April 1824 he had written to Francis Mewburn, solicitor to the Stockton and Darlington

Company, the following letter, which reveals a method of expediting correspondence in those days:

Dear Sir,

Your letter by this days post has cut me most sadly how to set off to London at such short notice I do not know as I am hemmed in with so much business and indeed I am not in a state of health for such a journey however I suppose I must go Lord Shaftesbury must be an old fool I always said he had been a spoilt child but he is a great deal worse than I expected I suppose the Dutchman has been making the best of him I think if you had been there you would have managed better. I have not seen Mr. Edward Pease nor yet Joseph and I suppose I shall not see them till to-morrow night—If you get this in time to give me a line back by the same coach saying whether there is any possibility of postponing my Journey I will have some one at the Coach office at night to receive it from the Guard.

I am Sir
Yours very sincerely
Geo. Stephenson*

Eldon Place
Newcastle
April 8th 1824

A major figure, who had entered into the lives of George and Robert Stephenson, some two years previously, was a Quaker named Thomas Richardson, a cousin of Edward Pease. Richardson was an influential banker, the founder of a firm known as Overend, Gurney and Company, discount bankers, with headquarters in the City, where he was well known. He had no doubts about his cousin's shrewd financial judgment, and advanced money to Robert Stephenson and Company in its early days and eventually became a partner in the Forth Street business. He also became interested in mining ventures in the New World, especially in countries, formerly exploited under Spanish rule for their mineral wealth, which had become independent and in some cases had allowed such activities to lapse. The Colombian Mining Association, a company of which Richardson was a promoter, had been constituted after a failure to get a similar scheme started in Mexico, and was seeking to obtain professional advice and mining expertise from Britain. The family relationship between Richardson and Pease was an obvious starting-point to make contact with Stephenson, whose basic engineering background of mining and steam plant pointed to him as one of the best consultants then obtainable. So Stephenson was brought into discussions on men, mining

* Someone has written, at the end of this letter 'Put this paper into the fire', evidently because of the remarks about Lord Shaftesbury.

methods, and machinery early in 1824; he was too cautious a man to become involved, but with much misgiving he and his partner, Michael Longridge, agreed to release Robert Stephenson from his responsibilities at the Forth Street Works to lead an advance party into the interior of Colombia. One can imagine how exasperating it was for Stephenson to be without his son's help at such a time, with the Stockton and Darlington line requiring as much supervision as could humanly be given, and the Liverpool and Manchester project looming up larger with each month that passed. Moreover, Robert was rapidly developing into an exceptionally gifted engineer, with every possible quality to fit him for leadership in the railway world that was dawning.

The original supposition was that Robert would not be in South America for more than one year, but in fact, his contract was for three. Robert sailed from Liverpool on 18 June 1824, less than a month after his father received news from Joseph Sandars that he had been officially appointed engineer to the Liverpool and Manchester Railway. Robert had just finished the design of the Brusselton Incline stationary winding engine for the Stockton and Darlington Railway.

To complicate Stephenson's life even further, he was caught up in an early proposal for a trunk railway from Birmingham to London, which was a very live issue at the time; although it languished after 1825, it was successfully revived in 1832. Stephenson's letters written between May and October 1824 contain numerous references to 'the Birmingham intended line'.

It is clear that Robert's departure for Colombia was not an over-night development; with his uncle Robert (Stephenson's brother) he had been on an extensive tour of South Wales and Cornwall early in 1824; a lively letter dated 8 March, describing his travels, is now a treasure in the Institution of Civil Engineers, and contains an ominous reference to 'this Mexican contract'.

On the subject of the Birmingham to London line, Stephenson wrote to Longridge, on 23 May 1824:

Dear Sir,

Your friend Mr. Forster and Mr. Hunt having called on me this evening and they being strangers of your roads, I have sent Hugh to conduct them to that highly characterized place, called Bedlington Iron Works—They are very anxious of me taking the Birmingham intended Line of Railway under my care; how must I do? I can get either Storey or John Dixon to assist me—We must not let such a valuable concern slip, but more of this when I see you—I am going to Darlington to-morrow; I shall either return in the evening, or with the mail on Tuesday morning, when I shall expect to meet you and the Gentlemen at breakfast. They must go to Hetton as the Engines are both better and travel with more waggons than the Killingworth ones and the Railway (is) in better order—

I am Dear Sir
Yours Very Truly
Geo. Stephenson

Forth Street
May 23rd 1824

The tussle between Birmingham and Liverpool interests is shown in a letter to Longridge, written a few days later:

Dear Sir,

On my arrival home this night a number of important letters were awaiting me one from the Birmingham Railway Committee wishing me to meet them as early as possible another from Mr. Saunders (Sandars) desiring me to set off for Liverpool immediately which I think I must be not later than Friday morning another letter from Charles saying they were going to be shipped at Liverpool I will therefore have a chance of seeing Robert how much I should have enjoyed your company to have gone with me but in the present state of things I cannot expect it could you possibly come over to morrow night and stop with us till the next day morning. You shall have the best bed and Mrs. Longridge's plan shall be adopted for your delicate feet I should like to see you before I leave—I am a little more chearful to night as I have quite come to a conclusion that there is nothing for me but hard work in this world therefore I may as well be chearful as not.

I am Dear Sir
Yours Truly
Geo. Stephenson

Forth Street
Newcastle.
June 7th 1824
Michael Longridge Esq

Stephenson's reference to 'nothing for me but hard work in this world' may well have been prompted by thoughts on the impending departure of Robert, who had become a most comforting support for his father, and a highly competent engineer into the bargain. As foreshadowed, Robert sailed from Liverpool on 18 June, and landed at La Guaira, Venezuela, on 23 July. Bad roads held up his journey to Colombia for two months, so he stayed in Caracas during the interval, after which he departed for Bogota, Colombia, en route for Mariquita, where the mining surveys were to be undertaken.

While Robert was on the high seas, his father (who had moved house from Newcastle to Liverpool in June, in readiness for his work on the proposed line to Manchester) again wrote to Michael Longridge about the Birmingham project, in a letter which shows how his reputation had soared, and with it the demand for his services:

Dear Sir,

I know you are scolding me for not writing according to promise but after telling you how I have been fagging almost night and day You will I am sure excuse me—I have now been through the whole of the Birmingham Line except the Branches and the greatest part of it is marked out. It will be a very fine Line the Undertakers are in great spirits about it. On my arrival at Birmingham a meeting of the most wealthy of the subscribers took place who would not hear of any other executing their work but myself of course I gave way to their wishes as I had also received the news as mentioned in your letter for the extension of time for depositing the plans They readily agreed to all my charges and I assure you it made me blush to ask it but the hardening lessons I had got from you made me stand to it and it was pleasant to find no one had the least objections—After all our business was settled the Company sat down to dinner you may imagine the style from what you saw at Sunderland—I think the greatest part of the Company had as much wine before dinner was over as would serve you and I to a great many—Foster is a warm hearted Gentleman he has accompanied me through the whole of their Line and I am sure he will not forget it as long as he lives—Some days fourteen hours without either bread or water rising at half past three and working till nine ten and sometimes twelve before we get to our quarters. Mr. Foster says he never slept so pleasantly in his life before closing his eyes when he laid down he opened them no more till he was called—

On my arrival at Birmingham I found yours of the 22nd Inst and this day have received yours of the 26th Inst. I think your Estimate for the drying machine is more than it would cost. We cannot say any thing about the Patent Right until we make some experiments. I told Gray before I left that the wheels for the Boiler waggons were to be made to move separate from the frames but he always forgets things as fast as I tell him. I have seen the Engineer at Birmingham he is rather a likely man but a few years older than I would wish I have some expectation of a younger person who I think would suit us better. We will settle these matters when I see you I am glad to hear that Mrs Longridge and her daughter are doing well—

I am Dear Sir
Yours Truly
Geo. Stephenson

Stephenson's almost superhuman energy and endurance were remembered for years afterwards not only by his engineering assistants but by his scribes also, to whom he would dictate letters until they themselves were at the point of exhaustion. Tom L. Gooch (a relative of Michael

Longridge and brother of the Daniel Gooch whose name is indissolubly linked with the Great Western Railway) and Francis Swanwick were among the succession of Stephenson's amanuenses.

A further letter to Longridge on the Liverpool and Manchester line now follows; it contains a reference to 'the Birmingham Line' which shows that, at that time, Stephenson clearly expected the project to come to fruition. He writes, on 7 July 1824:

Dear Sir,

I am now getting smoothly on with the Liverpool Line, and hope I shall accomplish it with ease—I have taken the Line through that part of the Country where we shall do away with the chief opposers to this undertaking, except the Canal proprietors, who will no doubt throw every obstacle in the way—The Opposers above alluded to are Lord Derby and Lord Sebgton (sic)—They have always been the terror of this undertaking I commence with the Birmingham Line tomorrow, and hope to get smoothly on with it also I expect to leave this place on Sunday morning I will spend one day at West Auckland as I return home—Time prevents me giving you a farther detail of our proceedings here.

I am Dear Sir
Yours Truly
Geo. Stephenson

The worries of Stephenson's perpetual travellings must have been formidable, as the next letter shows. It brings home the enormous benefits of a national railway system as compared with individual travel in the early nineteenth century. It also reminds one of Stephenson's concern for horses; he was always fond of them, and one celebrated steed, 'Bobby', carried him around for twenty years and went into retirement when his master took Tapton House. Stephenson writes to Michael Longridge accordingly:

Liverpool July 11th 1824

M. Longridge
Dear Sir,

Your favor came duly to hand. It astonishes me to find that such a mistake should be made by me as to post off a letter without a date. You speak of going to Wales and of meeting me at Manchester, but the time and place you have not mentioned which is equally as bad as an undated letter and rather worse. I expected to have set off with the mail this night but was detained by my horse breaking down on the road in passing from the Birmingham line to this quarter. This disaster put me too late for the Mail. The poor horses knees were broken in such a desperate manner that I did not know how to venture home with him. I had a fine kick up with the inn-keepers when I did get home. The only apology I could make was by proposing to buy the horse at its value—however with some difficulty we got matters made up. I have now got four sets of Surveyors upon the Birmingham line and shall have 8 or 10 sets more when I return from the north. The Liverpool line will soon be finished. I have Hugh and Mr. Galloway carrying on the levels who will manage the whole line without any other assistance. They have now got nearly half way and through the worst of the ground.

I shall set off to-morrow morn^{g}, for Newcastle. As I will stop one day at West Auckland; this will reach you before I arrive. I think I shall be at home on Wednesday night.

I hope Mrs. Longridge is doing well together with her little one.

I am Dear Sir
Yours truly
Geo. Stephenson

P.S. The sooner you get settled with the powerful iron-masters to manufacture the rails I think the better, as I am well aware there will be some alterations made to evade the patent right

G.S.

'Hugh', referred to in the foregoing letter, was Hugh Greenshields, who had also been one of the team which carried out the previous survey of the Liverpool and Manchester line, under William James, when Robert Stephenson had been a member of the surveying party. Galloway's name soon afterwards appears in connection with an ambitious proposal of Stephenson and his Newcastle partners to organize schemes for future railway construction in England and Wales upon a sort of regional plan, which included a London and Northern Rail Road; Robert Stephenson was to be the chief engineer, with Joseph Locke, Robert Taylor, and Elijah Galloway as chief assistants. It will be noticed that this role for Robert Stephenson was decided for him *in absentia*.

The volume of support for the proposed London and Birmingham line is clearly shown in a letter which Stephenson sent to Longridge four weeks later; his exhausting round of business journeys is indicated, too. The letter reads:

Swan Inn
Birmingham Aug. 8, 1824

Dear Sir,

On my arrival here I found yours of 3rd Inst. I have seen the Millwright but had not time to get the agreement signed. He expects to be at liberty in 8 or ten days, when I will immediately send him off to Newcastle. I think we shall be obliged to discharge 2 or 3 of our men the first opportunity; as I know, the whole of them are led on by them. I hope Mr. Fife will be able to continue until I return. I am quite aware of Mr. Johnson's anxiety about his railway but cannot help it at present.

I have had a letter from Mr, Thompson* of Brampton wishing me to visit

* Benjamin Thompson, also connected with the Brunton and Shields Railway.

them before the 21st which I shall endeavour to do. I shall inform you in my next of the time I expect to be there.

A very respectable meeting of the subscribers of this undertaking was held on my arrival here. They are quite determined to let no exertion be wanting to carry their point. They are making all the interest with ministers and men of power they possibly can obtain. The amount of the subscriptions when filled up will be £700,000 and it appears if double the sum were wanted it would be raised. The company will not allow any person to take more than One hundred shares. One gentleman applied since my arrival for six hundred shares of 50£ each: the company would not comply with his request; however, they have allowed him to take Two Hundred under different names.

I shall leave this place to-morrow for Newport: where I may be a couple of days: from thence I will go to Stourbridge where I will remain also two days: from the latter place to Newcastle under Lyne where I may spend the remainder of the week. I will endeavour to be at Liverpool on the Sunday where letters will find me.

I have an invitation from Boulton and Watt to dine with them to day.

I am Dear Sir
Yours truly
Geo. Stephenson

Meanwhile the Stockton and Darlington Railway was progressing with John Dixon as Stephenson's principal assistant. On 16 September 1824, the Forth Street Works received orders for the first two locomotives for that line, and an order for two stationary engines for the Brusselton and the Etherley Inclines.* The boilers for the stationary engines were constructed with the most astonishing expedition, for on 28 September 1824, Robert Stephenson and Company wrote to the directors of the Stockton and Darlington Railway:

Gent.

As the three Boilers are now delivered, we will be obliged by your accepting our Dft: for £500, as per Agreement.

And we will also feel obliged by your advancing us a further sum of £500—during the progress of the Work, for which we have also drawn.

We are Gent
Your obd[t] Serv[ts]
Rob Stephenson & Co

A certificate of delivery of the boilers of the stationary engines, signed by Stephenson, was worded thus:

* A printed notice, announcing the sale of these engines at the end of their working lives, was preserved in the Museum of British Transport, Clapham during 1963–73, and will presumably be included in the future National Railway Museum at York.

Newcastle upon Tyne 28th Sept
1824

I do certify that the three Boilers for the Brussleton and Etherly Engines are delivered at their respective stations.

Geo. Stephenson
Engineer for The
Stockton & Darlington
Rail Way Company

As the main purpose of the Stockton and Darlington line was the conveyance of coal for loading upon ships at Stockton, the provision of a quay now became an important feature of the Stockton terminus. Stephenson accordingly wrote to Dixon:

Newcastle Sept. 29th 1824

Dear John,

Before any plans can be made for the intended Quay at Stockton, boring must be made to prove the foundation. You will also have the goodness to make a sketch of the ground adjoining the river; the full length of that purchased by the Company. A section of the bank with the rise of the tide will also be necessary, and likewise the position the line of Railway runs through the said ground. You can forward those remarks to me at Liverpool, when I will immediately return you a plan and specification. I shall be obliged to set off to that place to-morrow: as the Rail-way Companies in that neighbourhood are out of all patience at my long absence. I must attend to them to get their plans and estimates finished. I have enclosed you a letter which I think it may be necessary to send to Messrs. Walkers of Rotherham for a tender for the Bridge. I also enclose a specification of my plan sent to Losh and Hawks. Is it yet decided whether the Bridge is to be Stone or Iron? Burrells will send you a few rails of the plan you want. Those that have come will join the crossing at the passing places. I expect you have by this time received a turn-rail. We will put another in hand as it is likely more will be wanted.

I am Dear John
Yours sincerely
Geo. Stephenson

The name of James Walker, who was to play an important part in subsequent discussions on the form of motive power for the Liverpool and Manchester Railway, appears in a letter from Stephenson to Longridge as early as 1824. Walker, already well known as a professional engineer, became President of the Institution of Civil Engineers after Thomas Telford. In the present instance, he was gaining first-hand acquaintance with railways and steam locomotives, with the help of their leading exponent. Benjamin Thompson later became associated with the Newcastle and Carlisle Railway.

Liverpool October 9th 1824

Dear Sir,

Mr. Walker, who I told you was to accompany me over the Liverpool and Manchester line, is from London and not from Gospel Oak, he is a Civil Engineer and I believe ranks high. He will very likely be coming to the North to see the loco-motive engines. I am not sure whether he is a friend of ours or of Mr. Thompson's I think there has been some communication between the latter and him. Thompson is a sly fellow, and I have no doubt is paving his way secretly. Walker is a deep Scotchman. I will give him a letter to you and I hope you will pay every attention to him. He will grapple in all the knowledge of rail-ways he possibly can as there is likely to be so much done in that system.

I am setting off to Birmingham but expect to be back to this neighbourhood the latter end of next week. I have sad work with the surveyors on the Liverpool line. The survey will be all to do over again and the lords of the land in this neighbourhood are most desperately against us.

I am Dear Sir
Yours truly
Geo. Stephenson

The trials of Stephenson's surveying parties during their work on the Liverpool and Manchester line is brought out in the postscript to a letter from Stephenson to Joseph Pease; the main subject of the letter, however, is the making of the iron bridge over the Gaunless for the Stockton and Darlington Railway.

Dear Sir,

Yours of the 16th has been forwarded to me—The remarks that the Rotherham people have made of the liability of the Cast Iron breaking when cast round the Wrought Iron is very erronious, for it is well understood at Newcastle upon Tyne not to have that effect, if a certain allowance is made for the bulk of metal in forming those junctions—I am well aware that none of those people will give themselves the trouble to erect such a Bridge; so long as they have more orders than they can execute, which is the case I suppose with every Ironmaster in the kingdom—As the price of iron has advanced so much lately, and is, still likely to advance higher, on that account I should advise a Stone Bridge to be erected if Mr. Bonomi thinks there is no risk of its tumbling down—I think it would be much safer if the abutment walls were allowed to stand over the dead of winter before the arch is commenced with—If a severe winter should come upon the new oak there might be danger of its settling more in one part than in another You can have Bonomi's opinion on these points—Did not Mr. Longridge send in an offer for the Bridge.

I am Dear Sir
Yours very Truly
Geo. Stephenson

Newcastle under Line
Octr 19th 1824

P.S. We have sad work with Lord Derby, Lord Sefton, and Bradshaw the great Canal Proprietor, whose grounds we go through with the projected railway—Their Ground is blockaded on every side to prevent us getting on with the Survey—Bradshaw fires guns through his ground in the course of the night to prevent the Surveyors coming on in the dark—We are to have a grand field-day next week, the Liverpool Railway Company are determined to force a survey through if possible—Lord Sefton says he will have a hundred men against us—The Company thinks those Great men have no right to stop a Survey It is the Farmers only who have a right to complain and by charging damages for trespass is all they can do—

G.S.

J. Pease Esqr

A very early railway in Lancashire was proposed about this time to connect the textile towns of Bolton and Leigh; alternative routes had been surveyed and the promoters, who were apparently undecided which to adopt, obtained the views of George Stephenson who, having considered the various surveys, set down his opinion with a finality and conviction that was typical of his practical outlook:

Liverpool Nov. 14th 1824

Gentlemen,

Having duly considered the various Lines of the intended Road proposed to Mr. Steel and having the Sections of two before me the practicability of the one and the impracticability of the other is so obvious that it is unnecessary to make any comment on either. The red line represents the intended line of Railway on both Sections. I am sorry I could not attend the meeting but I hope Mr. Steel will be able to make any explanation that may be wanted. I am very confident that the line I have laid out is the best that can be got.

I am Gentlemen
Your ob^t Servt
Geo. Stephenson

We may now go forward to the early part of the year 1827 in order to read Stephenson's own report on the Bolton and Leigh Railway, on which his brother Robert was engaged; it is included here as a characteristic example of Stephenson's views on the laying out of a new railway, a field of engineering in which he became extraordinarily skilled as a result of his widening practical experience:

To the Directors of the Bolton and Leigh Railway—
Gentlemen,

Agreeably with your request I met Messrs. Daglish and Seed at Leigh on the 8th Inst in order to examine the plans, as also the proceedings of the different works, on the line of the Bolton and Leigh Railway—

After seeing the Parliamentary Plan, and also the one prepared by Mr Daglish, we proceeded to that part of the line where it approaches the Leigh Canal, where I found the line had been altered, and brought nearer to Leigh, and certainly on much less favourable ground. For you will be aware that when this line was set out, it was determined to approach the Canal at that part where it could join the Liverpool and Manchester Railway, with the least expence and the most direct line. To do which the line was intended to be kept on as high a level in approaching the Canal, and also to obtain as high ground on the opposite side, as was possible; (the ground at Leigh being so much below the level of that part of the Liverpool & Manchester line where they would meet) now, the intended alteration at this place will actually throw the line into still lower ground, which to preserve the level originally intended, will require a higher embankment, and consequently be an additional expence; besides being a greater diviation from a straight line—

After seeing the ground, it does not, in my opinion, require a moment's consideration to determine which is the best line, and I think Mr. Daglish felt convinced that the alteration which he had proposed to make, was not for the better—

In proceeding up the line towards Checkerbent I did not observe much variation in the ground of the two lines until within half a mile of that place where it is not so favourable on the new line—It was originally intended to bring the Waggons up the assent from about half a mile from Leigh to Checkerbent, by two permanent engines, with a short flat between them, for the convenience of changing the waggons from one engine to the other—The new line shews two incline planes also, but with about a mile of flat intervening, the length of which level will be very obstructive. And an establishment of horses will oblige to be kept there, which will necessarily increase the rate of tunnage, as well as a loss of time—

I found that in crossing Wigan lane the line was lowered 7 or 8 feet more than the Parliamentary one was intended to be. In the latter it was proposed to be a slight uniform assent, so that a horse would take 8 tons towards Bolton. But as it now passes 7 or 8 feet lower at the Manchester and L'pool (line), and 10 or 12 feet higher at Daub-hill Bar, this assent will be such that a horse cannot take more than 6 tons. The expence of embanking would be the same in both cases, as the material produced from the cutts would be more than sufficient in either case. Mr. Daglish's explanation for such alteration, was to save a Bridge at Checkerbent, and also to save cutting at Daubhill Bar, but the sum of these alledged advantages, will by no means compensate for the loss of Loco-motive power by the increase of acclivity between these two places. The difference of expence in excavating, on these two lines, will not be much as both are on a level at one part of the cut, and the greater cutting increases in the form of a wedge in approaching Daubhill Bar, and it is at this place that the cutting is deepest—It is also said that a bridge is saved at Daubhill Bar, which is certainly the Case, but the expence of the walls on the side of the Turnpike road, together with the long slope forming a Roadway, will amount to nearly as much money as a Bridge. The spoiled banks on the sides of the deep cutting ought not by any means to have been made, as that material would have assisted in forming the inclined planes, which by this time might have been at work. If you calculate what expence has been incurred in making these banks into a tillaged state, you will find that it has exceeded their actual worth—This material ought to have been carried to the Inclined plane by wing or side Railways—

The Inclined plane towards Bolton, in my opinion is not laid out as it ought to be, and I can find no reason for any alteration, to the original plan, except a diminution of embankment before Mr. Carlisle's house, which I think will not lessen the compensation to Mr. Carlisle in any thing near the proportion of advantage which the Company would derive by keeping the original plan—

It appears that an engine of 50 Horse power is now making for this plane which I think is quite unnecessary—For the descending goods being so much more than the ascending ones, that little power will be required to assist the descending goods in overcoming the gravity of the ascending ones—A 10 Horse engine would be quite sufficient, and even this power might have been dispenced with had the plain been properly constructed—I do not see that much improvement can be made at the termination of the line at Bolton—As far as I have examined the Bridges, I find them good and firm but they would certainly have cost much less had they been built of Brick—My time was so limited that I could not examine them very particularly, but I think some of them might have been of less dimensions on the Roadway; particularly one which is called a Culvert, & I believe has been more expensive than any Bridge on the line, being 60 feet in length, and I think from 20 to 25 feet quite sufficient.

I examined the construction of your waggons which I certainly do not admire, and the cost I am informed is £24 each waggon—How this cost is made out I am at a loss to know, for I see nothing in their construction that warrants such a sum. We are now using waggons on the Manchester & Liverpool Railway for similar purposes, which I like much better than yours, and which cost us very little more than £5 each, and will carry as great a quantity of material as yours as well as being moved with half the trouble—

I have also examined the stone Blocks prepared for the Railway, they are much larger than I think is necessary, and you might divide each into two and they would still be large enough.

The unfavourableness of the day prevented me from going into the detail as I would otherwise have done; and the classified way in which the items of expenditure given to me, are arranged, I cannot enter into an investigation, whether those items are more than adequate to the work done, without some further information—

As the embankment now making on the decending Plane to Bolton, is much wider than it ought to be, I recommend you to diminish its width and make the joining as soon as possible—The line at the bottom of the Plane, ought to be now laid with the permanent Rails. If the material can be got in Bolton for the formation under the Blocks. As I shall be with you at the time these remarks will be mentioned, I shall endeavour to answer any further questions that may be required.

I am
Gentlemen
Your ob[t] Serv[t]
Geo. Stephenson

Liverpool
10th January 1827.

Stephenson followed up this report with a letter to the Directors of the Bolton and Leigh Railway, complete with estimated costs, as follows:

Gentlemen,

Agreeably with your wish I have made a close inspection of the Bolton and Leigh Railway and am now enabled to lay before you an estimate of the Capital that will be required to complete the Line, as I have taken the levels of the whole Line from Bolton to the Canal at Leigh and made sections of the same, from which you will see that my views a few weeks ago of the spoiled Banks were correct, as the quantity of material now to be excavated at Dean Moor is not sufficient to make the Embankments by about £2000 worth of labor, which, on examining the Books you will find these spoiled Banks to have cost.—

I have made some deviation in the Line near Chequerbent which will considerably lessen the expense of crossing the low ground in approaching that place—I have also made a deviation near Chowbent by running nearer that place, which enables me to make the 50 horse Engine work the whole of that Inclined Plane, the bottom of this Plane will be very convenient for taking or delivering goods at Chowbent—from the bottom of the Plane the Line runs very favourably towards the Canal.

The diviation which is made near Chowbent cuts through some broken sand stone banks which will supply suitable material for ballasting or finishing the road, and will not only be a great saving to the Comp[y] in the first offset, but will hereafter furnish a supply for keeping the road in order. Material can also be got in this quarter to form the Embankment necessary to cross the Canal, when it may be projected to join the Liverpool and Manchester Railway—

As the best or cheapest part of the excavation on Dean Moor is now done, in case the Contractor should not complete it at his present price, I have estimated 1s. per yard for the part that remains to be done—this makes a swell in my estimate, yet I think it necessary to lay before you the outside cost of what I think it will be done for—It will be seen by the section that it will be cheaper to lower part of the Inclined Plane approaching Bolton—

I should not recommend the Comp[y] to make any more warehouses or Depots than are necessary for Coals—

It must be considered that the value of the whole of the rails, chairs, waggons that are now in use, will be deducted from my estimate as they must be disposed of when the Line is completed—also the stone blocks which are already purchased must be deducted—I trust I shall get the blocks for $\frac{1}{3}$ less than I have estimated—I have laid before you the highest amount they possibly can cost—

The following Estimate will show the cost of the different items—

Estimate	£ s. d
10 Miles of Malleable Iron Railway	8250 ,, 0 ,, 0
Cast Iron Chairs for ditto	1760 ,, 0 ,, 0
Stone Blocks for ditto	3520 ,, 0 ,, 0
Laying the Way	2640 ,, 0 ,, 0
2 Permanent Engines	4700 ,, 0 ,, 0
Rollers for the Inclined Planes	594 ,, 0 ,, 0
Ropes for do	550 ,, 0 ,, 0
Keys and Pins for chairs	880 ,, 0 ,, 0
40 Small Waggons	240 ,, 0 ,, 0
40 Large do	960 ,, 0 ,, 0
Forming Emb^ts^ and Excavations	8331 ,, 1 ,, 6
Carriage of Rails, chairs, & blocks to different parts of the Line	2000 ,, 0 ,, 0
Bridge	300 ,, 0 ,, 0
Culverts	500 ,, 0 ,, 0
Fencing	880 ,, 0 ,, 0
Depôts at each end of the Line	800 ,, 0 ,, 0
Agencies & Casualities	1000 ,, 0 ,, 0
	£37905 ,, 1 ,, 6

Geo. Stephenson

Liverpool Feby 28th, 1827

To return to the year 1824, Russian interest in British railway developments was in evidence, not for the first time, for the first record of a visiting Russian to an English railway had taken place in 1812 (a momentous year for Russia) when the Grand Duke Nicholas, who became Tsar Nicholas I, visited the Blenkinsop rack railway at Leeds and saw the performance of the steam locomotives built by Matthew Murray, whose firm afterwards sent a model of a rack locomotive to Russia. Stephenson writes to Michael Longridge about this time:

Golden Lion Inn, Chester
Oct 23rd 1824

Dear Sir,

I have been hurried about from place to place which prevented me writing to you sooner—I wrote to Mr. Gordon in answer to his letter about Cabery I shall be in the neighbourhood of Liverpool and Chester the whole of next week—Will there be any good done with the Russian Railway people—I suppose I shall have the Russian Gentleman with me the next week—

What has been done with Mr. Locke—We are most sadly beset with Lord Derby, Lord Sefton and the canal interests—The coach is just going to move I must be off—

I am Dear Sir
Yours truly
Geo. Stephenson

Michael Longridge Esqr

The reference to Joseph Locke is interesting. He was then twenty years old, but had entered the services of Stephenson during the previous year; his father had been a fellow-employee with Stephenson at a colliery near Newburn. Young Locke's formal agreement to serve Stephenson as an engineer and clerk for two years at a salary of £80 per annum was not, however, signed until 11 January 1825, so it would seem that Stephenson, then heavily engaged at Liverpool, was wanting to know how Locke's time was being spent. Stephenson was also giving thought to the construction of the quay at Stockton, for he writes to Longridge, from Chester, as follows:

Chester, November 16th, 1824

Dear Sir,

I dare say Mr. Storey is the most proper person to send to survey the Docks, if the survey is to be done immediately. I am afraid he can not be spared from his present employment. Have you sounded Mr. Pease on the matter? I think Storey and the Darlington people are on better terms than they were; at least it appears so from his letters to me. As I will have to be in London early in the ensuing year—can the surveying of the Docks not be put off until then? At that time I can also superintend the erection of Messrs. McNay's paper machine.

There are nothing but railways and rumours of Railways in this country. I am desired to examine Lord Crew's Coalworks in the neighbourhood of Newcastle under line and give a report thereon; as I can make it convenient to do so. Several other Coalowners in this neighbourhood desire me to give similar reports. How I shall get all ends to meet I do not know. I think your words will come true. I shall have to work until I am an old man. I have a bag full of news to tell you on the defects of your rails. You have got your friends in the north as well as myself. The indirect secrets are getting out. It is astonishing the deep schemes that men contrive for the overthrow of their neighbour: and how often does it fall upon their own heads. I assure you I have been twisted backwards and forwards as I think few poor fellows ever were. Notwithstanding all those difficulties my spirits are still up, and I think I have got four times as much face as I had when I inhabited the north. I am sometimes obliged to use my tongue like a scolding wife.

I shall be in the neighbourhood of Liverpool and Chester all this next week.

My kind respects to Mrs. Longridge and your family: also to Mr. and Mrs. Birkinshaw: not forgetting my friend Mr. Gooch. It is now eleven O'Clock and a great deal of work yet to do. I cannot get to bed at your time.

I am Dear Sir
Yours very sincerely
Geo: Stephenson

P.S. You had better write to Richardson to see if the survey can be put off until I arrive in London: but do not lose the job for that. I will send a surveyor from here if we cannot do better.—G.S.

The allusion to defects in the rails manufactured at Longridge's works at Bedlington is perhaps connected with the splitting or flaking-off of laminations which occurred in the early days of their production. The Richardson mentioned in the P.S. was not the banker, of course, but Joshua Richardson who afterwards became resident engineer on the Canterbury and Whitstable Railway.

Stephenson's alertness to the possibilities of railway development (and of fostering an interest in what was being accomplished in the Forth Street Works) is shown in a letter, delivered by hand to John Buddle who was described by Rolt as 'the most celebrated mining engineer of the day becoming known on the Tyne as "The King of the Coal Trade" '; he had been Sir Humphry Davy's chief representative in the North of England. Moreover, Buddle was an associate of the Durham engineer, William Chapman, also a pioneer in locomotive construction. Stephenson writes:

J. Buddle Esqr
Sir,

It would give me great pleasure if you could spend a short time in looking through our manufactory some time to-day, as we are fitting up some Bearings for Waggon axles on the principle of the Mail-coach; which plan from your experience you must be aware is much wanted on Coal-waggons. Your opinion on this plan will much oblige me—I was thinking that as a railway is making under your inspection in the neighbourhood of Berwick this plan would be acceptable. Would you have the goodness to inform the Bearer whether you can favour me with your company, as I shall not have another opportunity of seeing you for some time, for I leave here for Liverpool on Monday.

I am
Sir
Yours obed^{t} Servt
Geo. Stephenson

Newcastle
Sept. 23, 1826

We must now come back to the year 1825, which proved to be one of the most eventful of all the crowded years of Stephenson's life, equalled only by that most historic period from the middle of 1829 to the middle of 1830, by which time his fame had soared to its zenith. The construction of the Stockton and Darlington Railway had been somewhat delayed by the appalling weather conditions of the long, cold, wet winter of 1824–5 which had made the ballasting extremely difficult and the transport of the materials almost impossible. However, the iron bridge designed by Stephenson was now in position over the River Gaunless, and a start was made in the organization of a locomotive department. In January a deputation of seven engineers visited Killingworth on behalf of the Committee of the Liverpool and Manchester Railway, in order to obtain first-hand impressions of the performance of Stephenson's engines. The party included James Walker. A fascinating description of the events of the day was recorded in *The Times* on 8 February 1825. Demonstrations were given with 'an old and imperfect engine' which did 4 m.p.h. with a moderate load, and with 'a superior engine' hauling a load of 48 tons at speeds varying from 7 to 9½ m.p.h. Walker, who had perceived the condition of the track, observed that 'had the Rail-way been good and well fixed, the result would have been higher'.

Another notable visitor was William Strickland, who arrived in 1825 from Pennsylvania on a fact-finding mission on canals and railways. He observed the Stephenson locomotives at Hetton Colliery and noted that Stephenson recommended the use of six wheels instead of four, to distribute the weight better 'and perhaps to increase the friction of the wheels on the railway'.

Stephenson, despite his major preoccupations at Liverpool, was also much concerned to see the Stockton and Darlington project through, and was now giving thought to the organization of its locomotive department. In 1825 the Company accepted his recommendation that Timothy Hackworth (then employed at the Forth Street Works) be appointed to take charge of it. Hackworth (1785–1850) was undoubtedly one of the most talented locomotive engineers of the day, and Stephenson's recommendation of him was absolutely sound.

Stephenson, now on the threshold of the most strenuous and exhausting period of his life, learned that on 21 March 1825 the Liverpool and Manchester Railway Bill had gone into the Committee stage in the House of Commons. The dreadful ordeal which he underwent during those dark days of 25 to 27 March, when he was brutally humiliated in the witness-box, must have left ineffaceable impressions. The story is told in every biography of Stephenson; here, where his letters are our principal concern, it is only necessary to recount that he found himself up against the most formidable opposition that could possibly have been assembled against him: the great landowners, whose power in those days was almost like that of feudal chiefs, and the canal promoters, whose supporters had concluded that their interests were being threatened with extinction. Unluckily for him, the accuracy of his survey was called into question, and he could not defend it because there were faults in it, serious enough to create doubts about the quality of his work. When one considers how he and his assistants had been harassed when attempting to carry out the survey—going in risk of their lives on some occasions—it is hardly surprising that errors should have occurred. The opponents of the railway, with their Parliamentary lawyers led by Alderson, had their time of triumph and the Bill was thrown out.

The Directors of the Company, however, decided to make a fresh attempt to get their Bill accepted, though this meant a wait until the next Parliamentary session. It speaks volumes for Stephenson's strong personality that, even at such a critical time, his confidence in the future for railways was as unassailable as ever, and continued to impress his directors, who did not really want to lose his services, as he was without question the most experienced railway and locomotive engineer of his time. But he did not shine in the witness-box; his way of speaking, though it could be impressive, was slow; his Northumbrian dialect was against him; and the Directors' most urgent need of the moment was for talents of quite a different order, which would excel in the cut-and-thrust of Parliamentary debate. Stephenson's reputation had been gained in the North; they needed a national figure. So they called in George and John Rennie, whose standing as civil engineers was of the highest, and under whose direction a gifted young engineer, Charles Vignoles, carried out a fresh survey, avoiding as far as possible the estates of the landed proprietors, and making closer approaches to locations where coal was to be got. Further, compensation was promised to landowners for full value of their land. A new Bill was submitted; it was read in the Commons for the first time on 7 February 1826 and passed with a majority of 47 on 5 May; the Lords produced only the Earl of Derby and the Earl of Wilton as dissentients. There were 200 clauses in the Act, as passed; it is remarkable that only one of them contains a reference to locomotives, but their use was certainly intended, as it was laid down that they should be so constructed as to consume their own smoke.

However, to return to 1825, the period between the defeat of the first Bill and the passing of the second must have been a time of intense depression for Stephenson, especially as some of his former friends and backers lost faith in him, and even Edward Pease appeared to waver in his usually staunch support. Joseph Sandars, however, remained unshaken in his belief in the soundness of Stephenson's ideas; but in general the cause of the steam locomotive had received a serious setback.

Stephenson, however, was far from idle at this time. He became associated with the Nantlle Railway, North Wales, which received its authorization in May 1825, and was to run from slate quarries at Cloddfarlon down to the quayside at Caernarvon. This line was remarkable for two very non-Stephenson characteristics: it was to have a gauge of 3 ft. 6 in. and was to be worked by horses. Stephenson's elder brother, Robert, supervised operations, aided by a young engineer named John Gillespie, who afterwards assisted with the Leicester and Swannington Railway.

It is one of the most heart-warming things about Stephenson that, in the midst of the worst of his worries about the biggest engineering project he (or anyone else in Britain) had yet attempted, he found time to keep in touch with old friends of his Killingworth days. The remorseless drive which he applied to himself did not diminish his efforts to help his former companions. The appended letter to Joseph Cabry (still 'exiled' in Cheshire) has a ring of sincerity, with an added interest in being one of the few surviving letters written in Stephenson's own hand:

London May 8th 1825
4 Norfolk Street Strand

My Dear Sir,

I duly received your favour for which I am much oblight to you we have

Fig 21. George Stephenson giving lessons in embroidery to Edward Pease's daughters (From a painting by A. Rankley)

hard fighting in parliament but I hope we shall get the Bill the great thing against us is time having so many witnesses to examine—it strikes me your family would like you to be in your own country now if you think any thing a bout it let me know I think I could contrive a suitable job for you and one that would please you all the day of your life and I am shore it would please you sons for it would a gain get you all to geather what can the job be you will be thinking it is to look after the whole of the men in our manufactry to keep each mans time and to see that every man attends to his work in time in the morning and to consult with the forman on all matters belonging to the concern you would have man (?) to work now I am shore there is not any thing I know would sute you so well as this—there is nothing will stop you but wages and I am shore when you get older you will have a gretter desire to be with your sons after you have duly considered this let me no—I have had a very flattering letter from Robert he has discovered 3 seams of Coals in Colombia one of them 8 feet thick and 1–3 feet and of exelent quality he does not say much about the gold & silver as he is not alowed to speak on that part to any one but the Company he has his health well and wrights in good spirart Mrs S joins me in best respects to Mrs Cabry and believe me

Dear Sir your faithfully
G Stephenson

(Addressed to: Mr. Joseph Cabray
Engineer
Neston Colliery
near Park gate
Cheshire)

Meanwhile, the Stockton and Darlington Railway was nearing completion; and when the summer of 1825 drew on, preparations were made for a grand opening ceremony, as the Directors were well aware that the inauguration would be a unique national event: there could never be another *first* public railway line. Although the transport of passengers was regarded as of much less importance than that of coal, the company ordered the first passenger vehicle; the framework was constructed at the Forth Street Works, but the bodywork, looking rather like a hen-house, was made by local craftsmen. Named the 'Experiment', this carriage had seats arranged lengthways, a table being planted between them. The vehicle was devoid of springs. It was completed just before the inaugural day.

Early in September 1825, Stephenson informed the Directors of the Company that the railway would shortly be ready for the opening ceremony and suggested Tuesday, 27 September, as the date. His recommendation was accepted, and the following historic notice accordingly appeared in the newspapers:

STOCKTON AND DARLINGTON RAILWAY

The Proprietors of the above concern hereby give notice, that their main line of railway, commencing at Witton Park Colliery, in the west of this county, and terminating at Stockton-upon-Tees, with the several branches to Darlington, Yarm, etc., being in extent about twenty-seven miles, will be formally opened, for the general purposes of trade, on Tuesday, the 27th instant. It is the intention of the Proprietors to meet at the permanent steam engine, erected below the tower at Brusselton, near West Auckland, and situated about nine miles west of Darlington, at 8 o'clock a.m., and after inspecting their extensive inclined planes there, proceed at 9 o'clock precisely, by way of Darlington and Yarm, to Stockton-upon-Tees, where it is calculated they will arrive about 1 o'clock. An elegant dinner will be provided for the company who may attend, by Mr. Foxton, at the Town's Hall, Stockton, at 3 o'clock, to which the proprietors have resolved to invite the neighbouring nobility and gentry who have taken an interest in this very important undertaking. A superior locomotive engine, on the most improved construction will be employed, with a train of convenient carriages, for the conveyance of the proprietors and strangers. Any gentleman who may intend to be present on the above occasion will oblige the company by addressing a note to their office at Darlington as early as possible.

14 September, 1825

Stockton & Darlington

Railway.

The Company's

COACH

CALLED THE

EXPERIMENT,

Which commenced Travelling on **MONDAY**, the **10th** of **OCTOBER, 1825**, will continue to run from *Darlington* to *Stockton*, and from *Stockton* to *Darlington* every Day, [Sunday's excepted] setting off from the **DEPOT** at each place, at the times specified as under, (*viz.*):---

ON MONDAY,

From Stockton at half-past 7 in the Morning, and will reach Darlington about half-past 9; the Coach will set off from the latter place on its return at 3 in the Afternoon, and reach Stockton about 5.

TUESDAY,

From Stockton at 3 in the Afternoon, and will reach Darlington about 5.

On the following Days, viz.:---

WEDNESDAY, THURSDAY & FRIDAY,

From Darlington at half-past 7 in the Morning, and will reach Stockton about half-past 9; the Coach will set off from the latter place on its return at 3 in the Afternoon, and reach Darlington about 5.

SATURDAY,

From Darlington at 1 in the Afternoon, and will reach Stockton about 3.

Passengers to pay 1s. each, and will be allowed a Package of not exceeding 14lb. all above that weight to pay at the rate of 2d. per Stone extra. Carriage of small Parcels 3d. each. The Company will not be accountable for Parcels of above £5. Value, unless paid for as such.

Mr. RICHARD PICKERSGILL at his Office in Commercial Street, Darlington; and Mr TULLY at Stockton, will for the present receive any Parcels and Book Passengers.

APPLETON PRINTER DARLINGTON.

Fig 22. Reproduction, postcard size, of Stockton and Darlington Railway poster announcing the 'Experiment' passenger coach.

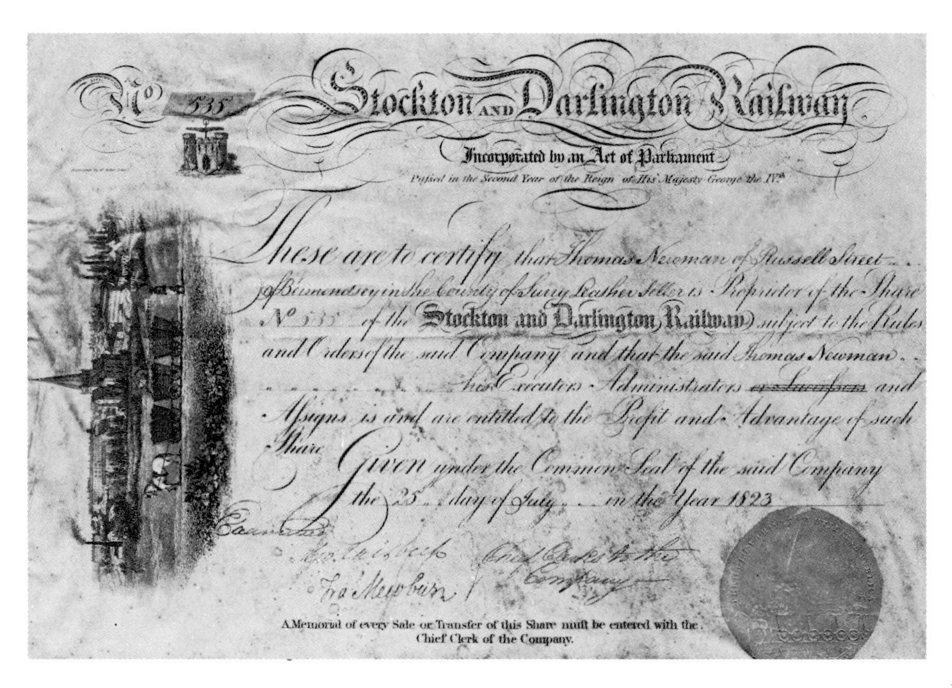

No 535 Stockton and Darlington Railway

Incorporated by an Act of Parliament

Passed in the Second Year of the Reign of His Majesty George the IVth

These are to certify that Thomas Newman of Russell Street of Bermondsey in the County of Surry Leather Seller is Proprietor of the Share No 535 of the Stockton and Darlington Railway subject to the Rules and Orders of the said Company and that the said Thomas Newman his Executors Administrators and Assigns is and are entitled to the Profit and Advantage of such Share

Given under the Common Seal of the said Company the 25 day of July in the Year 1823

Chief Clerks to the Company

Fra Mewburn

A Memorial of every Sale or Transfer of this Share must be entered with the Chief Clerk of the Company.

Fig 23. Share certificate, Stockton and Darlington Railway. (Photo : Science Museum, London)

Five days later a handbill was issued, to supplement the formal notice.

The railway was single track, with four sidings to the mile, to serve as passing places; there were no stations, platforms, or signals. From the start of the track at Witton, 470 ft. above sea level, the line rose to the top of the Etherley Incline, up which the trains were hauled by a 30 h.p. stationary engine (150 ft. rise in $\frac{1}{2}$ mile); when over the top they were lowered down the other side (312 ft. descent in 1 mile). The Brusselton Incline involved a rise of 150 ft. in $1\frac{1}{4}$ miles and was worked by a 60 h.p. stationary engine. In a description of the original railway, which appeared in the *Northern Echo* (Railway Centenary Supplement 1925) it was stated:

> In operation there were many accidents . . . the rope would stretch by as much as 70 fathoms in a single day! After stretching, the rope would break and the wagons rush down to destruction.
>
> For the upward journey Timothy Hackworth invented an ingenious device called a 'cow'. It consisted of iron bars which were held off the ground behind the last wagon by the tension of the rope. When the rope broke the bars fell on to the line and derailed the wagons.
>
> The wagons were lowered down the Shildon end of Brusselton Bank also by rope, but the 'cow' device was useless there, and lads had to be stationed at dangerous points to leap on to the wagons and apply the brakes in case of necessity or to throw the wagons off the line by means of wood blocks.

One can realize, from this description, why George Stephenson was so strongly in favour of locomotive haulage. But the notion of rope traction

Printed from a copy in the possession of
H. NICHOLSON, WHALLEY RANGE, MANCHESTER.

THE
STOCKTON & DARLINGTON
RAILWAY COMPANY
Hereby give Notice,

THAT the FORMAL OPENING of their RAILWAY will take place on the 27th instant, as announced in the public Papers.—The Proprietors will assemble at the Permanent Steam Engine, situated below BRUSSELTON TOWER*, *about nine Miles West of* DARLINGTON *at 8 o'clock, and after examining their extensive inclined Planes there, will start from the Foot of the* BRUSSELTON *descending Plane, at 9 o'clock, in the following Order:—*

1. THE COMPANY'S LOCOMOTIVE ENGINE.
2. THE ENGINE'S TENDER, with Water and Coals.
3. SIX WAGGONS, laden with Coals, Merchandize, &c.
4. THE COMMITTEE, and other PROPRIETORS, in the COACH belonging to the COMPANY.
5. SIX WAGGONS, with Seats reserved for STRANGERS.
6. FOURTEEN WAGGONS, for the Conveyance of Workmen and others.

The WHOLE of the above to proceed to STOCKTON.

7. SIX WAGGONS, laden with Coals, to leave the Procession at the DARLINGTON BRANCH.
8. SIX WAGGONS, drawn by Horses, for Workmen and others.
9. Ditto Ditto.
10. Ditto Ditto.
11. Ditto Ditto.

The COMPANY'S WORKMEN to leave the Procession at DARLINGTON, and DINE at that Place at ONE o'clock; excepting those to whom Tickets are specially given for YARM, and for whom Conveyances will be provided, on their Arrival at STOCKTON.

TICKETS will be given to the Workmen who are to dine at DARLINGTON, specifying the Houses of Entertainment.

The PROPRIETORS, and such of the NOBILITY and GENTRY as may honour them with their Company, will DINE precisely at THREE o'clock, at the TOWN-HALL, STOCKTON.—Such of the Party as may incline to return to DARLINGTON that Evening, will find Conveyances in waiting for their Accommodation, to start from the COMPANY'S WHARF there precisely at SEVEN o'clock.

The COMPANY take this Opportunity of enjoining on all their WORKPEOPLE that Attention to *Sobriety* and *Decorum* which they have hitherto had the Pleasure of observing.

The COMMITTEE give this PUBLIC NOTICE, that all Persons who shall ride upon, or by the sides of, the RAILWAY, on Horseback, will incur the Penalties imposed by the Acts of Parliament passed relative to this RAILWAY.

*Any Individuals desirous of seeing the TRAIN of Waggons descending the inclined Plane from ETHERLEY, and in Progress to BRUSSELTON, may have an Opportunity of so doing, by being on the RAILWAY at ST. HELEN'S AUCKLAND not later than Half-past Seven o'clock.

RAILWAY-OFFICE, *Sept. 19th*, 1825.

ATKINSON'S Office, High Row, Darlington.

Fig 24. Public notice of the opening of the Stockton and Darlington Railway.

by stationary engines was to remain entrenched in many quarters for some years. A delightful memorial of the occasion, which has come down to us, is the letter written by Stephenson to Joseph Swanwick, inviting him to the inauguration of the line. He was the father of Frederick Swanwick, described by W. R. Parsonage, in the paper on Stephenson which he presented to the Institution,* as 'the illustrious pupil, afterwards business associate and personal friend, of George Stephenson', who acted as his scribe during one of the most hectic periods of Stephenson's crowded life; few can have known the great man better. The letter was treasured in the Swanwick family and was made available to the Institution through

* *Proc. I. Mech. E. 1937*, vol. 136, p. 373.

Frederick's grandson, County Alderman E. D. Swanwick, M.A., of Chesterfield. The letter reads:

Newcastle on Tyne Sepr 18th 1825

Dear Swanwick,

I just have time to request that you will favour me with your company at the opening of the Darlington rail-way. As the rail-way system has met with so many checks since I last saw you, perhaps you may not be so warm an advocate in their cause as you were; but I am quite sure that a sight of this rail-way will give you as high an opinion of this mode of conveyance, as you ever had. Do favour me with your company,—the line will be opened on the 27th Inst.

My best regards to Mrs. Swanwick and all your family.

I should like young Mr. Javins of Liverpool to accompany you. Will you send him a note with my compliments?

I am, Dear Sir,
Yours very sincerely,
Geo. Stephenson

But to return to the opening ceremony: from daybreak people began to arrive in great streams from all directions to see the spectacle. Not all were well disposed towards the idea of railways; it has been suggested that, on that day, people who were friendly disposed towards the railway were outnumbered by its enemies who came along to gloat if it should be a failure. The vested interests in horses and canals for transport were very considerable.

The 'star' of this great gathering was 'Locomotion No. 1', which was given the honour of drawing the first official train. The *Northern Echo* account states 'she was the centre of a great crowd, who speculated as to the uses of her various parts' (one would give much for a tape-recording of this, if only it had been possible):

It was, therefore, under difficulties that the train was marshalled and attached to Locomotion. Three hundred tickets had been distributed (one for each shareholder, with extra tickets for every ten shares), but tickets were of no more use than—to give a modern instance—they were at the first Wembley cup-final. The crowd simply rushed the wagons and filled them to overflowing.

The railwaymen were there in force, each wearing a blue riband in his buttonhole, or, if he was on duty, a broad blue sash.

It is recorded that, before starting, Locomotion let off a little steam to the consternation of the 'Johnny Raws' around her, who fled in all directions.

George Stephenson and his brothers James and Ralph were on the engine and Timothy Hackworth is said to have acted as guard . . . 'All ready', shouted Hackworth, and the procession started with banners flying (four of them).

The blue-sashed men were all in their places—one between each pair of

Fig 25. George Stephenson's 'Locomotion No. 1, 1825' for the Stockton and Darlington Railway, now at North Road Station, Darlington. (Photo: British Railways)

wagons to brake when necessary— . . . the machine now moved forward at a rate of 10 to 12 miles per hour, with its train of 38 carriages, weighing some 80 tons or 90 tons.

A man on horseback preceded the 400 ft. long train, which was followed by a procession of 24 horse-drawn wagons, crowded with passengers. In the middle of the train was the Company's sole passenger vehicle, the 18-seater 'Experiment', proudly bearing the Company's arms painted on its side, together with the motto 'Periculum privatum, utilitas publica'. At Darlington, reached at 12 noon, six wagons were detached, their place being taken by two other wagons conveying respectively a group of local notabilities and the famous Yarm Band. Excitement grew and the train started out of Darlington

with people clinging to the wagons like a swarm of bees, so that the passengers numbered some 600 or 700 in all. Stockton was reached triumphantly at a quarter to four.

Down at the quay, a seven-gun salute was fired three times; the band then struck up the National Anthem. A procession of guests to the Town Hall was followed by a banquet at which 23 *official* toasts were drunk, starting with the Loyal Toast and ending with the toast of 'George

Fig 26. 'George Stevenson Esq.', portrait engraving by Moses Haughton, now in The Institution of Mechanical Engineers.

Fig 27. Copper plaque depicting the 'Locomotion' and the Bulmer Stone, Darlington, a gathering-point from which news was read and announcements made to the inhabitants (probably from Robert Stephenson and Company). (Courtesy: B. Lindqvist)

Fig 28. Reproduction of John Dobbin's painting, 'Opening of the first public railway – the Stockton and Darlington, 27 September 1825'. (By kind permission of the Borough Libraries and Curator of the Public Library, Darlington)

Stephenson, Esq., the Company's Surveyor'. The Chairman of the Company, Thomas Meynell, of Yarm, took the chair at this tremendous banquet.

The day must have provided an unforgettable spectacle for all who saw it, and no one can have been more relieved than Stephenson that it went off without mishap, despite the frightful risks taken by the passengers in the 'convenient carriages'. A journalist eye-witness writing for 'The Scotsman' was captivated by what he saw that day:

> Nothing could exceed the beauty and grandeur of the scene. Throughout the whole distance the fields and lanes were covered with elegantly dressed females and all descriptions of spectators. The bridges, under which the procession in some places darted through with astonishing rapidity, lined with spectators cheering and waving their hats, had a grand effect. . . . At one time the passengers by the engine had the pleasure of accompanying and cheering their brother passengers by the stage coach which passed alongside and observing the striking contrast exhibited by the power of the engine and the horse—the engine with her 600 passengers and load and the coach with four horses and only 16 passengers.

A more symbolic portent of the challenge to the stage coach by the railway could hardly have been imagined; it must have been, also, a tremendously heart-warming occasion for Stephenson after his grim conflict with Parliamentary lawyers six months earlier. His belief in railways and in steam traction was vindicated—temporarily, at least—and the Stockton and Darlington line was in operation. As a distinguished railway historian of our day, R. M. Robbins, pithily put it:

Its inception and business management were due primarily to Edward Pease; its technical features were due to George Stephenson practically alone.*

Stephenson did not relax his efforts in the slightest degree after this great personal triumph. Within a few days he had gone to Canterbury, in connection with a proposal to build a railway to Whitstable; a fortnight later he had joined Longridge in a journey to Edinburgh and Glasgow. His physical endurance was phenomenal. It was certainly going to be needed in the next great stage of his career.

* Robbins, R. M. *George and Robert Stephenson*, Oxford University Press (The Clarendon Biographies), 1966.

2

Struggle for the Adoption of the Steam Locomotive, 1825–31

The successful start of the Stockton and Darlington Railway must have reinforced ideas which had been germinating for a long time in Stephenson's mind—ideas for his taking the initiative in the establishment of a main line railway network for the whole country, perhaps inspired by William James's visions of a like nature. The railway-construction firm of George Stephenson and Son (as distinct from the locomotive-building and marine engineering firm of Robert Stephenson & Co.) had already made (as we have seen) a tentative national plan, envisaging certain specified railways for different regions. This plan was discussed on 31 December 1824, in great detail, and the allocation of Stephenson's assistants to the construction of these lines was agreed. It was a cardinal principle of Stephenson's, in railway development schemes, to rely on one main line between the great termini, with various branch lines (dictated by industries, traffic potential, and local geography) acting as feeders. The proposal to construct the London and Northern Rail Road under Robert Stephenson, was made while he was in South America, but with the expectation that he would not be away from England for more than a year. The fact that he was absent for three years put a severe strain on George Stephenson and Son, which was gradually transformed into a consulting engineering firm, eventually with offices in London which Robert Stephenson in later life made his own.

George Stephenson, throughout many years, had cherished the notion of a coastal railway between Newcastle and Edinburgh, which in due course would become part of an Edinburgh–London rail link. While Robert was struggling to organize his forces in Colombia, George paid a visit to Michael Longridge, who described it in a letter to Robert, written at Morpeth on 2 November 1825. He writes:

I am here to accompany your father who joins me to-morrow when we go together to Edinburgh and Glasgow—and return by way of Carlisle. This recalls to my recollection the day when, at the same place and nearly at the same time of the year, I entered the self same coach and found you, your Father, Mr. Hill, and our friend James seated 'Cheek by Jowl'—'alas, how time escapes, 'tis even so'—but why should we regret the escape of Time? It makes us wiser and ought to make us better . . . my imagination pictures the time when seated around my fire-side at Bedlington Iron Works—my head still more 'Silvered o'er with age' than it is now, I shall see you with your God-daughter sitting on your knee, and listening to the Traveller's Tales which you promise, for I shall regret if you suppress any real occurrences which befel you. I had rather given some license to high colouring than have a bare detail of dates and journeyings. I feel to-night as though I were sitting talking to you, and can hardly bring my pen to narrate such common matter-of-fact subjects as that we continue to be overwhelmed with business at Bedlington Iron Works.

Interruptions during Longridge's travels in Scotland with Stephenson caused the letter to be disjointed; it was continued, from Glasgow, on 8 November, and completed, from London, on 27 February 1826. It is an important letter, as its last portion deals with the very attractive offer made to Robert, through Thomas Richardson, under which the Colombian Mining Association would retain Robert's services as their chief agent, or Director. Longridge fervently hoped Robert would decline; in the event, George Stephenson also was brought into the correspondence, for Robert's prolonged absence was seriously affecting the direction of the Forth Street Works, at which Michael Longridge was acting only as a caretaker Director until Robert's return. In fact, Robert fulfilled his contract in Colombia to the letter, and declined any further appointment with the Mining Association. Longridge concludes his letter thus:

I feel anxious for your return, and I think that you will find your Father and your Friend considerably older than when you left us. Pray take care of your own (health) and let us see you able as well mentally as physically to fill up our stations.

The Stockton and Darlington Railway, still in its infancy, was a source of much concern to Stephenson at this time; without Robert beside him, he was deprived of a most valuable aid, especially in connection with the locomotives—a field in which Robert, even at the age of twenty-three, was exceptionally talented. Much responsibility, therefore, rested on Timothy Hackworth, who in 1825 had been appointed to take charge of locomotive maintenance for the Company, under the general surveillance of Thomas Storey. A letter from Stephenson to Hackworth, preserved in the Science Museum, is of interest:

Newcastle Jan 12

Dear Timothy,

If you have any fear or trouble with the cranks let me know by return of post: and I will send the long ones over and two single crank pins: to fit the large holes of the Wheel. It appears to me; that one of the side rods, must have bent to let the other get over the Centre: otherwise it could not get past.

How does the new plan of wheels do? is there any appearance of working loose? How does the old Engine get on?

I hope by the time you have got the Shops covered in, so as to get the Engines under cover to repair them.

I hope Robert Morry will get his heart up and try to do better it certainly was a sad mistake in him to leave the Engine as he did at Darlington last Saturday night.

We will not be long in getting another Engine ready for you—so that you will have more time to repair—

I am dear Timothy
Yours truly
Geo. Stephenson

But Stephenson now had to turn his attention to the Liverpool and Manchester Railway, which was to be his main concern for the next four years.

The Directors of the Company at first decided to engage the services of the Rennie brothers; it was then agreed that one of the two brothers, George, should be chief (or consulting) engineer, who should make six visits annually to the line, and should have under him a resident engineer for construction (to be appointed) and an operative engineer (George Stephenson or J. U. Rastrick). Rennie, however, had second thoughts, informing the Directors on 17 June 1826 that, though he would not object to Mr. Jessop or Mr. Telford or any member of the Society of Engineers being consulted, he would not be associated in any way with Rastrick or Stephenson. Probably the line taken by Rennie with the Directors was too high-handed, for they declined to accept his terms; then Joseph Sandars withdrew Rastrick's candidature (as his terms were stated to be unacceptable), so that the door was left wide open for Stephenson, who was appointed chief engineer of the railway at a salary of £1,000 a year. He was to devote practically the whole of his time to its construction; further he was not to undertake the making of any other line till the Liverpool and Manchester works were completed. This restriction afterwards became irksome for Stephenson, as he had to decline the post of chief engineer to several railways, and had to suggest Robert, or an assistant, for any such position. His request to take the Canterbury and Whitstable appointment led to the famous remark by the Chairman of the Liverpool and Manchester Railway, 'No; thirty-one miles is enough for any man'.

Charles Vignoles was still 'on the strength' as acting engineer, and this rather uncomfortable situation (for him) lasted until February 1827 when he resigned, largely because of temperamental differences between him and Stephenson. He later became a very celebrated engineer, specializing in railways.

For the time being, however, Vignoles and Stephenson went over the line on a fresh survey. When all was ready for construction to begin, Stephenson divided the line into three sections and appointed an assistant to take charge of each. John Dixon was transferred from the Stockton and Darlington Railway to take charge of the eastern section, which included the notorious morass known as Chat Moss; William Allcard, who had worked during 1825 on a survey for a line from Birmingham to Liverpool (which was not built as originally planned) had the central section; and Charles Vignoles initially took over the western section. Thomas Gooch was appointed chief draughtsman.

Fig 29. Silver loving-cup presented by William Allcard to 'Geordy' (George Stephenson).

Dixon began his work by attacking Chat Moss without delay, after an inauspicious start—he fell into it and had to be rescued by Joseph Locke. Dendy Marshall in his classical *Centenary History of the Liverpool and Manchester Railway* writes:

> Much testimony was given in Parliament as to the impracticability of making a line over the Moss; one witness estimating the cost at £270,000.* In the end, it turned out to be only £28,000. The method adopted was to spread hurdles,

* This witness was Francis Giles (see p. 141).

Fig 30. Chat Moss, Liverpool and Manchester Railway. (From an aquatint by J. T. Bury, published by R. Ackermann, 1831)

interwoven with heather, in a double layer with their ends overlapping, thus forming a floating road. In the centre it was found useless to dig drains, as they filled up as quickly as they were made, so lines of empty tar barrels were laid and covered with clay, to form a course for the water.

The worst part was at the Manchester end; months of work produced no apparent effect, and there was talk of abandoning the job. Stephenson's determination won the battle, however, and this part of the line was finished by 1 January 1830. Dendy Marshall writes:

It eventually proved to be the most satisfactory part of the line.

Fig 31. Olive Mount Cutting, Liverpool and Manchester Railway. (From an aquatint by J. T. Bury, published by R. Ackermann, 1831)

In September 1826 construction of the tunnel at the Liverpool end, which was to convey trains to Wapping (Liverpool) for shipment of their contents, had begun under Vignoles, and continued until he was replaced by Joseph Locke. Liverpool itself was reached by a spectacular cutting at Olive Mount, where it passed through the red sandstone rocks. The length of the cutting was about two miles; in places the depth exceeded 100 ft. About 480,000 cu. yd. of rock had to be excavated. The length of the Edgehill tunnel was 2,240 yd., and construction was difficult, because sand and water were present. Care had to be taken to prevent any falls of rock, and to obviate damage to the land surface. The excavation was divided into several lengths.

The whole line required the construction of 63 bridges, of which Rainhill Bridge is of special interest; it is perhaps the first instance of skew bridge construction in masonry. The road crosses the railway at an angle of 34 deg. The great Sankey viaduct, of brick, faced with stone, carried the line on nine arches across the Sankey Valley; its building cost was £45,000. It is an impressive monument to Stephenson's genius. There were notable bridges also at Newton, and over the River Irwell (Manchester) and above Water Street, Manchester (which bridge was demolished in 1910).

At the Liverpool end, the first terminus was at Crown Street, approached by the celebrated Moorish Arch (later demolished). The gradient down to Wapping was 1 in 48.

Stationary engines were used to haul the trains up the steeper gradients, always known as 'inclined planes'; such an installation was provided at Edgehill; other stationary engines were erected at the tops of the inclined planes (gradients of 1 in 96) at each end of the Rainhill level portion, and were known as the Rainhill and the Sutton engines respectively. It is rather curious that Stephenson, with his disapproval of stationary engines, did not modify the plan of the line so as to avoid these stationary-engine workings, even though they were common practice in the collieries among which he grew up. However, it must be remembered that the incorporation of the inclined planes did reduce the earthworks very considerably, and hence the constructional costs, and they did not form a very large proportion of the total length.

The worries of the Liverpool and Manchester Railway (for it should be remembered that no civil engineering project on such a scale had ever before been attempted) would have been enough even for Stephenson; but there were also worries arising from the Forth Street Works, where Robert's talents were sadly needed to direct the enterprise. Michael Longridge was doing his best to keep an eye on operations there, but the time he was able to spare was limited. However, by the end of 1826 it was estimated that £12,000 worth of orders had been carried out by Robert Stephenson & Co.

In fairness to Stephenson, it must be remembered that he did try to get business for his firm, as the following letter to John Buddle (p. 83) will show:

J. Buddle Esqr
Sir,

It would give me great pleasure if you could spend a short time in looking through our manufactory some time to-day, as we are fitting up some Bearings for Waggon axles on the principle of the Mail Coach; which plan from your experience you must be aware is much wanted in Coal-waggons. Your opinion on this plan will much oblige me—I was thinking that as a railway is making under your inspection, in the neighbourhood of Berwick, this plan would be acceptable. Would you have the goodness to inform the Bearer whether you can favour me with your company, as I shall not have another opportunity of seeing you for some time, for I leave here for Liverpool on Monday.

I am,
Sir,
Your obed^t Servt
Geo. Stephenson

Newcastle
Sept. 23, 1826

About this time one of the longest letters ever written by Stephenson in his own hand was sent to Robert:

Liverpool Feb. 23rd 1827

My Dear,

Robert your very welcom letter dated Oct 26 1826 we duly received and was glad to here such good newes from Columbia respecting the mines—but at the same time greatly disapointed at you not geting home so soon as was expected however I hope all will be for the best, and I must waddle on as well as I can until you get to joine me. There has been a florishing a count of your men in the English pappers and great creadit is given to Robert Stephenson for his good management of them. I must now let you know how we are geting on in this quarter. Yore mother is geting her tea beside me while I am riting this and in good spirits. she has been in Liverpool a bout a fortnight. we have got a very comfortable home, and a Roume set a side for Robert and Charels when they arive in England. We are getting rapitly on with the tunnal under Liverpool it is 22 feet width & 16 feet high we have 6 shafts and driving right & left we have also got a great deal done on chat moss and on the same plans that I prepared befor parlament 2 years a go which plans was condemed by almost all the Engineers in England these plans is by cuting & imbanking with the moss some

of the laths 12 feet high and stand remarkably well—it was said that Renney had some of the best surveyors in England with him here and one of the best was left with me which I supposed was expected by menny of our directors to be a guid[e] to me & set him to surveye the tunnal and mark out the different shafts after which I found a meathat of cheking his work and found eny shaft out of the line this was after we had spent about 1000£ in that part thr . . . a finishing blay [blow] to Renny & his . . . my asstance is now all of my own chosen—the Bolton line which was clandistanly got from me when we were in parlament with the Liverpool bill has been given to me—a welsh line 9 miles long has been put into my hands a line at Canterbury is in my hands likewise—we have a most magnificent Bridge to build a cross the sankey valley near newton it will be 70 feet high so as to cross the masts of ships that navigate that canal I have drawen a plan on the gothick principal there will be 20 arches of 40 feet span. it will be quite a novel(ty) in England as there will be a flat arch sprung between the centre of the tops of the gothick and so on it has a fine a pearance in the plans we have also 2 bridges in hand at present one at the river adjoining chat moss and the other crossing the duckes (Duke's) cannal near manchester the one 30 feet span and the other 25—and for 3 Railroad on the top land is bought for 4 lines but only 2 will be laid at first the Rails is 35 pound per yard. we have just advertised for 400 waggon wheels & 200 axels and strange to say Robert Stephenson & Co. offer was lower than any other house and we have had offers from almost all the best (?) houses in England—my plans of wheels is now put up like the maile Coach axels but still fast so that one greaseing per day is a nough—the locomotive engine is working very well at Darlington—and a great many Coaches on the line I think a bout 6 and each drawen (by) one horse which take a bout 30 pasengers and run to Stockton in 1½ hours and many come from a great distance to ride in those Coaches it is expected that a line will be made from Darlington to York and I have been asked to take the survey—but hope it will be cept back untill you come to England—this line will sute Mr Charels. I think the projected tunnal under the thames was talked of befor you left—it is now got a good way under the river but will cost a great deal more money than was expected. This is however a very common case with engineers—the estimate for this concern is 500000£ and I daresay it will require it all the line passes Rainhill very near the same place where Jameses line passed
we shall want one steam engine at that place and a nother at near parr moss also one at the top of the tunnal I want these engines to be constantly moveing with an endless Rope so that the locomotive engines can take hold of the Rope and go on with out stoping. the Incline plane will only be 3/8 of an inch per yard. so that the poor (power) of the locomotive assisted by the perment (permanent) ones will get the traffict on in grand stile. we most (must) go at 10 miles per hour I think I told you about my new plan of locomotive it will be a nuge job the Cylinder[s ?] is intirly within the Bolior and neaither Cranks nor chain will be wanted. I have no fire door (?) and I will not use more than the coals that has heather (hither) to been used you will think I have mistaken some ideas about this but I think not—and you may depend upon it that if you do not get

home soon every thing will be at prefecttion and then there will be nothing for you to do or invent—however we will hope that some usfull Ideas will be brought from the western world.—the coal trade has been very bad in Newcastle last year you cannot immagine how kindly Mr. Lambert inquires after you Mr. Charels weatherly is now a father—I think I told you of his mariage last year—Mr. Wood is expected to be maried very soon of a young lady with a great posithen (?) she be long to Alnwick he got a quainted with her at the election—your mother expects (you will not forget the presents you must bring more than one as Mrs Robert Stephenson will want one by & by—and we expect Mr. Charels will bring plenty of amarica plants seeds for our (garden) cannot you bring your favorate mule with you I trust (this?) letter will just catch you befor living (leaving) the country my kindest love to Charels I am my Dear Dear Robert your affectionate father Geo: Stephenson.
I hope you will make a fair holing in your shaft it is a very dificult job to work from Compass in such a situation Renny man got one of our shafts 13 feet from the line and none of them in the line my methet of prouf was by pendulumns in the arc suported by 3 triangles legs so that I had a plume (plumb) line from the top to the Bodom (bottom) and got the sights over the tops of the houses.*

This long epistle, difficult in parts to decipher, is one of the most interesting of all Stephenson's letters; it reveals several of the parallel lines of thought that were going through his mind, and gives clues to his character. The vividly remembered setback over the first Liverpool and Manchester Bill is in evidence; the irksome presence of Rennie's men checking his line of the tunnel is there too—and Stephenson's satisfaction in having got one of Rennie's staff to join his own team of surveyors. Though his fundamental métier was mechanical engineering, he had had to learn and apply the full range of civil engineering involved in the construction of railways; as this letter shows, he was much concerned with bridge design, a field in which his son was to achieve even greater fame. But the most fascinating part of this letter is the reference to the experimental locomotive, the history of which was wrapped in mystery for generations. The great interest in the design was that it had horizontal cylinders both driving on to the same crankshaft, the first engine to incorporate this feature. These cylinders were sunk into the boiler barrel, at the firedoor end, and operated a countershaft from which long connecting rods drove the leading pair of the six coupled wheels. To have Stephenson's own reference to it when it has been the subject of lengthy speculation is fortunate; it fixes the date, and it confirms his talents as a locomotive designer.

The whole story of this remarkable engine has been lovingly chronicled by Warren; his account of it is a miniature classic, and every word of it is

* The author is indebted to Brigadier C C Parkman, CBE, FICE, of the consulting engineering firm of Ward, Ashcroft, and Parkman, Liverpool, for assistance with this letter.

worth reading. The locomotive was under construction at the Forth Street Works in 1827, when two important visitors, Carl von Oeynhausen and Heinrich von Dechen, mining engineers from Prussia, paid a visit; during their tour they made an intensive study of railways, and wrote a very full account of the Stockton and Darlington line.* But the dramatic find concerning this locomotive was the discovery of J. U. Rastrick's notebook in which he had sketched the 'Experiment', as it was known, and had noted many of its details. Rastrick certainly made good use of his time; his presence in the North-East, in company with James Walker, was the result of a request by the Directors of the Liverpool and Manchester Railway, who wanted a first-hand account of the operation of the Stockton and Darlington Railway.

The 'Experiment' was, so far as can be ascertained, the first locomotive to be fitted with springs, a feature which represented a most vital step forward in locomotive design, bearing in mind the vulnerable nature of the rails of those days. The furnace contained an internal water drum within the single flue, and water-tube firebars, in an early attempt to improve circulation. It would seem that the engine remained for some months at Forth Street, possibly for extended trials, but by January 1828 it had been sold to the Stockton and Darlington Railway, where it became their No. 6.

It should be mentioned at this point that Timothy Hackworth was now beginning to develop his own ideas on locomotive design; these differed in certain important ways from Stephenson's, but nevertheless he was a very sound engineer who produced and maintained a number of steam locomotives well adapted to current conditions on the Stockton and Darlington Railway. His success is all the more remarkable when it is remembered that his Directors held the purse-strings very tightly; but Hackworth could, when occasions arose, surmount such an obstacle in style. Thus when he saw a locomotive being offered at £380 by a Mr. Wilson, of Newcastle, he got his Directors to take it on trial for one month. It was listed as No. 5 in the Company's books and was named 'Chittaprat' (it is said, in imitation of the noises it made); although not a success in its original form, important parts of it were used by Hackworth in a rebuilding operation, after which it went into traffic as the 'Royal George' and was famous as the largest and most powerful locomotive at work in the country. Hackworth, while remaining on good terms with Stephenson, was a formidable rival at the Rainhill Trials in 1829.

The Forth Street Works apparently constructed a similar experimental locomotive about the same time; and when in November 1827 the Stockton and Darlington Railway Directors were contemplating the acquisition

* The Newcomen Society have published a translation of their writings (see also p. 173).

of another locomotive, they instructed Timothy Hackworth to write to Robert Stephenson & Co. accordingly. There was, at first, some objection to an engine weighing 7 tons, but by November 1827 the Railway Company was told that the weight would be guaranteed not to exceed 6 tons 15 cwt., and the engine was sent to Darlington for trials. The notion of water-tube firebars clearly worried Edward Pease, for a letter dated 24 October 1827, sent to him on behalf of the makers, by Harris Dickinson, clerk to Robert Stephenson and Company, is worded thus:

In answer to thy favour of the 20th inst., respecting our new locomotive engine, we are of opinion that there is little or no more risk attending the engine than the former ones. The only danger, I apprehend, is from the bars burning away, and so blowing out the hot water and scalding those who may be employed at the engine; but how can these hollow tubes burn away so long as they are filled with water? And if, from any neglect, the communication between the boiler and fire tubes should be stopped, so that the tubes burnt into holes, there could not then be any water to blow up.

Harris Dickinson must have been of the fraternity (they have existed in all ages) who could sell refrigerators to Esquimaux. He seems to have been a very thrusting type, for the reports of Oeynhausen and Dechen contain a section headed 'Locomotives of Stephenson and Dickinson at Newcastle'; they evidently thought he ranked with the partners in the business.

George Stephenson, though he may have had no illusions about the rapidity of the postal services between England and Colombia, must have been getting anxious about Robert's return. Robert had refused requests for him to continue in South America, but he wished to honour his contract absolutely; on 16 July 1827 he wrote to Michael Longridge:

The period of my departure from this place has at last really and truly arrived, though not longer than a month or two ago I was despairing of being able to get away without incurring the displeasure of the Board of Directors.

He knew of the increasing difficulties that had arisen in the direction of the Forth Street Works, and realized that it would fall to him to put the whole business on a sure footing. Without him, the enterprise would have probably perished at an early age; with his return, it was rapidly transformed into a flourishing factory. Robert did not actually disembark at Liverpool until late November 1827, his return journey being a series of adventures and disasters: at Cartagena, he accidentally met Trevithick, who was returning from Peru to England, sailing to Falmouth; he himself chose to return by way of New York; his ship encountered survivors of a shipwreck in the West Indies, and picked them up in the last stages of starvation. Then, when only a day's sailing from New York itself, the ship ran on to rocks in a hurricane and the hull disintegrated. No lives were lost, but Robert arrived without money or possessions. He managed, however, to obtain credit in New York, and saw something of the United States and Canada before joining the Liverpool-bound ship 'Pacific' which brought him home. George Stephenson had moved house from Eldon Street, Newcastle, to Upper Parliament Street, Liverpool, in 1824 so it must have been a quick and easy reunion after Robert's ship had berthed.

During 1827, at such times as he could get away from his major task of constructing the Liverpool and Manchester line, Stephenson was prospecting for a branch line from the Stockton and Darlington Railway to what is now Middlesbrough, then completely undeveloped; this project was engendered by perennial delays on the part of the Tees Navigation Company to improve the port facilities at Stockton. The subsequent building of this Middlesbrough branch and its opening as a line for coal shipment gave great impetus to Middlesbrough as an industrial centre and marked the beginning of a decline for Stockton. Foreseeing that this would be the outcome of a Middlesbrough line, Thomas Meynell, the Chairman of the Stockton and Darlington Railway, resigned rather than be a party to this body-blow to his city.

Another concern of Stephenson's at this time was the progress in the construction of the Nantlle Railway in North Wales, which his brother Robert had surveyed some two years previously. Brother Robert, who earlier had laid down railways for the Hetton Colliery owners, was without doubt much the most talented of Stephenson's three brothers; he was now engaged on the construction of the Bolton and Leigh Railway. Later he became chief engineer of the Pendleton Collieries.

While the present book was being proofed the following letter came to light at an auction held at Sotheby's on 28 November 1972; it was obtained by the Science Museum whose authorities have kindly given permission to quote it in full:

Liverpool 19th March 1827

Dear Sir,

I received yours of the 17th Inst. this morning. Since I wrote you last, I have been so much harassed about that I have been prevented in getting the Plans finished for the Canterbury engines although they are in a forward state. And I am obliged to be off tomorrow to meet Mrs. Hughes, and from thence to Chat Moss. After I have finished there, I shall have to spend a day or two at Bolton. As soon as I return I shall set about finishing them. In the mean time I have (although you may think it premature) wrote to Newcastle, to order them to get forward with the cylinder & Boiler, giving them the proper dimentions. The Company have certainly a right to receive offers from where they think proper, but I feel concious of giving a just tender. On these grounds, knowing there was no time to be lost I put the cylinder in hand.

I think it will be better for me to tender for the rollers, without the gallows or frames as I think they will be best made at Canterbury, or perhaps cheapest at Portsey near Portsmouth. Proper allowance will be made from my estimate for these items, and I think the Company ought to let the building of the houses to some other contractor than us. I also think the Company ought to lead the materials to the spot from the Shipping place, as horses can be got more conveniently by them than us, a deduction of which will be made in my estimate.

I am

Dear Sir

Yours truly—

Geo. Stephenson

Lister Ellis Esq[r]

P.S. I had intended to have staid up the greatest part of to night, working at your plan, but I feel so tired with a hard days work, that I must go to bed sooner than I intended.

Messrs Moss and Lawrence have been at the Moss, which I dare say Dixon would tell you, he and these gentlemen all agreed that I had weakened his for . . . [illegible because of sealing wax]* to much in draining. Mr. Moss stuck very closely to it today, urging that more drainers should be set on, and I stood as warmly against it. I think I convinced the Directors that I was right.

G.S.

Your plan of Gallows is very good

The letter is of interest in showing that, in spite of the general restriction placed on Stephenson by the Directors of the Liverpool and Manchester railway, which prevented him from giving more than a very small fraction of his time to other railway projects, he had become involved with the Canterbury and Whitstable line, proposed in 1825, construction of which was now proceeding. John Dixon deputised for Stephenson, and took over the Canterbury work on his behalf, working on it from 1825 to 1827, when Stephenson summoned him to the Liverpool and Manchester Railway.

The 'gallows' referred to were the brackets for the rollers which guided the rope on the sections to be worked by stationary engines. Portsmouth or 'Portsey' (Portsea) would be sensible places to go to for the manufacture of such rollers, as the Royal Navy base ensured the permanent establishment there of machinery for comparable products.

Dendy Marshall, in *Early British Locomotives* (Locomotive Publishing Company, London, 1939) refers to the entry in the ledger of the Forth

* The illegible word may be *formation*.

Fig 32. Sankey Viaduct, Liverpool and Manchester Railway. (Ackermann's print No. 4)

Street Works which records, on 31 October 1828, an order by 'George Stephenson for Canterbury railway 3 25H.P. high pressure engines with boilers, rope rolls, etc. £850 each'.

But on the Liverpool and Manchester Railway sites, George Stephenson's testing time was now reaching its climax; the Directors of the Company, and those engineers who were in a position to know the formidable task presented by Chat Moss, were wondering whether Stephenson's nerve and his physical endurance would crack before the Moss had been vanquished. The phenomenal determination shown by Stephenson, at this time, compels one's deepest admiration. He was engaged on the greatest engineering project ever attempted in Britain; and he was solving its problems without any previous experience to guide him. It must have been a profound relief to him to have his son back at the Forth Street Works. To his son Robert, Stephenson wrote:

Liverpool, 3rd March 1828

Dear Robert,

I have received yours of the 27 Ult. with the invoice of the wheels, they are certainly very high which I think will be against their adoption, however they appear to be a good job—I have sent your letter to Cabry—I wish you could contrive to come up here to stay a week or a fortnight; we shall want more wheels and axles here and I should like to bring it forward while you are here that you may make the agreement—You ought to know the lowest price you

STOCKTON
AND
HARTLEPOOL
RAILWAY.

£5.
REWARD.

WHEREAS
Some evil disposed person has removed and taken away several stakes, or level pegs, and thereby caused much inconvenience and damage to the works on the said Railway.

THIS IS TO GIVE NOTICE,
That the above Reward will be given to any person giving such information as may lead to the apprehension and conviction of the offender.

JOHN FOWLER,
Resident Engineer.
Greatham, Feb. 15th 1840.

From the Office of J. Procter, Hartlepool.

Fig 33. Notice warning against removal of surveying pegs, 1840. (Photo: British Railways Board)

can take for the wheels before you leave Newcastle as there is an American Engineer here who wants a number of the same kind and I think he will also want four Loco motive Engines—

There is also a neighbour of mine who will want a Steam Mill Engine, and I think it will be better for you to be here to close the bargains yourself in case we can agree for prices—I expect now in a few weeks to receive orders to proceed with the Canterbury Engines. The Bill is now in Parliament and is expected to pass shortly, to enable Mr. Ellis to take the lease of that concern and I suppose as soon as it goes forward I must deliver my profits up to Robert Stephenson and Co. I think it is likely the Chester Line will go forward which I was speaking to Mr. Longridge about—I only returned last night from examining the ground—I send in my report tomorrow of the practicability and expence of the Line—I am glad to hear you have got a Horse to suit you, but if it is a cheap one I think it is very likely to be a shabby one and very unfit to come by the side of mine; the whole of which are as fat as Pigs—

I am
Dear Robert
Your Afft. Father
Geo. Stephenson

Knowing the restrictions placed upon his father by the Liverpool and Manchester Directors, on engaging in the construction of other railways, Robert could (and did) now look forward hopefully to securing the appointment of engineer to the Canterbury and Whitstable line. He was more than usually interested, in this instance, as the journey to the south would bring him so much closer to London where, in the City, lived a merchant whose daughter, Fanny Sanderson, he afterwards married; he had in fact met her before his departure for Colombia. He did not, however, propose to her until late in 1828; they married on 17 June 1829 which, as we shall see presently, was a time of most feverish activity, centred on the construction of the 'Rocket'.

During the crowded year 1828 the Directors of the Liverpool and Manchester Railway ordered a locomotive engine in the design of which Stephenson had been working with the Company's energetic and versatile treasurer, Henry Booth; in fact, as early as 30 April 1827, the Directors had given authority for the experimental work to be done. The relevant minutes state:

The Treasurer reported that he had discovered a method of producing Steam without Smoke, which he considered might be applied to Locomotive and other Engines; Mr. Stephenson attended and having given his opinion that the Invention, if it succeeded on a large scale, would be highly important to the Company, he was directed to make any experiments necessary to decide the real merits of the scheme, it being understood that an expenditure of £100 would be sufficient for the purpose.

A drawing of the boiler was shown to the Directors on 7 January 1828, when it was agreed that construction should proceed; the engine would weigh about 6 tons, and the expected cost would be £550. As the Liverpool and Manchester Railway construction was not sufficiently advanced, the engine was to be sent to the Bolton and Leigh Railway. Warren states that Robert Stephenson's biographer, Jeaffreson,

consulted a number of letters between the two Stephensons dealing with the vital question of boiler design; but all trace of the originals has now been lost.

However a few scraps of these exchanges survive. Writing from Liverpool to Robert, George Stephenson, on 8 January 1828 advised him that

the small tubes will not require to be so strong as the other parts of the boiler, and you must take care that you have no thick plates and thin ones, as is often the case with those which come from Bedlington. You must calculate that this engine will be for all the engineers in the kingdom—nay, indeed, the world—to look at.

On 31 January 1828 Stephenson again wrote to his son,

With respect to the engine for Liverpool, I think the boiler ought not to be longer than eight feet. The engine ought to be made light as it is intended to run fast. Mr. Booth and myself think two chimneys would be better than one, say eight inches in diameter and not to exceed fifteen feet.

Robert found himself up against formidable practical problems in making this boiler; concerning which he received the following not too sympathetic comment dated 15 April 1828, in a letter from his father:

I am quite aware that the bent tubes are a complicated job to make, but once in and well done it cannot be any complication in the working of the engine. This bent tube is a child of your own, which you stated to me in a former letter.

Five days later Stephenson wrote further to Robert from Liverpool:

I duly received yours dated the 16th inst. I do not think there can be much difficulty in cleaning the refuse matter of the fire from the locomotive-engine boiler. I would make the nozzle pipe that goes in from the blast to be a kind of grating rather than a conical shape, and to project about two feet into the fire. The grating to be on the upper side. The nozzle piece to be made with a flange, fitting very nicely to the plate at the front of the fire to prevent the escape of air, and kept on by a bolt and cotter, or two screw-bolts. This nozzle piece could easily be taken out at any time and the fire cleared at the hole. This I think may be done while the engine is working upon an easy part of the road. It appears to me it will be found better to feed one time with coke and the next with coal. I think the one would revive the other . . .

To prepare Timothy Hackworth for possible alterations to Stockton and Darlington locomotives, to work on this principle, Stephenson wrote to him on 25 July 1828:

Liverpool 25th July 1828

Dear Timothy,

Brandreth has given a report here that you are going to lay off the Locomotive Engines, Is it so? It was a great pity that these accidents took place with the tubes. It appears Brandreth has got my plan introduced for the horse to ride which I suppose he will set off as his own invention. It is more than two years since I explained this to Brandreth—Canterbury was the place where I meant to have put it to use, but as that Company have now determined to work the Line by steam power it will not be wanted.

We have tried the new Locomotive Engine at Bolton, which works beautifully there is not the least noise about it we have also tried the blast to it for burning coke, and I believe it will answer—there are two bellows work(ed) by eccentrics underneath the tender—The Line will be opened on the 1st Augt—

It is too far for you to come, or I should be glad to see you—Write me about the Engines by return of Post if you can.

Yours Truly

Geo. Stephenson

P.S. John Dixon and every Director at Canterbury can speak to my plan of carrying the Horses, which I mentioned to them two years ago, but I never considered it ought to be tried at Darlington, as I then considered the Locomotive Engines a better thing—

G.S.

T. S. Brandreth, to whom Stephenson refers, was a Director of the Liverpool and Manchester Railway, so he must have had opportunities for conversations with Stephenson. It was Brandreth who devised the horse-operated 'Cyclopede' for the Rainhill Trials in the following year. Stephenson had evidently devised his own form of 'dandy cart', a flat wagon with side-rails forming the last vehicle in trains on railways embodying inclined planes. The horse pulled the train to the top of the incline; then the horse was detached and led back to the dandy cart at the rear, on to which it stepped, after which the brakes were released and the whole train would descend the incline, with the dandy cart and its horse-passenger bringing up the rear.

It must have been a shock to Stephenson when the rumours ascribed to Brandreth began to circulate in Liverpool. On the Stockton and Darlington Railways, at that time, things were beginning to improve after the bad patch of 1825–6, when the steam locomotives were less reliable; but from 1827, under the skill and determination of Timothy Hackworth, the situation definitely improved—a point which does not appear to have been sufficiently appreciated by Brandreth. But Brandreth seems, in any case, to have had a preference for horse traction in those days.

It is made clear that the 'blast' in question was not created by exhaust steam but was produced by forced-draught equipment. The anxiety to achieve successful steaming with coke on locomotives was due to a virtual ban on coal as fuel, by a clause in the Liverpool and Manchester Railway Act. It appears that the bent tubes which caused Robert so much trouble in manufacture were not a success, but after modifications the engine performed very satisfactorily.

The 'Liverpool Travelling Engine' was a definite landmark in steam locomotive development; vertical cylinders were abandoned and the engine was mounted on springs. Although the horizontal disposition of the cylinders (as in the 'Experiment') now gave way to an inclined position, which might be regarded as a retrogression, yet the former side-levers were superseded by direct drive; and the location of cylinders inside the boiler was given up. The twin flues enabled a lighter boiler to be used, with increased heating surface. An ingenious early attempt to secure expansive working of the steam was also incorporated.

In the modifications referred to, a simpler form of return-flue boiler was used, with notable success. The exhaust steam was turned into the chimney. As thus altered, the 'Liverpool Travelling Engine' was renamed 'Lancashire Witch' by Mrs. Hulton (whose husband was the Chairman of the Bolton and Leigh Railway) during the inauguration of the line on 1 August 1828. The 'Lancashire Witch' was cited by Robert Stephenson as evidence to refute the findings of Walker and Rastrick in favour of stationary engines for the Liverpool and Manchester Railway; he stated* that

> deductions from its performances would have approximated nearer the truth than data drawn from the Darlington engines that have been several years in use and working under great disadvantages.

The 'Experiment' and the 'Lancashire Witch' were definite landmarks in the escape from the cumbersome beam-engine structures of the earlier locomotives, with the cylinders sunk into the boiler, and each cylinder driving a separate axle. That primitive layout, derived directly from stationary-engine practice (what else was there to go on?) was not especially ill-suited to Stockton and Darlington conditions, where heavy, slow-moving mineral trains (interspersed with horse-drawn chaldrons or passenger-carriages) formed the traffic, and the traffic itself was mostly over short distances downhill, under full loads, with only the returning light empties required to ascend the gradients. The Stephensons well understood that the Liverpool and Manchester line was to be of quite a different character, with much longer runs, and no dominant downhill profile with gravity helping virtually one-way traffic. From now onwards, their locomotives would have to run at higher speeds than anything previously achieved. Their belief in the future of steam locomotion, shown by the completeness of their preparations for it on the Liverpool and Manchester line, was not, however, shared by all the Directors, whose desire to obtain the maximum amount of professional advice, without necessarily committing themselves to accepting it, is clearly shown in the series of events and proposals that preceded the opening of the line.

By showing confidence in their chief engineer, the Directors could have saved themselves a great deal of time and trouble by plumping in favour of steam locomotives; but this was not their way. It must be remembered that they were business men, mostly without any technical knowledge, and that they were involving themselves in a venture which had no parallel in the nation's history, and no one really knew if it could succeed.

* Robert Stephenson and Joseph Locke, *Observations on the Comparative Merits of Locomotives and Fixed Engines: A Reply to the Report of Mr. James Walker* (1830). See also Warren, p. 148.

Further, there must have lingered in their minds some recollections of the disastrous *débâcle* of 1825, when Stephenson had been so mercilessly attacked by the counsel opposing the Liverpool and Manchester Bill that some of them had their confidence in him badly shaken. They knew that on the Stockton and Darlington Railway it was possible to observe the performance of horses, steam locomotives, and stationary steam engines so, according to their records, on 29 September 1828:

A discussion took place on the various and contradictory accounts which prevailed with respect to the power and relative economy of Locomotive Engines on the Darlington Railway, as compared with Horses. The subject being of first importance it was considered desirable that one or two of the Directors, accompanied by the Treasurer should proceed to Darlington to ascertain as correctly as practicable the result of the experience on that Line, taking into the account, first cost, wear and tear, both of the Engines and the Road, and as far as possible all the circumstances involved in the question.*

The Directors appointed James Cropper to accompany Henry Booth (the treasurer) on this fact-finding mission; they represented respectively, the 'anti' and the 'pro' followings of steam locomotives, Booth being strongly in their favour, and Cropper (who supported stationary engines and ropes) against. Edward Pease accordingly instructed Timothy Hackworth to prepare for the arrival of the deputation ('have the engines and men as neat and clean as can, and be ready with thy calculations, not only showing the saving, but how much more work they do in a given time').

Returning to Liverpool, the deputation gave their opinion in favour of stationary engines. It seems doubtful whether Booth can have had much say in their report; not many months previously he had been experimenting with Stephenson in connection with the 'Liverpool Travelling Engine' and is hardly likely to have altered his opinion so quickly. Cropper always seems to have been evilly disposed towards Stephenson, and even carried on his vendetta to make trouble for Robert Stephenson a few years later. One can imagine the feeling of disgust which must have engulfed Stephenson when the deputation's findings were reported to him. On 22 October 1828 he therefore replied with a truly formidable broadside in the form of a report to the Directors; it is preserved in the Institution of Mechanical Engineers' Library, and runs to about 4,000 words—too long to be given here, but of absorbing interest and a magnificent example of Stephenson's power in marshalling facts and figures. The upshot of his main argument was that serious operating difficulties would occur with rope haulage whenever a failure of a stationary engine occurred paralysing the whole system, or whenever a wagon was derailed.

* See Warren, p. 165.

The Directors lost no time in holding a meeting immediately after receiving Stephenson's report, for on 6 November 1828,

> a discussion of great length took place, after which it was Ordered, That Mr. Stephenson's Report be lithographed for the use of the Directors: and the Treasurer was instructed to write to Mr. Ben Thompson to enquire whether he would object to a Deputation (including one or two professional or scientific men) visiting his Railway with a view to ascertain what quantity of work could be performed in 12 hours, on two successive days. Also the power of the engines and such other particulars as may be found requisite to afford complete information on the subject.*

One may suspect the influence of Cropper in this policy, for Benjamin Thompson was known to be strongly in favour of stationary engines; some years previously he had engaged in a wordy battle with a lifelong associate of Stephenson, Nicholas Wood, who was a powerful supporter of steam locomotive haulage. The Directors met again, on 17 November 1828, and after listening to the reading of

> several letters from Mr. Braithwaite and Mr. Cropper, decidedly recommending the use of this latter power on the Liverpool and Manchester line

they resolved to request James Walker and John Rastrick to make a journey to Newcastle, Darlington, and the surrounding region,

> to ascertain by actual inspection and investigation the comparative merits of Fixed Engines and Locomotives . . . and to visit Liverpool on their way to the North, in order to receive from the Directors more specific instructions. . . .

There was clearly building up within the direction of the Liverpool and Manchester line a strong feeling in favour of stationary engines; it is not too much to say that the whole future of the steam locomotive was now in the balance, and Stephenson was almost alone in his unshaken championship of it. Among the Directors themselves, Joseph Sandars was notably in its favour, but between his clear-cut and unwavering support (which he shared with Henry Booth) and the hostility of James Cropper there was a large proportion of the 'don't knows'. To be fair to the stationary-engine supporters, they could point to a higher degree of reliability in their favoured motive power, contrasting with the steam locomotive, still in its infancy and largely an unknown quantity; at that stage in its development, dependability had hardly yet been achieved.

The investigation carried out by Walker and Rastrick was very thorough. Conducted in the depth of winter, it must have involved them in a great deal of highly uncomfortable travel.

* See Warren, p. 170.

At that time, the locomotives known to have been at work comprised:

Four Blenkinsop rack-rail engines at Middleton Colliery, Leeds.
Three Hedley 'Puffing Billy' type locomotives at Wylam Colliery.
Four Stephenson locomotives at Killingworth Colliery.
Five Stephenson locomotives at Hetton Colliery, Sunderland.
Five Stephenson locomotives on the Stockton and Darlington Railway.
One Hackworth locomotive on the Stockton and Darlington Railway (the 'Royal George').
Two Stephenson locomotives at Springwell Colliery, Newcastle.
One Stephenson locomotive on the Bolton and Leigh Railway (the 'Lancashire Witch').
One Rastrick locomotive on the Shutt End Railway, near Stourbridge (the 'Agenoria').

Most of these 26 engines were inspected by Walker and Rastrick. The status of these machines is described by Dendy Marshall*:

In some places to which engines had been supplied they had been discontinued, owing to their unsatisfactory working. The fate of the locomotive was hanging in the balance; no-one, except a few enthusiasts, believing that it had 'come to stay'. In fact, since 1814, not one had been built, so far as is known, by anyone except Stephenson. Not only hampered by its own crudity and imperfections, due perhaps even more to lack of the skill and facilities required for manufacturing it, than to poverty of design, its chief obstacle lay in the track, which was far too weak to carry it, and continually broke under the strain. The usual rate of progress was not much more than a walking pace, perhaps sometimes not even that, and it had to meet all the same kind of opposition that the motor car encountered, seventy years later.

Even those who had been sufficiently enterprising to take the plunge and adopt it as a means of haulage, were inclined to waver in their faith, and wonder whether horses were not better after all. Edward Pease is quoted as having written to William James on 4th February 1826, speaking of the Stockton and Darlington Railway, 'they have placed locomotive engines on the line for the haulage of coal (only), before it is creditable to them, or of advantage to the Company'.†

Smiles describes this period as 'the darkest hour of the locomotive'.

But the Walker and Rastrick tour of inquiry, although it did on the whole come down rather half-heartedly in favour of fixed-engine haulage, had one tremendously important result. The two engineers reported back separately to the Directors on 9 March 1829, and one of them, James

* *Centenary History of the Liverpool and Manchester Railway*, p. 6.
† *The Two James's and the Two Stephensons* by E.M.S.P. London: G. Phipps, 1861.

Walker, offered in his findings the epoch-making suggestion to the Directors that

> to enable you to take advantage of improvements which might be made (in steam locomotives); with a view to encourage which, and to draw the attention of Engine makers to the subject, something in the way of a premium, or an assurance of preference, might be held to the person whose Engine should, upon experience, be found to answer the best. The Rainhill (stationary) Engines would at the same time enable you to judge of the comparative advantages of the two systems, and if upon any occasion the trade should get beyond the supply of loco-motives, the horse might form a temporary substitute.*

To James Walker, therefore, belongs the credit for an idea which was to have such far-reaching consequences upon the nation's industrial future. His report, and Rastrick's, were regarded as so important that the Directors ordered 500 copies of them to be printed.

George Stephenson immediately set to work to produce his own observations on the reports of Walker and Rastrick; these were considered by the Directors, who, wishing for more time to produce their decision, adjourned the meeting. But neither George nor Robert Stephenson was prepared to give up the principle of steam locomotion, in which both had such implicit faith. †It was at this time that Robert wrote:

> We are preparing for a counter-report in favour of locomotives, which I believe still will ultimately get the day, but from present appearances nothing decisive can be said: rely upon it, locomotives shall not be cowardly given up. I will fight for them until the last. They are worthy of a conflict.

For some months preceding these developments the Liverpool and Manchester Directors had been wading through deep financial waters. The construction of the line was far from finished, and they were running short of money. They therefore applied for a loan from public funds. The Exchequer Loan Bill Commissioners had already advanced £10,000; but much more was now needed. The Commissioners naturally required some reassurance as to the viability of this great venture into unknown territory, and they requested a report on the present state of the line. Their engineering adviser was the famous Thomas Telford, President of the Institution of Civil Engineers, expert organizer of canal and road construction, and the doyen of the civil engineering profession. After receiving some rather disturbing reports from one of his staff, on the unorthodox methods of construction and of payment of labour, Telford decided to make a personal inspection, and traversed the whole of the line in company with Stephenson. Telford noted all that had been done, as

* Warren, p. 172.
† Jeaffreson, *Life of Robert Stephenson*, vol. I, p. 124.

well as the large number of works to be finished, and considered that construction could not be completed till 1830; it was then January 1829. The question of motive power, being still undecided, drew forth Telford's criticism, but eventually, upon the Directors agreeing to take action in the light of Telford's several adverse comments, it was agreed that the Loan Commissioners should advance £100,000 to the Company. Stephenson knew that the future of the railway—and of all railways—was at stake during these critical months, and entered into an agreement with the Directors to have the construction finished in 1830.

One cannot escape the feeling that Stephenson, notwithstanding his unrivalled genius in railway construction, had too many irons in the fire at this time. In his own field, he was the most successful engineer in the country; doubtless he knew it, and he therefore found it hard to resist participation in new railway ventures which were being proposed in various places. If he could secure the goodwill initially, which would enable the constructional supervision to come to his son, he could feel assured that the job would be in good hands, and the Forth Street Works would benefit in due course. His Quaker partners, keenly interested in the financial side of the firm, would give him every encouragement, or even apply some pressure, to ensure that the business flourished. It was picking up well, after Robert's return had transformed the once-languishing factory into an energetic establishment.

So, although it seems almost incredible, Stephenson, in company with Robert, in the midst of appalling worries over the Liverpool and Manchester Railway, attended a meeting in Leicester, on 12 February 1829 (while still awaiting the Walker and Rastrick reports!), which was arranged by William Stenson, a partner in a Leicestershire colliery, to discuss a proposal for a railway from Swannington to Leicester, some sixteen miles, which would enable the price of coal, in that city, to be brought down to a competitive level. Stephenson had prepared himself, for he had already visited Swannington and had returned duly impressed. A committee was set up that same evening, with John Ellis as chairman. Ellis later achieved special distinction as the unifying force in the considerable amalgamation of lines which were in 1844 combined to form the Midland Railway; the Leicester and Swannington Railway thus became the senior company involved in the merger. Robert Stephenson, already engaged on the construction of the Bolton and Leigh Railway, and the Warrington and Newton Railway, now had the Leicester and Swannington line added to his responsibilities. However, the committee appointed a local surveyor to carry out the preliminary work, and in due course construction was begun.

We now come to the most exciting period in the history of the Liver-

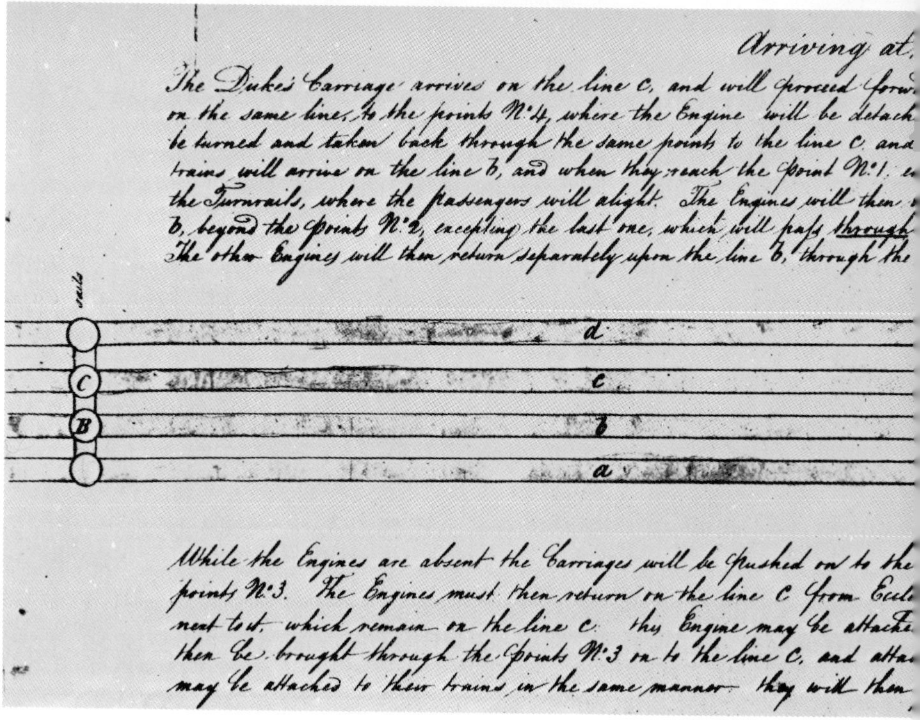

Fig 34. Diagram showing arrangements for the opening of the Liverpool and Manchester Railway, 1830 (Courtesy The Institution of Civil Engineers).

pool and Manchester Railway. The Directors took up James Walker's suggestion of a premium, for award in respect of locomotive design, and on 20 April 1829, while careful to record that their minds were not yet made up on the question of locomotives versus rope haulage by stationary engines, they resolved to offer a premium of £500.

for a Locomotive Engine which shall be a decided improvement on those now in use, as respects the consumption of smoke, increased speed, adequate power, and moderate weight, the particulars of which shall be specified in detail by the Preparation Committee.

The Directors already had a steam locomotive on order from the Forth Street Works; this was the 'Liverpool Coke Engine' which was specifically designed to burn coke, in anticipation of the service conditions of the railway; it had twin vertical boilers, each with its own chimney which resulted in its being known as 'Twin Sisters'. It was carried on six wheels, but only one pair was driven. The cylinders were inclined; the drive was direct on to crank-pins. The engine had to be constructed and delivered in a great hurry; it apparently was ordered on 16 March 1829; shipped from Newcastle *via* Carlisle, and by 13 July had arrived in Liverpool, and was used on the construction of the line where, according to a *Manchester Guardian* journalist (in the issue dated 25 July 1829), it would propel 12 wagons each weighing 1 ton and each containing 4 tons of clay, at 6–7 miles an hour.

Less than a week after their historic meeting on 20 April, the Directors issued their set of conditions, to be complied with by all entrants for the

Manchester

...ils, where the party will alight, and the Engine and Carriage return
through the points No 4. No 2 and No 1, to the Turnrail A, where it will
...ts Carriages, and then proceed forward to the Eccles Water Station. The
...ass into the line a, and the Carriages proceed along the line b, towards
...is upon the Turnrail A, and return through the Points No 1, along the line
...d No 4 on to the line c. and proceed on that line to the Eccles Water Station
No 4, on to the line c, and thence forward to the Eccles Water Station.

No 3 No 4 South line
No 1 No 2 North line
A

c, and will be turned on to the line c. and brought forward to the
the Points No 3 on to the line d, excepting the Dukes and the Engine
...d proceed a little forward on the line c. the next Engine must
proceeding a little forward, so that all the Engines upon the line d
line c, to Liverpool, the Dukes Carriage taking the lead.

locomotive trials. These have been published so often that perhaps the Conditions for the Rainhill Trials (Appendix I) will suffice. It seems likely that Stephenson would have advised the Directors on the conditions to be imposed. He thus had only 5 days' start over any competitors, but it can safely be assumed that Robert would have been supplied with the details by the next post. On 18 May the Directors considered an application by Timothy Hackworth; other firm entries were received from Mr. T. S. Brandreth, Mr. T. Burstall, and Messrs. J. Braithwaite and J. Ericsson (jointly). But a vast number of inquiries were received, which showed that every possible and impossible mode of propulsion was being considered, not omitting perpetual motion; the Company was inundated with questions on the eligibility of this or that form of transport.

Stephenson entrusted the design details of his locomotive to Robert, but there was close collaboration between them, and both were well aware that the engine would be a new stage in locomotive development. It was to be lightweight, built for speed rather than heavy haulage, to demonstrate what steam could achieve on a railway laid out with the rapid conveyance of passengers as a principal aim, as contrasted with the heavy mineral traffic of the pioneer public railway from Darlington to Stockton. This most famous of all locomotives was named 'Rocket', and was entered jointly by George Stephenson and Henry Booth, whose vital contribution to the design was the notion of a multi-tubular boiler instead of the usual single—or return—flue types then in general use.

No other locomotive has had so much written about it; and it is probable that a good many more accounts will appear in the future. Just before the writing of this narrative a further excellent publication, most painstakingly written and superbly illustrated, has appeared*; it makes a welcome addition to the great classics by J. G. H. Warren and Dendy Marshall.

The chief draughtsman at Forth Street, G. H. Phipps, was in frequent contact with Stephenson over details of locomotive design; on 13 August 1829, a letter to Phipps from Stephenson contained the following passage, which is of interest, because the turning of the exhaust steam into what later became known as a 'blast pipe' was a feature which Stephenson and other locomotive builders had adopted for some years past, in attempts to create an induced draught:

> As I understand Robert is gone to Canterbury I may mention to you that I have put on to the coke engine a longer exarsting pipe, riching nearly to the top of the chimeney but find it dose not do so well as putting it into the chimeney lower down. I think it will be best near the level of the top of the boiler, by doing so it will look neater. The coke engine is doing extremely well—but the 'Lankshire Witch' is rely doing wonders. A statement of her performance you will see in the papers in a few days.

Robert cannot have had much time for a honeymoon! He had been married four weeks when the foregoing letter was written by his father.

With the Exchequer Loan providing much-needed capital, good progress was now being made on the Liverpool and Manchester line; and about this time Stephenson wrote to Michael Longridge:

Liverpool Aug[t] 23[d] 1829

Dear Sir,

One of our Directors, Mr. James Bourne desired me to order 10 Tons of Rails similar to the Liverpool and Manchester Railway ones, for their own private use. You must let him have them at as low a price as if it had been a large order, as he is one of your friends. Direct them to Mess[rs] James and Peter Bourne Liverpool.

The Warrington and Newton Railway Co are very much in want of the Rails that are ordered; there is no doubt of your getting the full order for this Railway. If you had tendered the same price for the Kenyon and Leigh Junction Railway you would have got an order for them likewise. Foster's price was 11£ for the Harrington and 10£–10s for the Kenyon & Leigh; delivered at Leigh.

The New Locomotive Engine works well and makes no smoke.—Huskisson visited the greater part of the Line with the Directors,—of course I was one of the party. We first went to the great Viaduct, then along the Line to the Skew Bridge at Rainhill: then to the commencement of the deep cutting at Olive

* 'The Rocket'; *Loco Profile No. 7*, by Brian Reed. Dec. 1970, Profile Publications, Ltd, Windsor.

Mount where we were met by the Locomotive Engine which took the whole party amounting to about 135 through the deep cutting at the rate of 9 miles an hour to the great delight of the whole party.—The Engine really did well.—We next went to the Tunnel, where a train of waggons was in readiness to receive the party. Many of the first families in the County were waiting here to witness the procession which accompanied by a band of Music occupying one of the Waggons descended in grand style through the Tunnel which was brilliantly lighted up, the gas lights being placed at intervals of 25 yards. The whole went off most pleasantly without the slightest accident attending our various movements. Huskisson expressed himself to me highly delighted with what he had seen—Mr. Huskisson and the Directors dined with Mr. Lawrence in the evening—The Engineer was one of the party, and a most splendid set out there was I assure you.—The evening was spent in a very pleasing manner.

Yours always truly
Geo. Stephenson

The occasion just described was evidently a welcome break for Stephenson during the rigours of construction of the line. William Huskisson, the M.P. for Liverpool, had taken a great interest in the railway, on which he was destined to die so tragically a year later. Charles Lawrence was the first Chairman of the Company. Difficulties had been encountered over the completion of the line to the projected terminus in Manchester; in fact, the Directors had to get a fourth Act passed (in May 1829) 'to enable them to enter the sacred precincts of Manchester after all', as Dendy Marshall has recorded.* He goes on:

It included clauses strictly forbidding the use of locomotives in Manchester or Salford, except on the lines as authorized. Apparently there was a fear of the engines running loose on the streets, like wild beasts.

On 31 August 1829 the Directors of the Liverpool and Manchester Railway published the location for the locomotive trials: 'the level space between the two inclined Planes at Rainhill'. Double track was laid down to provide a run of $1\frac{1}{2}$ miles with $\frac{1}{8}$ mile extra at each end for getting up speed and for braking. Eventually only the 'Rocket', by Stephenson, the 'Sans Pareil', by Hackworth, and the 'Novelty', by Braithwaite and Ericsson, remained as serious competitors.

The extremely important part played by Booth in the design and construction of the 'Rocket' is shown by a most illuminating series of letters written to him by Robert Stephenson in August and September 1829; they are quoted extensively by Warren, and throw light on the heavy manufacturing difficulties which Robert had to surmount. Hackworth was doubtless having comparable problems to solve; Braithwaite

* *Centenary History of the Liverpool and Manchester Railway*, p. 15.

Fig 35. Railway entry into Manchester, Liverpool and Manchester Railway.

and Ericsson modelled their 'Novelty' on the engines of the steam cars that were just beginning to appear on the roads.

The trials began on 6 October 1829, and were concluded on 14 October, when the 'Rocket' alone was running; the engine achieved a speed of 35 m.p.h., which as Parsonage* has remarked, must have been

> a terrifying speed, a performance requiring courage if the engine and permanent way are considered.

The trials were carried out with great care and the results were noted in detail by the three judges. Warren has recorded this epoch-making event very fully. But one wonders how many of the 15,000 spectators realized that they were witnessing the birth of a new 'Age of Speed', which would transform the daily life of the country and convert England from a mainly agricultural to a largely industrial kingdom. There could now be no longer any doubt as to the motive power of the future. The £500 was duly claimed by Stephenson and Booth, and was well and truly earned, for the 'Rocket' alone fulfilled every requirement comprised in the Trials. In less than a month, the Forth Street Works had received

* The 'Rocket's' driving wheels were 4 ft. 8½ in. diameter equal to the track gauge—also almost equal to 1 r.p.s. (revolution per second) at 10 m.p.h. (*Trans. Newcomen Soc., 1928–9* vol. IX, p. 83).

Fig 36. Dr. J. Bradbury Winter's silver model of the 'Rocket'.

an order for four locomotives for the Liverpool and Manchester Railway, and these were delivered the following Spring.

It was especially hard for Stephenson that at this time of his greatest triumph, petty animosity on the part of James Cropper should have created a situation in which Stephenson had to defend himself vigorously against interference with his recognized right to appoint his own staff. Cropper, hoping perhaps to discover some sign that Stephenson would not be able to complete the line in 1830, despite his definite agreement to do so, decided on an investigation of the state of the Works, and a certain William Chapman was duly appointed. But Stephenson was highly incensed when Chapman brought about the dismissal of one of the enginemen for not answering questions satisfactorily, and sent in a furious report to the Directors (quoted in full by L. T. C. Rolt*) which is worth reading *in extenso*. Authority to engage and control his own staff was a most important matter to Stephenson; here he is, writing again to his Directors, on 19 December 1829, when he wished Joseph Locke to carry out a task in connection with a Bill for a line at Stockport:

It will I think be perfectly within your recollection that one of the conditions on which I accepted my present office, was that I should have the appoint-

* *George and Robert Stephenson*, by L.T.C. Rolt, Longmans, London, 1960.

Fig 37. Glazed tile showing the 'Rocket' locomotive. (In author's possession)

ment of my own assistants, so as to have them under my own control, which understanding was, I think, fully confirmed by the circumstances attendant upon the withdrawal of Mr. Vignoles; being urged by several members of your Board to accept that gentleman's services, I did so, but afterwards, finding that they were likely to be disadvantageous rather than beneficial, I intimated to your Chairman that the Company might retain Mr. Vignoles in their employ if they thought proper, but that I would not be responsible for him.

Stephenson naturally had to rely—especially in so great an undertaking as the Liverpool and Manchester Railway—pretty considerably on his assistants, many of whom had received their training under him. The experience must have been very valuable to them, as there was hardly any other way in which practical railway engineering could have been learned—at least where public railways were concerned. Perhaps it might be likened to young men in the 1970s training for space flight. Joseph Swanwick, a friend of Stephenson's who had been invited by him to the opening of the Stockton and Darlington Railway, made inquiries about a formal apprenticeship for his son Frederick; Stephenson's reply was as follows:

Liverpool March 30th 1829

Dear Swanwick,

If you intend your Son Frederick to be bound an apprentice to me there is now an opening for him to come into my house—I think I have told you my terms before—you will oblige me with an early answer.

I did expect to have given Mrs. Stephenson a treat to Chester before this but have really been so much engaged that I have not been able to find the time to do it; however if the weather gets warm I may possibly come upon you some day suddenly & take a family dinner with you.

Yours Very Sincerely,
Geo. Stephenson

Arrangements for the apprenticeship of young Frederick Swanwick were duly made. A form of receipt dated some months later has been preserved with family papers:

Jany 29 1830

Jos. Swanwick
Dr. to George Stephenson
By Board of F. Swanwick for 26 weeks at 15/– per week £19–10s–0d

Young Frederick Swanwick, as we have seen, turned out to be an illustrious pupil; only a few months later in the same year (1830), he was one of the favoured young men entrusted with the driving of one of the locomotives—the 'Arrow', distinguished by a pink flag—during the great Opening Day of the Liverpool and Manchester Railway.

Stephenson was as good as his word concerning the completion of the line. Chat Moss was conquered and on 1 January 1830 a trial trip was made across it. A month later two further locomotives were ordered, to be in readiness for the opening of the line.

About this time Stephenson wrote to Michael Longridge the following letter, in his own hand:

Leverpool Feb. 8, 1830

My Dear Sir,

You quite alarm me with the newes contained in the times, we must have something new or we will be in the back ground, Fordham is certainly shewing of with his arc bubbles & herapath very justly says if nothing happen gurney we shall see somthing. but it is my oppinion that somthing will happen boath with G* and F. I think you have nothing to feer from the above with the errection of the mell in Wails do you intend to let Losh of paying any more patent right have you not an agrament with him woent the Law compell him to fullfill his agrament—I think you have mannagered badly with the N.le (Newcastle) & Carlisle Railway to let it out of our hands, I suppose Losh & his friends has been prepared to meet you—will your frends still be subscribers to the work and if they do not will the work go on, we must have it ultimatly—.
Locke has not withdrawen himself from me, I was under the nessisity of taking him from this concren to go on with the stockport bill as I could not go on with it my self on account of the marques of stafford and Robert could not get to it

* Francis Giles.

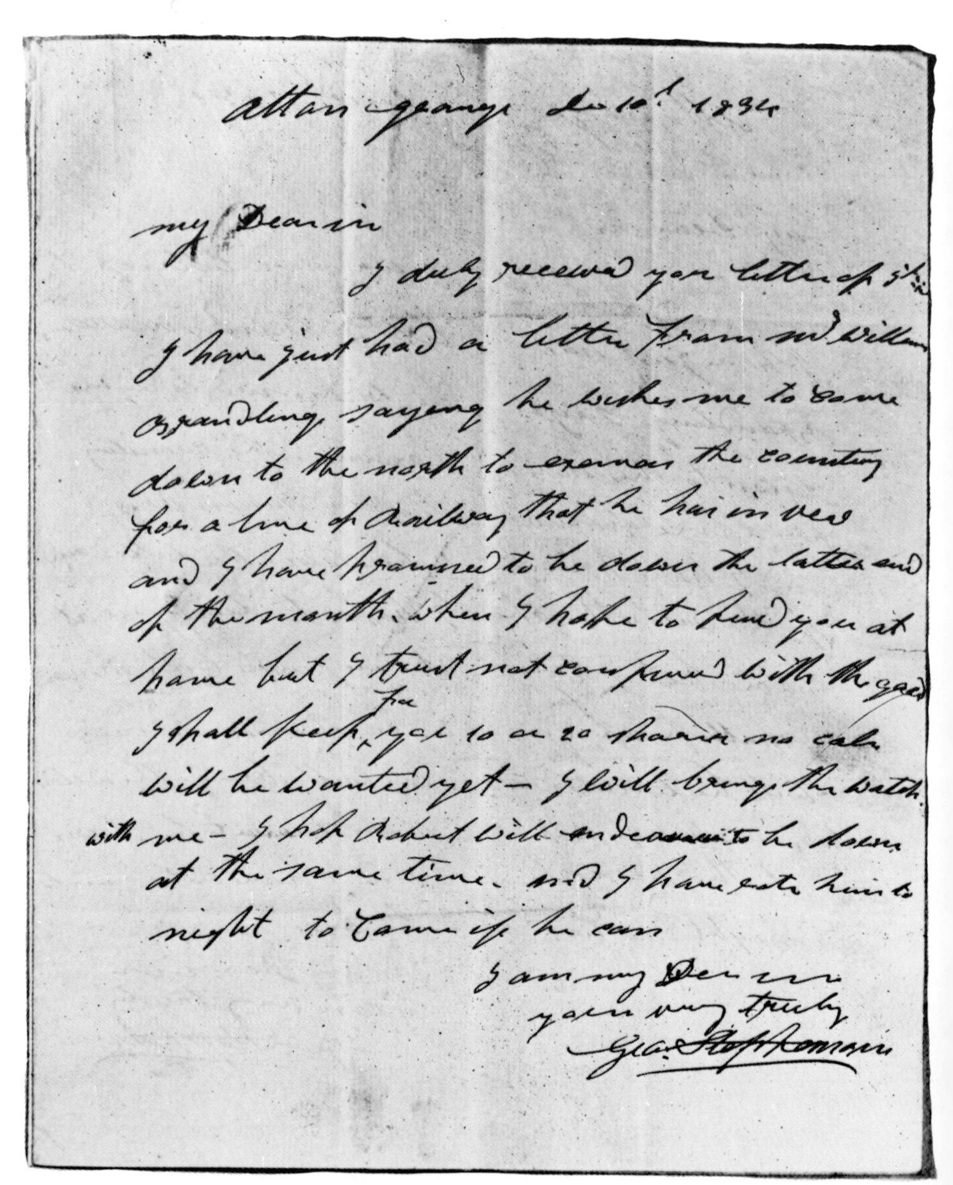

Alton grange Dec 10th 1836

My Dear Sir

I duly received your letter of 5th

I have just had a letter from Mr William
Brandling saying he wishes me to come
down to the north to examine the country
for a line of Railway that he has in view
and I have promised to be down the latter end
of the month when I hope to find you at
home but I trust not confined with the gout
I shall keep for you 10 or 20 shares no cash
will be wanted yet— I will bring the watch
with me— I hope Robert will endeavour to be down
at the same time. and I have wrote him to
night to come if he can

I am my Dear Sir
yours very truly
Geo Stephenson

Fig. 38. Facsimile of a typical letter written in George Stephenson's own hand.

in time to look after the sirveying—the severe winter has pervented us geting on with our masoncry so much that we can not be opened before the latter end of may or, the begining of june as soon as I can spare time you know you & I are to go and set the Railway out from the meditirranean to the Red Sea. & we shall send the young men to execute it after it is done we will take a trip to the east indes by that rute, and set them to work in that quarter after which there will be plenty of orders for boath Losh you and all the manufacturers in England I hope you will come this way to London—

I am Dear Sir
Yours truly
Geo. Stephenson

While the latter stages of construction were being reached on the Liverpool and Manchester line, a notable event took place in the south: the Canterbury and Whitstable Railway was completed, and celebrated its opening in great style on 3 May 1830. It was a small concern, with only one steam locomotive, the 'Invicta', which was built by Robert Stephenson & Co. and sent by sea to Whitstable. A good deal of the steeply graded line was laid out for fixed-engine haulage. But the 'Invicta' behaved well and the line was opened amid great celebrations, 'without a single mishap' (as Robert Stephenson wrote, three days later, to Thomas Richardson). The locomotive had the inclined-cylinder layout that was the latest practice in the Forth Street designs, but contained a definite advance in that the cylinders were at the front; in this respect 'Invicta' was in advance of the 'Rocket'.

Back in Liverpool, Stephenson's phenomenal energies were directed to the completion of the line to Manchester. By July 1830, the end was in sight, and the Directors enjoyed a trip over the whole length of the rail-

Fig 39. Portrait of George Stephenson, by Briggs.

Fig 40. Railway Office, Liverpool, in the early days of the Liverpool and Manchester Railway. (*From a postcard issued by the London and North Western Railway*)

way. The locomotive was the 'Arrow'. A letter describing this event, written by Stephenson to Michael Longridge, has survived:

Liverpool July 4th 1830

My dear Sir,

I duly received yours of the 26th of June. I am well aware that the sentiments expressed in it are sincere, and I know no one who rejoices more than you do at my welfare. The trip was a very delightful one to me, as we took the Directors and a load along with us for the first time. Mr. Bald from Scotland was with us and was I believe highly gratified. If I had slacked the Reins of our horse on that day, they would have run over the ground in less time.

Being as you know a very cautious man and desirous of doing things moderately, we were much longer than we need have been.

In coming back with the Directors not more than half the power of the engine was applied on many parts of the line. On our return home Mr Lawrence had a splendid dinner provided for the party.

The formal opening of the Railway it is intended shall take place on the 15th of September, when I shall be glad to see you, and hope you will come a few days before, by doing which you will have an opportunity of seeing the different horses training on the ground. You ought I think to bring Mrs. Longridge with you, as it will I should imagine be a treat to her. I will take care to have Lodgings provided for you either at my house or elsewhere.

I am dear Sir

Yours allways truly,

Geo. Stephenson.

Mic: Longridge Esqr.

P.S. You shall have my opinion on the form of Rails in the course of a few days. I think the I Rails an infringement of your Patent, I have seen Foster and told him so.

G.S.

At Manchester, the Directors agreed the following resolution unanimously as a tribute to Stephenson:

> That the Directors cannot allow this opportunity to pass without expressing their strong sense of the great skill and unwearied energy displayed by their Engineer, Mr. George Stephenson, which have so far brought this great national work to a successful termination, and which promise to be followed by results so beneficial to the country at large, and to the Proprietors of this concern.

Everything was now turned towards the preparations for the opening day. A beautiful description of a trip over the line, personally conducted by Stephenson, was written on 26 August 1830 by Fanny Kemble, who was to become one of the great figures in the nineteenth-century theatre. She rode on the footplate, and captured the atmosphere with such vividness that her account has been reproduced in numerous books on early railways.

An early visitor to the scene was James Nasmyth, of steam-hammer fame, who arrived on 11 September and saw the line and its locomotives. The 'Rocket' had *already* become, in his own words, 'this distinguished and celebrated engine'; the locomotive was taken for a number of short runs by Stephenson, as driver, with Robert as fireman. Alexander

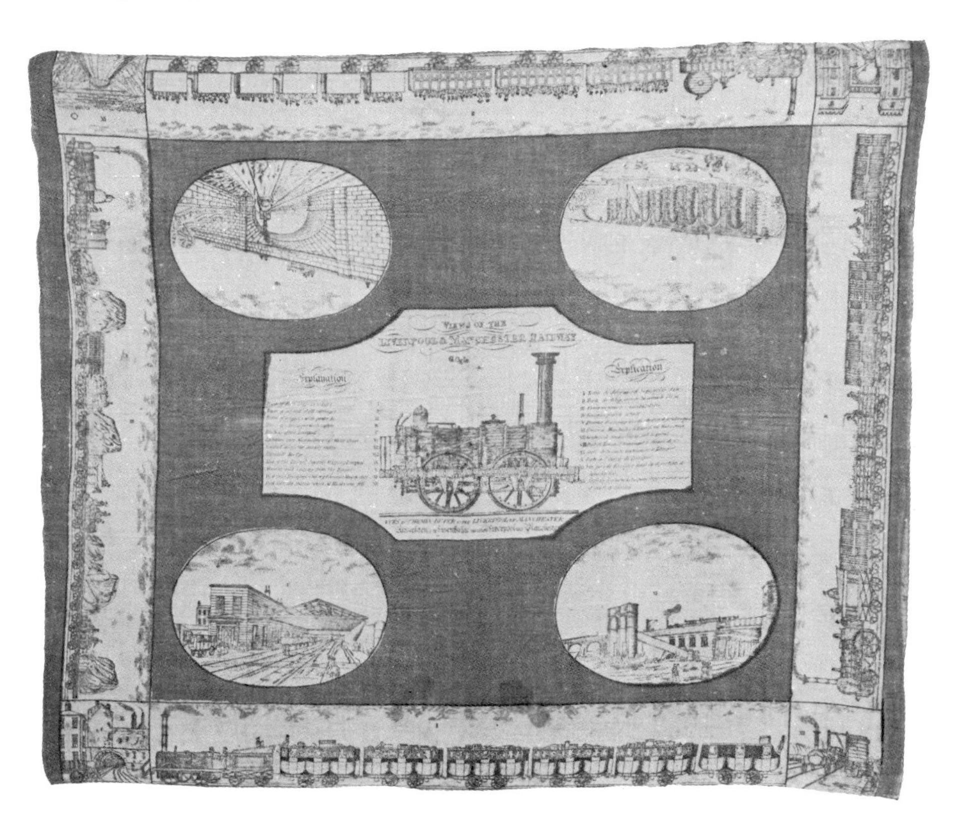

Fig 41. Handkerchief (framed) as souvenir of Liverpool and Manchester Railway. (Photo: British Railways Board)

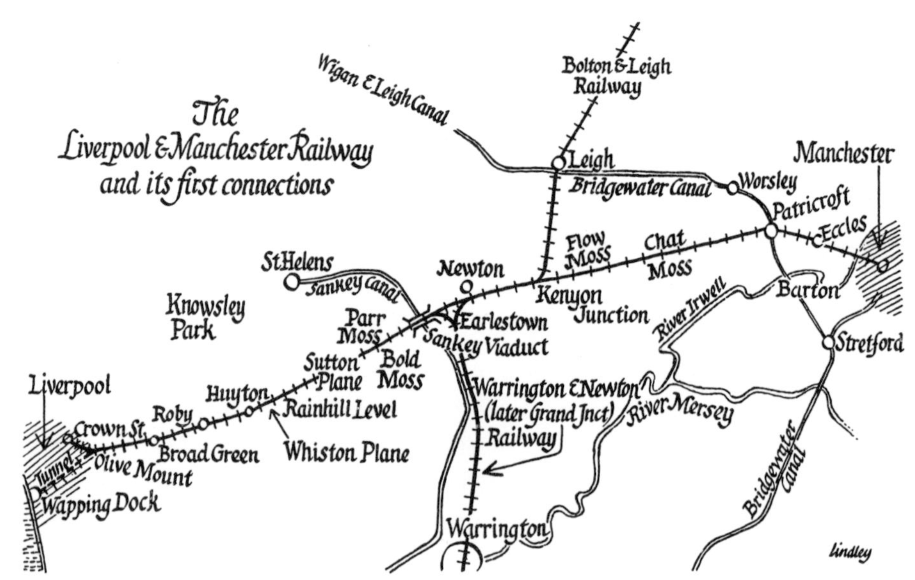

Fig 42. The Liverpool and Manchester Railway (From George and Robert Stephenson, *by L. T. C. Rolt).*

Fig 43. Aquatint showing the 'Northumbrian' locomotive (not yet named), being got ready by George and Robert Stephenson for the Liverpool and Manchester Railway.

Nasmyth has left us a delightful drawing of the contemporary scene; the Stephensons are shown preparing an engine (then unnamed, but evidently the 'Northumbrian') for a trial run.

Countless descriptions of the opening of the line have been written, and no doubt more will appear in the future. Warren, Rolt, Dendy Marshall, and Smiles have all provided us with admirable accounts.

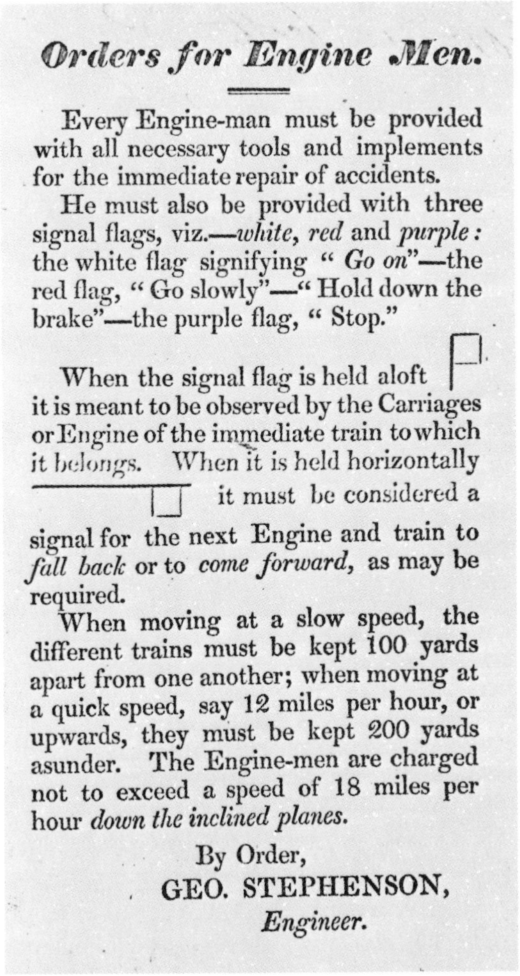

Orders for Engine Men.

Every Engine-man must be provided with all necessary tools and implements for the immediate repair of accidents.

He must also be provided with three signal flags, viz.—*white*, *red* and *purple*: the white flag signifying " *Go on*"—the red flag, " Go slowly"—" Hold down the brake"—the purple flag, " Stop."

When the signal flag is held aloft it is meant to be observed by the Carriages or Engine of the immediate train to which it belongs. When it is held horizontally it must be considered a signal for the next Engine and train to *fall back* or to *come forward*, as may be required.

When moving at a slow speed, the different trains must be kept 100 yards apart from one another; when moving at a quick speed, say 12 miles per hour, or upwards, they must be kept 200 yards asunder. The Engine-men are charged not to exceed a speed of 18 miles per hour *down the inclined planes*.

By Order,
GEO. STEPHENSON,
Engineer.

Fig 44. Orders for enginemen issued by George Stephenson for the opening of the Liverpool and Manchester Railway.

The precautions taken to avoid any accident on the opening day, 15 September 1830, were fantastic. To obviate any possibility of collisions or the straying of vehicles from one track to another, every crossing (except one, at Huyton) was removed for the inauguration. Though the occasion was marred by the dreadful accident to William Huskisson—run into by the 'Rocket' when he was going to speak to the Duke of Wellington (then Prime Minister), who opened the line—the railway acquitted itself well; it is a sad thought that this tragic event is almost the

Fig 45. Woven silk picture showing George Stephenson with locomotives. (Photo: Science Museum, London)

Fig 46. Masonic Jewel (Wylam Lodge) showing the 'Rocket' at speed.

only thing remembered by the general public about that memorable day.

Concerning Huskisson's fatal accident, a sidelight on the circumstances appears in the Journal of the Stephenson Locomotive Society which is worth quoting*:

When the L. & M. Railway was first laid out, the space between the tracks (the 'six-foot') was made only 4 ft. 8½ in. wide, some genius having the idea that it would be possible to run goods wagons on this centre track at night, carrying very wide, out-of-gauge loads. This 4 ft. 8½ in. centre space was a contributory cause to the fatal accident to Mr. Huskisson, at Parkside, during the opening ceremony in 1830, and it gave the L.N.W.R. a great deal of trouble at a later date, structures having to be moved or altered to the normal 'six-foot'. George Neele, in his 'Reminiscences' records an accident attributable to this cause as late as 1874, at Huyton Quarry (the next station to Rainhill), where the 'six-foot' space was only 4 ft. 8½ in.

Fig 47. Medal to commemorate opening of Liverpool and Manchester Railway, 15 September 1830.

* Rollason, M. H., *Journ. Stephenson Locomotive Soc.*, vol. 30, 1954, p. 331.

The opening ceremony must have been wonderfully impressive, as well as exciting, for the spectators. Eight locomotives, all built at the Forth Street Works, took part, and about 600 passengers were taken along the line. The first locomotive in the procession was the 'Northumbrian', driven by George Stephenson, then came the 'Phoenix' driven by Robert Stephenson, followed by the 'North Star', driven by Robert Stephenson (George's brother), and the 'Rocket' driven by Joseph Locke. The next engine was the 'Dart' driven by Thomas Gooch; the remaining three engines, the 'Comet', the 'Arrow', and the 'Meteor' being driven respectively by William Allcard, Frederick Swanwick, and Anthony Harding.

It seems likely that the Mr. Harding who drove the 'Meteor' was the engineer who was afterwards associated with G. P. Bidder in experiments proposed for the Gauge Commissioners in 1845.

The great opening-day celebrations were followed by a period of intensive railway development, once the issue of locomotive versus stationary engines had been settled; this applied to the motive power department in particular. One might say that the progress in locomotive design during the 5-year period 1829–34 was unmatched at any other stage in its history.

3

Growth of Public Railways in Great Britain after 1830

It is a salutary thought that, until Stephenson's great triumphs with the success of the 'Rocket' and the opening of the Liverpool and Manchester Railway, the fate of the steam locomotive hung in the balance; and though its adoption probably would have been extended in collieries and on mineral lines, its use on passenger-carrying railways was very largely the result of Stephenson's own efforts. There was still in 1829, a widely held view that stationary engines were preferable; they did not break down so often, and their use obviated the need for track that would take locomotive axle-loads. Moreover they could haul trains up gradients that were too steep for locomotives, and for that reason a line could be laid with less expenditure on earthworks. Objections, too, came from the canal promoters, who saw the extensive system of inland waterways, many of them of quite recent construction, as a perfectly adequate means of transporting goods; while for passengers requiring something quicker there was a well-established network of stage coaches, regarded by many as the most enjoyable form of travel.

It should not be supposed, either, that on the Liverpool and Manchester Railway, everything ran smoothly from the start. Engineers were in the process of learning, often by painful and humiliating experiences, the limitations of their locomotives and rolling stock, and of the materials used in their construction, and were striving to improve them by every known means. Stephenson wrote to Michael Longridge, who had become one of the country's foremost suppliers of railway material:

Railway Office, Liverpool
Oct. 11th, 1830

Dear Sir,

Upon my arrival here I examined the broken wheels, And found that one of the hoops which has given way was scarcely at all welded. This says very ill for your Blacksmith's work and alarms me very much about the axletrees; For, should one of them break you are quite aware how serious an accident it would be. It is the cranked axletrees of the Engines to which I allude. The axletrees should all be numbered at your Works, and the name of the Maker inserted in a book.

Fig 48. Semicircular panel, with portrait of George Stephenson on central portion, on a gold background. (Photo: British Railways Board)

Another of the Carriage wheels that has broken is quite 'cold Short' Iron. These hoops had better be $\frac{1}{4}$ of an Inch thicker. Would it not be better to make these hoops of Foreign Iron, or perhaps the best Low Moor.—I do not think that Scrap Iron is safe, it varies so much in its quality.

Mr. Rennie is stirring as much Interest as possible to get part of the London Line. I hope you will do all you can with <u>your</u> friends to counteract this. Tooke the Solicitor is I think Rennie's principal man; You are quite aware that Rennie will be very much in the way, and will most likely spoil the job.

Yours truly,
Geo. Stephenson

Mic. Longridge Esq.

Cranked axles were just beginning to be acceptable for use on railways; in 1830 the Forth Street Works produced the locomotive 'Planet', which marked a most vital step forward in design, in that it comprised inside cylinders under the smokebox, and a cranked axle, and a multi-tubular boiler. The inside cylinders were believed to have been the result of a conversation between Robert Stephenson and Richard Trevithick when they were on their way back from South America; Trevithick having said that a 40 per cent increase in the 'duty' (performance) of Watt's engine (worked expansively) in Cornwall, was derived from putting a jacket on the cylinders. The 'Planet' can be regarded as the forerunner of what became the established layout of the British steam-locomotive. At the same time (1830), Timothy Hackworth designed his first inside-cylinder engine, the 'Globe', for the Stockton and Darlington Railway. It does not appear that Stephenson's apprehensions about crank axles were due to any misbehaviour on the part of the 'Planet'; a study of Warren's account of her suggests that she was a very satisfactory engine. But railway promotion was now beginning to 'snowball'; and Stephenson, allowing himself no respite after the completion of the Liverpool and Manchester line, was much in demand for advice on the lines to be followed by proposed railways. He worked on his reports at high speed; after being consulted for a railway at Preston, he wrote on 26 October 1830 to B. P. Gregson, of the Lancaster Canal,

> I have determined upon the leading points of alteration in the Railway near Preston, but I have not yet been able to make out my Report on the subject;—if I possibly can, I will let you have it in time for the meeting on Friday.

The line through Preston was destined to become an integral part of the through route to Scotland; there can be little doubt that Stephenson's vision of a trunk line between the English and Scottish capitals was in his mind at this period. He wrote to Michael Longridge the following letter, in his own hand (the day of the month was omitted, which was not at all characteristic):

> Liverpool Dec: 1830
>
> My Dear sir,
>
> I expect to be able to get off to Scoetland (glasgow) on tuesday next—it would give me great pleasure if I could have you with me. I posiably may take Swanwick with me as I intend to draw up my reports before I return—if I do not see you in Scotland I will return by (way) of Bedlington—It is rely shamefull the way the countrey is going to be cut up by Railways we have no less than eight Bels (Bills) for Parliament this sissions.
>
> Your truly
> George Stephenson

A brief mention has already been made of proposals for a railway between London and Birmingham; support for it had cooled, however, during the Liverpool and Manchester developments, but it was revived again in 1830, and on 18 September, only three days after the inauguration of the Liverpool and Manchester line, an agreement was signed by both George and Robert Stephenson to survey a railway from London to Birmingham. The closeness of these two dates must be coincidental, for pressure to proceed with a survey must have been building up for some time beforehand; yet it is remarkable how the Stephensons should have taken on the greatest engineering challenge of their time when they already had so many commitments. They were commissioned to carry out surveys of alternative routes, one by way of Banbury and Oxford and the other through Rugby and Coventry. George Stephenson's association with this great undertaking was advisory rather than executive; the agreement, however, appointed him only in connection with the preliminary survey, which actually was done under Robert's direction. The London and Birmingham Railway was, in fact, to become Robert's major pre-

Fig 49. Replica of First Class coach, Liverpool and Manchester Railway. (Photo: British Railways Board)

occupation from the first application before Parliament in February 1832 until September 1838 when the line was officially opened.

Early in 1831 the partners in Robert Stephenson and Company began to realize that there would be far more orders for locomotives than they would be able to supply, so they concurred in Robert's idea of establishing a locomotive-building works in the Liverpool area; the project was successfully launched in 1832, the new firm being known as Charles Tayleur, Junr. & Co. (Charles Tayleur was a Liverpool engineer), and the works as the Vulcan Foundry, situated at Newton-le-Willows, near Warrington. This firm prospered, and achieved a very long and honourable record in the locomotive-building business; its name was changed officially to Vulcan Foundry Ltd.

With a big demand for locomotives becoming likely, several other firms entered the field throughout the 1830s and 1840s, some of which gained considerable renown.

During the year 1831, the Forth Street Works supplied two powerful total-adhesion locomotives named 'Samson' and 'Goliath' which, in the layout of their cylinders and frames, were of the same type of construction as the 'Planet'; but their four wheels were coupled, and the boiler diameter, firebox dimensions, and cylinder diameter were all increased. These engines were for the operations on the 1 in 96 gradients at Whiston and Sutton on the Liverpool and Manchester line, which were laid out for stationary-engine haulage; when the line was planned it was believed that no locomotives could haul trains up such gradients until Stephenson, during the Rainhill Trials, gave a masterly demonstration with the 'Rocket' by taking her up Rainhill 'at a galop' (John Dixon's description) with a coachload of about 20 people.

A period of recession, which must have been brief (as Stephenson predicted it would be) seems to have occurred on the Liverpool and Manchester Railway about a year after its opening. Possibly a great many passengers travelled on it in its earliest days simply out of curiosity, so they would never have become part of the regular traffic. Projects for new railways (Manchester to Leeds, and Manchester to Sheffield) also tended to draw attention away from the Liverpool and Manchester line. Writing to Nicholas Wood, Stephenson comments:

Lpool Nov 9th 1831

My dear Sir,

I have this day received yours of the 6th Inst and so far from pleading guilty to your accusation of having forsaken you, I intend to be in Newcastle some time next week. as I have some business in that neighbourhood, and may probably reach Newcastle towards the latter end of the week.

Railways are not certainly in such good repute here just at present as they were this time last year; this indifference will however disappear in the course of 6 months, and they will rise again to their proper level.

The Report made by the Directors to the last General Meeting was made as unfavourable as it could with any appearance of truth, in order to throw a damper upon a Rival scheme the 'Lpool & Leeds' Railway, but notwithstanding their attempts, they will not long be able to keep them back.

The Bill for the 'Sheffield & Manchester' Railway has as you would be aware, been obtained. I find upon enquiry that your £25 was paid. The work will not be commenced before next spring. To give you some idea of my own Estimate of Railway projects I will let you know what number of shares I myself hold.

In the 'Lpool & Manchester"	6
In the 'Wton & Newton"----	24
In the 'Leicester & Swannington"	45
Robert & myself have in the "Shefd & Mantr"	20

I have about 80 more in Railway projects that have not yet obtained Acts.

With respect to Mr. Losh's wheels I will look at these when I am in N.Castle: the price I think will be considered too high even at 30/– per cwt. However it is only fair that they should be tried. and I will make arrangements about them.

I shall be able to speak to you more decisively about Giles's Tunnal when I see you. If the sand is pretty sound and compact, the Brickwork which he proposes is sufficiently thick. The Radius of the bottom however is too great if there is any unsoundness in the bottom, and in any case so long a Radius should not be used as the expence is very nearly the same for a flat curve as for another. If the Work is well managed then Tunnelling should not cost more than £16 per lineal yard. The mode of working the Tunnel depends altogether upon the sort of material that is to be driven through. You state the quantity of excavation in the open cutting to be 122000 I think you must mean 1,220,000 c. yds. I think Mr- Giles must be afraid of not holing right when he speaks of driving an experimental drift, for there is no occasion for it whatever, in fact it is safer and far less expensive without it. If Giles were in as bitter repute in the North than he is here he would not long remain on the N.Castle & Carlisle Railway. I enclose you a circular which will shew how he is liked by parties who have been employing him.

If I am to be able to be in N.Castle before the end of the week I will write to you, and if you will meet me there we will drive down to Losh's, and dine with him for old times' sake.

Mrs. Stephenson joins me in best respects to Mrs. Wood and to your sister, from whom Mrs. S. would be glad to hear

I am dear Sir
Yours truly
Geo. Stephenson

a copy of the circular spoken of to you cannot be obtained. Its object was to expose the gross injustice of Mr. Giles's demands upon the "Chester & Lpool" Railway; the amount of his bill for pointing out and advocating one of the very worst lines that it was possible to select amounts to the small sum of £1500, the charge for his own valuable time being £7. 7s. per diem.

Geo. Stephenson
Nov. 9 1831

The preceding paragraph (about Giles's fees) was added in a different hand and the signature following it is not Stephenson's.

Francis Giles was an adversary of old. He had poured scorn on Stephenson's method of conquering Chat Moss, and in 1830–31 was trying to secure a leading place for himself on the London and Birmingham Railway construction. Robert Stephenson refused to have him as a joint engineer for the project. L. T. C. Rolt calls him a middle-aged canal engineer, not equal to the demands of the railway age. However he did get himself appointed as engineer to the Newcastle and Carlisle Railway and, later, the London and Southampton Railway.

Mention has already been made of the Leicester and Swannington Railway, the preliminary survey for which had been conducted by George Stephenson. In 1829 the committee for the line had appointed Robert Stephenson as its engineer, and construction was duly begun. There was one major work on the railway, the Glenfield Tunnel, a mile long, the line of which went through a bed of sand, which created difficulties and added greatly to the cost. George Stephenson visited the line and discussed its progress with Robert who made some observations destined to have a profound effect on his father's life.

The Leicester and Swannington Railway, as we have seen, was built primarily to serve coalfields. While superintending its construction Robert, who had grown up among collieries and had acquired a very considerable knowledge of their operation, formed the opinion that the Leicestershire coalfields could be made to yield much more, and that the area was suitable for exploitation. There were, he was sure, deeper seams ready to be worked, as well as the existing ones nearer the surface. George Stephenson, whose knowledge of collieries was profound, was impressed, and on his return to Liverpool he discussed this possible development with his friend Joseph Sandars, his great champion in the Liverpool and Manchester enterprise, and with Sir Joshua Walmsley. The three men went into partnership and purchased land at Snibston, adjacent to the Leicester and Swannington Railway. George Stephenson, by now a man

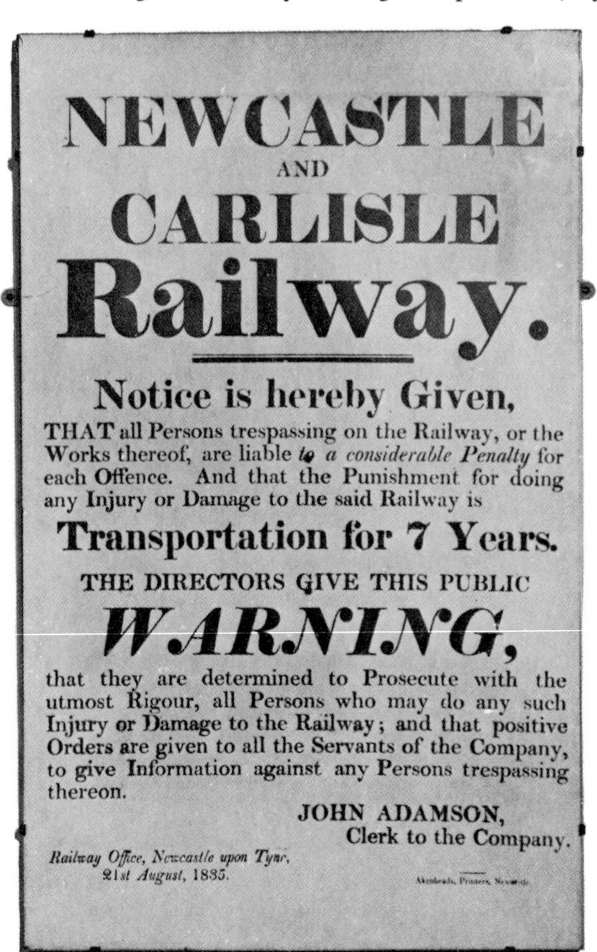

Fig 50. Newcastle, Carlisle and Grand Junction Railway: notice threatening offenders with transportation (1835). (Photo: British Railways Board)

of substantial means, took to the new venture with such enthusiasm that he gave up his house in Liverpool and moved to Alton Grange, Ashby-de-la-Zouch, an attractive house near Coalville, which he occupied for about seven years. He was now near the centre of England and could set off in any direction in which railway schemes requiring his attention were being promoted. This move was, therefore, an important step in his life, and during the 1830s, though Stephenson's name occurs less in connection with locomotives, it was continually increasing in the field of railway planning and construction.

The Snibston colliery enterprise was not without its setbacks, in its early stages. Water in the workings, during the sinking of the new pits, provided great difficulties; and the deeper strata included some very hard volcanic rock, 22ft. in thickness. Stephenson, finding that local labour was inexperienced and too easily discouraged under these tough conditions, offered jobs to a number of miners from his old Killingworth district; thus a highly skilled force was built up, and eventually the hard rock was penetrated, and Stephenson and his partners were rewarded by the first-rate quality of the thick seam of coal which had been reached. The workings included three shafts; and Stephenson found himself involved in a highly profitable venture. It is of interest that Stephenson's elder brother James came to take up a job at Snibston.

During his last days in Liverpool Stephenson was on 19 September 1831 requested by the Directors of the Liverpool and Manchester Railway to report to them on a rather weird-looking locomotive, the first ever to be built in Manchester, which had been constructed by a firm named Galloway, Bowman, and Glasgow. It was a side-lever engine with vertical cylinders driving a dummy crankshaft and exhausting into a chimney over the boiler barrel; presumably the boiler was of the return-flue type. Stephenson's opinion is summarized in Warren's history of the Forth Street firm*; the Liverpool and Manchester Directors stated that they would object to any new engines with vertical cylinders being put to work on the Liverpool and Manchester Railway; and Dendy Marshall, in his Centenary History of the line, records that in its original form it was said to lift itself off the rails.† It was rebuilt a year later, with a more normal boiler, and the dummy crank axle amidships, and was renamed the 'Caledonian'; the Directors of the Liverpool and Manchester Railway agreed to pay £800 for it, and it appears to have done rather better after being rebuilt. When they sold it to the London and Birmingham railway in 1837 they recouped themselves to the extent of £400.

Meanwhile a rather complicated situation was growing up around the

* Warren, pp. 288–9.
† *Centenary History of the Liverpool and Manchester Railway*, pp. 89, 90.

promotion and construction of a most important line to connect Birmingham with the Liverpool and Manchester Railway. It was, of course, realized that to join these two major routes together would be of great advantage to each of them; hence the origin of what became known as the Grand Junction Railway, which was to go roughly north from Birmingham and link up with the Liverpool and Manchester line at Newton, from which a branch line to Warrington was being constructed under the direction of Robert Stephenson, who had been appointed engineer-in-chief.

The Liverpool and Manchester Directors, keenly interested in the prospects of this vital new railway, encouraged George Stephenson to give his attention to it; as a result, Stephenson requested John Locke to carry out a survey from Birmingham to the Warrington and Newton Railway. The divergence of Locke from Stephenson, on professional grounds, was yet to come; Stephenson must have been torn between the desire to retain Locke (who had become one of the most competent railway engineers in the country, with a career of great promise opening before him) under his absolute control and the alternative of allowing him freedom to play a far greater part in new railway construction. The two men had travelled to Ireland together, and from 18 to 24 February 1832 they were working on a scheme for a line from Dublin to Kingstown; a list of Locke's expenses, which has survived, was posted to Stephenson on 25 December 1832. But relations became rather strained, and eventually a compromise was effected, so far as the Grand Junction Railway was concerned, by assigning the construction of the northern half of the line to Locke and the southern half to George Stephenson. But this failed to work, and in 1835 Locke was appointed to the chief's position for the whole undertaking, and Stephenson was no longer associated with it. Some of Locke's letters to Stephenson (or portions of them) are preserved at Chesterfield, and testify to the deep respect shown by Locke to his old chief. They are of great historic interest, showing the fierce scramble for jobs on the London and Birmingham line (letter dated 30 June 1832), also a proposal by 'the Dublin Co.' to offer £500 for the best Locomotive Engine (evidently inspired by the Rainhill Trials) in a letter dated 14 November 1832.

Concern at Stephenson's absence from a dinner party in December 1832, at the Adelphi, Liverpool, is expressed in a letter to Stephenson by Locke who writes:

> . . . I don't know at this moment where you dined, and was ignorant until this morning that you felt hurt at our apparent neglect. I beg to assure you that Allcard and myself would have gladly availed ourselves of your company, that we were both disappointed at not seeing you, and that we came purposely to

(Newton?) on the following day to make up for that disappointment. After that explanation I am sure you will acquit us. . . .

Through the kindness of Mr. Adin Hull, A.I.Mech.E., three generations of whose family served successively the London and North Western Railway and the London, Midland, and Scottish Railway, a collection of fifteen unpublished letters written by Stephenson to John Moss and to J. R. Chorley, about the construction of the Grand Junction Railway, have been made available for the present volume. Chorley was a lawyer in Liverpool engaged by the Railway Company during its development; Moss a Liverpool banker interested in the promotion of the Grand Junction. The letters are given below *in extenso*. The letter about the Broughton family's quarries is of particular interest, showing Stephenson's characteristic realism in such matters as the exploitation of the land through which his railways were intended to run.

Chedion Hotel, Leicester Square
March 19th 1832

My dear Sir,

I am duly in receipt of your's of the 14th inst. for which I am obliged. Before I left Liverpool the other day I agreed to take 20 shares from Mr. Henry Booth which he held in the London & Birmingham Railway. This will prevent me taking the shares in the Liverpool & Birmingham.

We have great expectation in getting our Bill – Our opponents appear to be getting weaker and weaker every day.

I will take care to send you a plan & section as you request by Clay.

Yours faithfully
Geo: Stephenson

J. R. Chorley
Messrs. Pritt, Clay & Swift
Solicitors
Liverpool

Alton Grange: June 30th 1833

Dear Sir,

I beg to acknowledge the receipt of your letter of June 29th stating you had paid the amount due to me from the Grand Junction Company into Mr. Moss's Bank which is quite right.

I am
Dear Sir
Yours truly
Geo: Stephenson

J. R. Chorley Esq.
Grand Junction Railway Office
Liverpool

Dear Sir,

Understanding from the Birmingham Directors that you expected to have my report on the deviated line, laid before you on Wednesday next – I am sorry that I cannot have a full report ready by that time, and therefore you must not expect one before the end of the week, and I think it will be better to defer the consideration of the subject until the next meeting – I am now examining the nature of the bridges that will be required – Mr. Turner has been so obliging as to accompany me over the Line so as to enable him to say – how far, in his opinion, the deviated Line will interfere with any gentlemens residences.

I am
Yours truly
Geo: Stephenson

Penkridge 9 Sep. 1833

John Moss Esq.
Liverpool Bank
Liverpool

Dear Sir,

I have been making every exertion in my power to have the plans prepared for Your inspection on Friday, but find it impossible to get them ready in time.

If however you could have the meeting put off till Monday next, I shall be able to have them ready on that day, and will have also collected for Swift a list of the parishes and townships which we pass through.

I have taken the levels of another line with a view to keep out of sight of Mr. Gough's House: and should Lord Dartmouth be willing to let us take a small portion of the Hampstead park (a small estate some miles nearer Birmingham than his Residence) we shall be almost enabled to Keep Clear of Mr. Gough's land and will be in such a situation, where we pass through his property as to be within the limit prescribed by the act. I shall however be able to describe this part much better upon the plan, and when Mr. Lawrence and yourself accompany me over the line, You will be able to estimate the damages likely to be done to his property.

Mr. Turner and Mr. Ledsam who were on the spot with me this morning, both think, that Lord Dartmouth may probably accede to the alteration, as it will be an accomodation [sic] to the Gough Family to whom he is very friendly.

I am dear Sir
Yours faithfully
Geo: Stephenson

P.S. I hope that by Friday, Mr. Locke will have prepared the plans necessary for purchasing the land between the Mersey & Weaver.

John Moss Esq.
&c &c
Liverpool

Stafford
Dec. 24th 1833.

Dear Chorley,

I have desired Mr. Swanwick to go down to Lpool for the purpose of entering into any explanation of the Accts which I handed you the other day, that may be required by the Finance Committee.

You will oblige me by paying to (?) M.S. the Balance due to me at the end of the year together with the amount of the other accounts.

Yours truly
Geo: Stephenson

John Chorley Esq.
Grand Junction Railway Office
Liverpool

Betley 4 Jany 1834.

Dear Sir,

I have very minutely examined the quarries belonging to the Broughton family, and I can now inform you that the stone is not worth one shilling to the Company – there is plenty of it that may be fit for bridge building and similar purposes – but none of it hard enough for blocks – the expence of getting it would be considerable owing to the immense covering there is on it – stone of the same quality may be got in Mr. Brittain's land nearer to the Railway and at a much less cost – whoever gets the Contract for forming the Railway in that district would be able to pay a good rent for Brittain's quarry rather than have that of the Broughtons for nothing. There is also another quarry belonging to a Mr. Coates which would be more advantageously worked at a fair rent. – In the Madeley Park estate there is a quarry of stone of superior quality to any above alluded to, and which would be worked much cheaper than Mr. Broughton's.

Mr. Barker has got 5 copies of the Plan & Section which I believe is sufficient for his purpose – one copy will have reached you in Liverpool ere this – I expect to be with you on Tuesday next when I will call at the Bank. –

I am
Dear Sir
Yours truly
Geo: Stephenson

John Moss Esqre
Bank
Liverpool

Birmingham Jany 25. 1834

Dear Sir,

I have again been called up here, to examine some deviations (proposed by Mr. Jesson) where the line passes through the property of Mr. Gough, which as they are only trifling I have consented to.

I have seen Mr. Dawson, Lord Dartmouth's Steward, at Mr. Barker's who says, that although the arrangement had not been finally made, he had no doubt but that the result would be favourable.

The Plans preparing at Stafford, for Parliament, will be finished about the end of next week, when that office will be no longer necessary.

I am going to London this evening to see my son, but will be here again on Tuesday, as Mr. Barker thinks it may be necessary.

I am, dear Sir
Yours truly
Geo: Stephenson

John Moss Esqre
Liverpool

Stafford Jany 27th 1834

Dear Sir,

I returned to Birmingham this morning according to my intention and called upon Mr. Barker expecting that something relative to the treaty with Lord Dartmouth might have required my presence, Mr. Dawson however did not meet Mr. Barker as expected, and accordingly I came down here, ready to return when necessary.

A clause should be inserted in the bill for the Extension Line empowering the Company to stop or to divert the Canal during the erection of the Bridge on the site of the proposed Crossing. I think that the diversion of the Canal may be on the whole the most expedient mode.

I will endeavour to let you have a *general* Estimate of the Line by next Wednesday, which I trust will be sufficiently correct and detailed for the present, all the details however I cannot hope to have prepared so early.

I am, dear Sir,
Yours truly
Geo: Stephenson

John Moss Esqre
Liverpool

Newcastle on Tyne
Feb. 23rd 1834

Dear Sir,

I received yours of the 21st. I shall be with you on Tuesday and if necessary I can proceed to London that night.

With respect to Sir John Wrottesley observations about the plan being promised for crossing the Staffordshire and Worcestershire Canal, I saw the Clerk after I promised to give the Plan and made a full explanation of the manner of crossing, after which I did not think it necessary to give a plan – There is also a Clause in the Bill which completely protect them from any inquiry.

If a plan is necessary Swanwick can give it them in London as he perfectly understands my mode of crossing the Canal.

I am Dear Sir
Yours truly
Geo: Stephenson

J. Chorley Esq[re]
Grand Junction Railway Office
Liverpool

Stork Hotel Birmingham
April 7th 1834

Dear Sir,

In consequence of your letter which I received in London I came down to Birmingham this morning and have seen Parker with whom I have been engaged the whole day in considering the propositions of several parties who require arrangements to be made with the Coy. We have considered the Clauses proposed by the Birmingham Canal Coy most of which have been agreed upon. There is one point on which I think their demands unreasonable and to which therefore I cannot allow the Directors to agree: it relates to the width of the aqueduct under the Walsall Branch Canal, which they insist shall be not only of the full width of the Canal & Towing Path, but of the additional width of a slip of sand they have on one side of the Canal. The demand is so unreasonable that I think they cannot insist upon it.

With respect to [. . .] of the T.P. [Turnpike] Roads I am to meet the [. . . . .] to-morrow to endeavour to come to a *final* arrangement with them on some of the points which they seemed disposed to insist on, and which thinking unreasonable I have previously refused to give up; on these I think we shall be able to-morrow to come to some arrangement. The care of the old Bham & Walsall T.P. Road is I think in train for being settled, either by their consenting to the proposed diversion or if they decidedly dissent, we must make the sacrifice of a few hundred Pounds.

I am turning my attention towards the Alton-Park case and hope as the first step towards an arrangement allowing of the diversion still taking a portion of the Park, to see Mr. Watt to-morrow. If the interview is favourable to our wish of remaining in the Park, I will lay down a line and after getting the Section I will inform you as to the cost of it.

If nothing occurs in the Watts case to detain me here I hope to be with you on Wednesday.

I am dear Sir
Yours faithfully
Geo: Stephenson

J. Moss Esq[re]
Bank, Liverpool

I send you a copy of the Plans & Sections of the two lines, which has just been completed.

Alton Grange, Septr 8th 1834

My Dear Sir,

Since writing the accompanying letter [not now with *this* letter] I have considered it may be better for me to proceed at once to Mr. Forster's to see if I can get the rails that I ordered, forwarded to Liverpool. On this account I may not be able to get to Liverpool to attend the Board on Wednesday, unless I travel on Tuesday night, & I have got a bad cold & am rather unfit for travelling at night.

Yours truly
Geo: Stephenson

P.S. I have this moment received a letter from Mr. Forster, stating that he hopes to forward the rails & chains for the Grand Junction Railway by the end of next week. I still think it will be better for me to see them before they are sent off, & shall set off for Stourbridge tomorrow.

G: S

J. R. Chorley Esqre
Grand Junction Railway Office
Mersey Chambers
Liverpool

Liverpool June 13th 1835

Dear Sir,

I have read over Mr. Locke's report upon the different rails he has laid before the Directors. I shall also be able to lay before you, in a few days, my views upon the same.

I am compelled to be in London on Tuesday next, which prevents me waiting upon the board on Wednesday. I hope however to be with you the next week.

I am, dear Sir
Yours truly
Geo: Stephenson

John Moss Esqre
Liverpool

Alton Grange, 15th Sepr 1835.

My Dear Sir,

I beg to acknowledge the receipt of your Letter of the 15th inst. and to enclose a Receipt for the £799.12.4 paid to Mr. Sandars on my account.

I am Dear Sir
Yours very truly
Geo: Stephenson

J. R. Chorley Esq.
Grand Junction Railway Office
Liverpool.

Angel Inn Liverpool
Sunday 14th 1835

Dear Chorley,

I am obliged to leave here without seeing you, having to go into the witness-box in the Lords, on Tuesday.

Will you be so kind as to remit me £100, say one hundred pounds, to the Albion Hotel, Cockspar Street, London.

I am sorry I had not the pleasure of your company over the line. Do contrive to be with us the next time – I hope to be in Liverpool again in about a fortnight. –

I am,
Yours truly
Geo: Stephenson

J. R. Chorley Esqre
Grand Junction Railway Office
Mersey Chambers

To return to the year 1832, the opening took place of the Glasgow and Garnkirk Railway which, as Warren reminds us, was the fourth public railway to be opened with locomotives built by Robert Stephenson and Company; the two engines supplied were stated, at the time, to have 'fully sustained the high character acquired for their engines by these eminent engineers. They are quite similar in their construction to those of the Liverpool and Manchester Railway, with all the improvements up to the date of their making'. The locomotives were named 'St. Rollox' and 'George Stephenson'; the latter naming was a handsome Scottish compliment to the famous engineer, who was himself the grandson of a Scotsman. Incidentally, the Stockton and Darlington Railway named one of their locomotives 'Stephenson', but not until 1850, shortly after his death; their locomotive naming policy in the 1850s turned rather more than in the past to famous men associated with the line, including 'Meynell' (the first chairman), 'Hackworth', 'Edward Pease', and 'John Dixon'.

The Glasgow and Garnkirk locomotives were basically of the 'Planet' and the 'Goliath' types; the gauge was 4 ft. 6 in. originally. An excellent publication, *Views of the Opening of the Glasgow and Garnkirk Railway* was compiled by D. O. Hill and published in 1832.

Stephenson still retained his appointment with the Liverpool and Manchester Railway, which he did not relinquish until 1833; he was frequently consulted by the Directors on technical matters, one of which (then causing increasing concern) was the axle loading of the latest locomotives. When one reflects that in 1829 the *total* weight of the 'Rocket'

Fig 51. The 'Rocket' on arrival at South Kensington, 1862. (From a photograph in the author's possession)

was $4\frac{1}{4}$ tons ($2\frac{1}{2}$ tons on the driving wheels) and that by 1831 the 'Samson' had over $5\frac{1}{2}$ tons on the driving axle and a total weight of about 10 tons, one can understand their anxiety about the life of the track. Even in early colliery locomotives, the problem had been attacked by increasing the number of axles; and this solution was the subject of a discussion at a Directors' meeting on 5 November 1832, when Stephenson was present. He was asked to report on the respective merits of four-wheeled and six-wheeled locomotives, and must have taken some satisfaction in doing so, in favour of the six-wheeled engine, the ultimate need for which he had foreshadowed in an earlier report which he had submitted to the Directors in 1828. Further, it implied disapproval, on his part, of the four-wheeled designs to which his rival, Edward Bury, was to cling so tenaciously.

The development of the six-wheeled locomotive followed rapidly, under Robert Stephenson's direction. As early as October 1832 a working drawing was completed at the Forth Street Works for an elongated 'Planet' type locomotive, to run on six wheels, the two front axles being coupled. Soon after, on 3 January 1833, a design was prepared for a locomotive with six wheels, but with the driving axle uncoupled. These were not the first six-wheeled engines, for Stephenson had constructed one before 1815; and much more recently the six-wheeled 'Twin Sisters' had been put to work on the Bolton and Leigh Railway. But the developments of 1832–3 marked a definite trend in locomotive designs towards the six-wheeled type, which soon blossomed forth in the 2–2–2, 0–4–2, and 2–4–0 wheel arrangements (as well as some examples of the 4–2–0 variety, especially in the 1840s).

The Leicester and Swannington Railway, upon which Stephenson, now living at Alton Grange, could keep a watchful eye, was progressing well; the first portion, from Leicester to Staunton Road, had been opened on 17 July 1832, and the line was completed in 1833. This railway was thus the oldest component of the great amalgamation of lines which took place in 1844, to become the Midland Railway.

Fig 52. The 'Rocket' locomotive to-day. (Crown copyright: Science Museum, London)

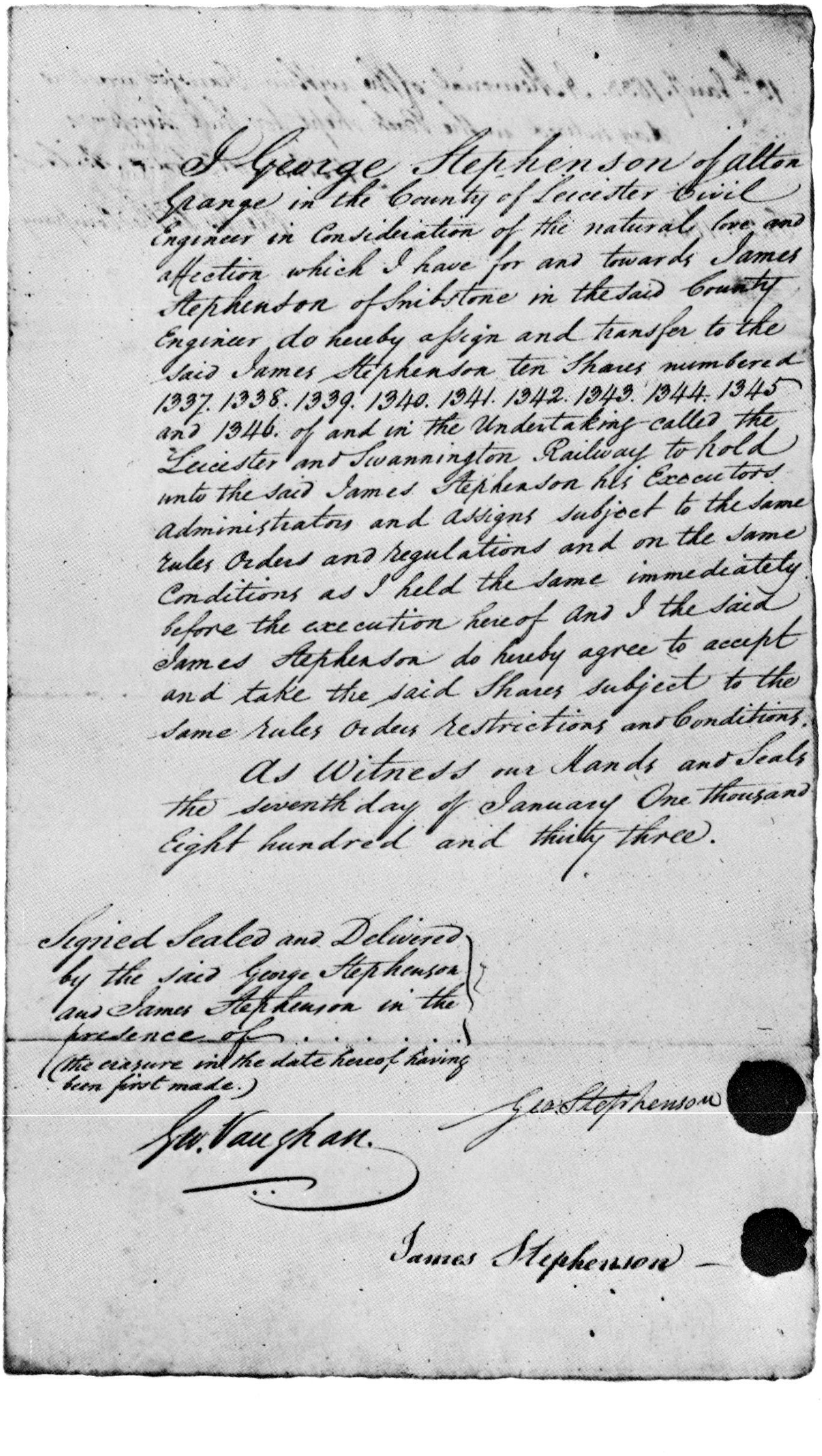

I George Stephenson of Alton Grange in the County of Leicester Civil Engineer in Consideration of the natural love and affection which I have for and towards James Stephenson of Snibstone in the said County Engineer do hereby assign and transfer to the said James Stephenson ten Shares numbered 1337. 1338. 1339. 1340. 1341. 1342. 1343. 1344. 1345 and 1346. of and in the Undertaking called the Leicester and Swannington Railway to hold unto the said James Stephenson his Executors administrators and assigns subject to the same rules Orders and regulations and on the same Conditions as I held the same immediately before the execution hereof And I the said James Stephenson do hereby agree to accept and take the said Shares subject to the same rules Orders restrictions and Conditions.

As Witness our Hands and Seals the seventh day of January One thousand Eight hundred and thirty three.

Signed Sealed and Delivered by the said George Stephenson and James Stephenson in the presence of (the erasure in the date hereof having been first made.)

Geo. Vaughan.

Geo Stephenson

James Stephenson

Fig 53. Deed of Gift (transfer of shares) from George Stephenson to his nephew James Stephenson, 1833.

Stephenson was a notably generous man to his closer relations, and upon his brother John's death in an accident at the Forth Street Works in 1831, which left a large family fatherless, he undertook to support them; in similar manner he also supported the family of his sister Eleanor, whose husband Stephen Liddell died after an accident at Newcastle; he was working for George Stephenson at the time. Again, in January 1833 Stephenson effected a Deed of Gift to his nephew James Stephenson, by a transfer of shares to the young man.

The Stephensons' participation in the Leicester and Swannington Railway provided an opportunity for gaining experience with the six-wheeled locomotives recently developed. The design, together with some specified details such as the provision of a steam brake, were the subject of a patent taken out by Robert Stephenson on 7 October 1833, while the construction of a remarkable locomotive was in progress for the Leicester and Swannington Railway. This engine, which was the fourth to be completed under the patent, had all six wheels coupled, and represented a phenomenal increase in size and power over other engines. The weight is not known, but has been estimated at 17 tons. What is so important about the design is that it became the pioneer of the ordinary six-coupled goods locomotive, with inside cylinders, and the firebox between the driving and trailing axles—the type which has been the most generally useful design throughout the long history of British steam locomotives.

The Grand Junction Railway Act was passed on 6 May 1833; as we have seen, Stephenson was initially in charge, though he relinquished it by degrees to Joseph Locke. Nevertheless for the ensuing two years, it was one of Stephenson's many responsibilities. In 1833, too, the London and Birmingham Railway Bill was safely passed, and on 20 September Stephenson had the satisfaction of seeing Robert appointed to the chief engineering position for the construction of the line. Other railways then under consideration were the London and Southampton, the London and Brighton, the Liverpool and Preston, the Preston and Wyre and the Stanhope and Tyne. The London and Greenwich Railway, incorporated in 1833, and the London and Croydon Railway soon followed. By no means were all of these Stephenson lines; but George and Robert certainly had their full share at this exciting time of railway development.

Stephenson kept in contact with his Stockton and Darlington friends, and with his first public railway which had now 'grown up' and had abolished horse traction, for which Timothy Hackworth must have been truly thankful, for a line on which steam-hauled trains were interspersed with horse-drawn chaldrons, in a glorious 'free for all', could not have hoped to increase its revenue, even though there were various traffics awaiting its attention. This reform dated from 1833. Edward Pease wrote to Stephenson from Darlington in April 1834, exhorting him to

make more width between your lines of way than we have.

(it must have had similar spacing to its successor, the Liverpool and Manchester Railway).

—if rails can be made that both the upper & under surface were exactly alike, it would be an advantage, then so soon as lamination in the slightest degree or deflection took place, the other surface to be immediately resorted to.

We have already seen the effects of this spacing of tracks on the Liverpool and Manchester line; it appears that Stephenson, in choosing it, was simply following his earlier practice, and it is a salutary thought to reflect how railway development would have been inhibited if it had become widespread. This early notion of reversible 'bull-head' rails is interesting; that form of rail section eventually became practically *de rigueur* for railways in Britain, but the idea of reversibility failed because it was not appreciated that, owing to the action of the wheels of the trains, the rails would wear hollows on their under-surfaces, wherever the rails were supported by chairs, and these hollows were sufficiently pronounced to make the under-surfaces unusable. The laminations to which Pease refers were a frequent worry to railway engineers in those days but were gradually eliminated or reduced by improved manufacturing methods.

Pease concludes on a personal note, and his son Joseph adds an appeal for employment for an acquaintance who had fallen on hard times:

. . . And now my friend George (old & tried) it is well known to thee that I cherish so warm an interest in thy happiness & prosperity, thou should have told me something about thyself: if thy coal had begun to realize thy expectations; or that all thy hopes were, where the hopes of all miners are, underground yet old men count little of advantages, till they come into the pockets & when thine is full I shall conclude Leicestershire mining is a good trade & not before

With much regard,
Thy sincere Friend
Edward Pease.

Isaac Coutes (John's younger brother) cannot make his Iron trade answer and would be glad to accept a salaried situation at a moderate rate—he would render himself useful in any way—understanding more than a little the working on railways—Iron Waggon building &c—Canst thou help him

Joseph Pease Jnr.
Kind regards.

A very momentous meeting took place in the summer of 1834 between Stephenson and George Hudson, who later became known as the 'Railway King'. Hudson was a native of Whitby, Yorkshire, and Stephenson was visiting the town in connection with a proposal to provide a railway to York. Hudson had inherited a large sum of money seven years before, which he used in order to build up his railway kingdom, and he cherished schemes for making York a great railway centre.

It is curious how well the two men got on together; their characters were so different and yet their friendship lasted for some ten or twelve years. Hudson was a flamboyant, bombastic personality, who used many devious tricks to secure his ascendancy over several of the railways in Britain; Stephenson was a man of the highest integrity in all his dealings, whose cautious nature restrained him from taking risks, financial or otherwise. But they both had an insatiable interest in railways; and now that the heaping of obloquy on Hudson has become less fashionable, it can be seen that some of his schemes, such as the formation of the Midland

Fig 54. Idealised picture of George Stephenson's family. The seated woman on the left is Fanny (Henderson) Stephenson, George Stephenson's first wife, with her arm round their daughter, who died at the age of three weeks; the other seated woman is Elizabeth Hindmarsh, who became George Stephenson's second wife. The standing woman is Mabel Stephenson (George Stephenson's mother). George Stephenson is shown seated, holding his miner's safety lamp. Robert Stephenson is shown on the right, with dogs. In the background are shown Heaton and Morpeth Bridge; 'Dial Cottage' at Wylam; the 'Blucher' locomotive driven by James Stephenson (George's brother); and the Killingworth High Pit. (Photo: Science Museum, London)

Railway, were based on sound ideas. An important outcome of the meeting between Stephenson and Hudson in 1834 was the promotion by Hudson of the York and North Midland Railway, to link York with the North Midland (a line in which Stephenson was much interested) at Normanton. To effect this junction, Hudson had to give up his previous idea of a York and Leeds Railway, but the York and North Midland was to become a vital component in the great spread of railways in the 1835–40 period, which gave a line of communication between London and York, via Birmingham and Derby.

About this time there was a move by the two brothers, Charles and Robert Brandling, to promote a railway between Gateshead and South Shields, and with Monkwearmouth. This became known as the Brandling Junction Railway; and both George and Robert Stephenson were associated with it from 1835 onwards. Towards the end of 1834 another Brandling—William—appears to have been interested in it. The Brandling family, of Gosforth Hall, north of Newcastle, had known Stephenson since his early days. Stephenson, on being invited to inspect the location of the proposed railway, saw an opportunity of calling on his friend and ally, Michael Longridge, at the same time, and accordingly wrote (in his own hand) as follows to Longridge at Bedlington Iron Works:

Alton Grange Dec 10th 1834

My Dear Sir,

I duly received your letter of 5th. I have just had a letter from Mr. William Brandling saying he wishes me to come down to the north to examen the country for a line of Railway that he has in vew and I have promised to be down the latter end of the month, when I hope to find you at home but I trust not confined with the gout (?) I shall keep for you 10 or 20 shares no cash will be wanted yet—I will bring the watch with me—I hope Robert will endeavour to be down at the same time and I have rote him to night to come if he can

I am Dear sir
Your very truly
Geo. Stephenson

The survey apparently went well, and on 3 February 1835, Stephenson sent the following letter (now in the possession of Mr. R. J. Duncan, of Gosforth, by whose kind permission it is reproduced here):

Dear Sir,

Having now thoroughly investigated the projected line of Railway from Gateshead to South Shields and Sunderland as to its practicability, I am enabled to inform you that the nature of the country is extremely favourable to its formation—I have also as Mr. Robt W. Brandling requested duly considered the coal district belonging to the Dean and Chapter of Durham and also to Lady Barrington, as to whether the line could in any way be improved, so as to work the coal under these estates in the most advantageous manner.

It is my opinion that the line is laid out in the best possible manner for working the Coals under these Estates, not only with reference to the part leased by yourself and Mr. Robt W. Brandling but also to all the Coal (belonging to them) and lying many miles above Newcastle which must eventually join this line. Indeed it is the only feasible route that can be taken for working the coal, lying between the Tyne and Wear, which belongs to the Dean & Chapter of Durham, Excepting that part which will be taken up by the Stanhope & Tyne Railway.

I may however inform you, that the line must be worked upon the most economical plan, in order to render it a profitable speculation

I am, Dear Sir,
Your most obdt Servt
Geo. Stephenson

John Brandling Esq.,
Kenton Lodge.

Stephenson's intense activity was indeed a trial to each of his current scribes in turn; about this time, one of them observed that in a busy season, in a single day Stephenson dictated 37 letters, several of them embodying the results of much close thinking and calculation. On one occasion he dictated reports and letters for 12 hours, non-stop, until his secretary pleaded for a suspension of the labour. Smiles, on this aspect of Stephenson's work, writes:

This great mass of correspondence, although bearing on the subjects under discussion, was not, however, of a kind to supply the biographer with matter for quotation, or give that insight into the life and character of the writer which the letters of literary men so often furnish. They were, for the most part, letters of mere business, relating to works in progress, Parliamentary contests, new surveys, estimates of cost, and railway policy—curt, and to the point; in short, the letters of a man every moment of whose time is precious.

He was now firmly established as a man of the highest reputation in the new world of railways, and his renown was spreading abroad, so that he soon became a much sought-after international figure. In the following letter to Michael Longridge, he refers to the development of railways in Belgium, which he had recently visited, and on which his advice was being sought. It is included here, although the growth of railways abroad is dealt with in the next chapter:

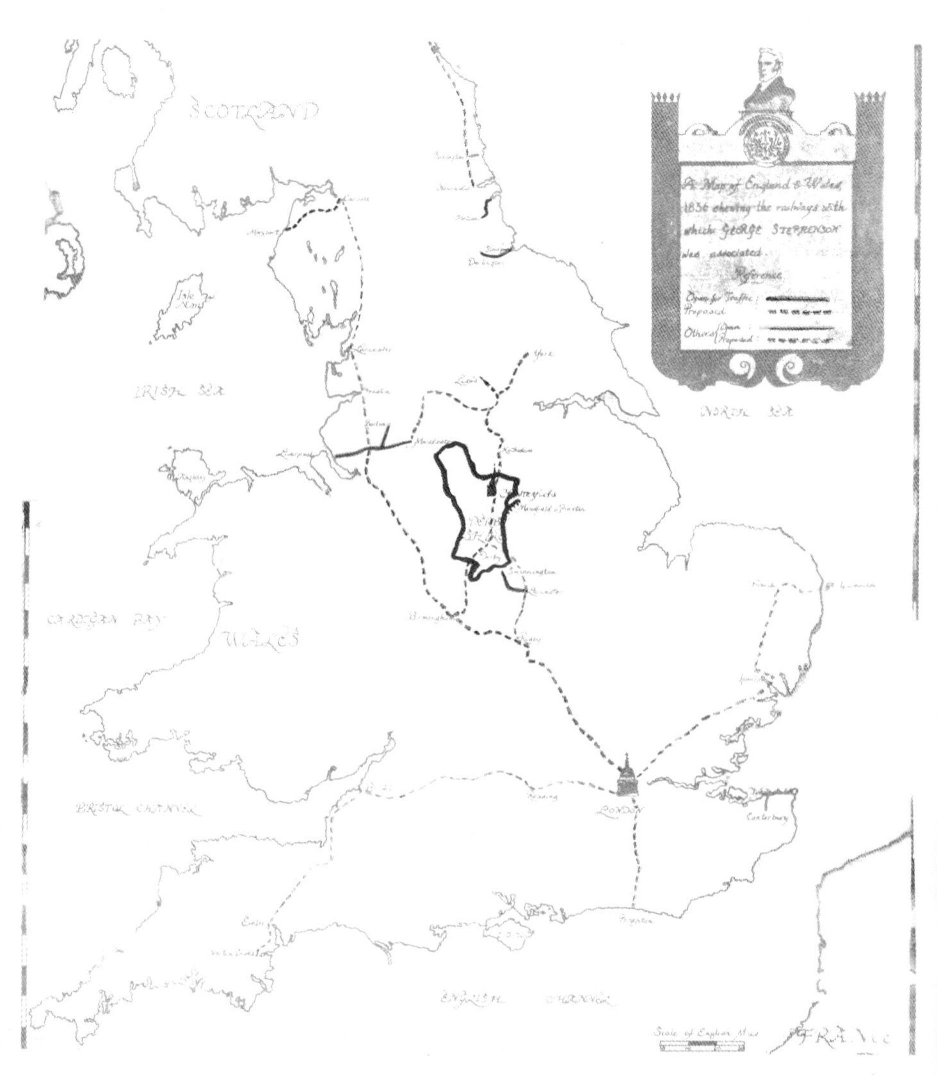

Fig 55. Map showing railway associations of George Stephenson in 1836. (Courtesy: The Chesterfield Public Library)

Alton Grange June 5, 1835

My dear Sir,

I duly received your letter of the 25th ultimo in London. I had not forgotten the Bridges, as you were kind enough to imagine I had.

I was at home about a fortnight ago, and made search for the plans of the Bridges; but could not find them. On my arrival again in London, I found that Swanwick had taken them to Whitby to have another copy made; and I assure you I was no little annoyed about it and gave Swanwick such a reprimand, that I am sure he will not dare to do it again.

They are still at Whitby and must remain there until Swanwick returns.

I wrote a long letter to Simmons about 3 weeks ago giving them some useful information; and as I have received no answer, am afraid it has miscarried. The money was paid to the person who collects the letters* at the Inn, and he has I fear kept the money and destroyed the letter. When you write again, would you ask if he has received it.

* In the original wording '. . . collects the letters' was '. . . collects the money'; the word 'money' was then crossed out and 'letters' substituted.

I yesterday wrote a letter of thanks to the King of the Belgians, and also one to the Minister of the Interior, which Robert will deliver to the Ambassador on Monday. I called upon the Ambassador about a week ago; to enquire as to the form of addressing the King. He received me with very great kindness indeed.—When I called he could not be seen for some time, Starbuck* was with me, and advised me to send up my Card. This done we were order'd up instantly, where he and several Belgians were at breakfast and he received me in as kind a manner as—King Leopold did, and stated he was very glad indeed to have the honor of my acquaintance. He seemed quite delighted with what had taken place in Belgium about the Railway.

The Brighton Railway is carried on under Robert's guidance, he cannot attend to it more than examining the particulars laid before him. I have strong expectations of having the Great Northern Railway carried in another direction. Robert and I think it ought to come off at Coventry to Ashby, Derby, Chesterfield, Sheffield and Rotherham to York. We are requested to give our opinion to some of the monied men in London. This will be done as soon as I return to London, which will be in 8 or 10 days. I shall only be two days at home as I have to go to Birmingham, Liverpool and some other places, in the meantime.

I cannot yet fix, when I shall be at Newcastle, nor yet when I can go abroad, but I can most certainly assure you that I am most anxious to go abroad if my engagements can be made to suit it: I am quite sure that nothing can be more important for James† at present than to let him attend to the proportions of Steam Engine building. When I come to Newcastle, I will give him work to do in drawing. I left London last night and arrived here this morning, without the repetition of the upset I had in going up by the 'Hope' which I dare say you would see by the papers: I saw she was going to upset and being inside made use of a little science, which brought me off safe. I never saw such a sight before, passengers like dead pigs in every direction: and the road a sheet of blood, two I apprehend will die.

I am, Yours very truly,
Geo. Stephenson

Michael Longridge Esq[r]

This letter is crammed with interest; it shows the crowded events in Stephenson's life at this period, many of them of great importance to him personally and to the development of railways generally, both at home and abroad. The Whitby episode probably relates to the line to York, for which Stephenson had prospected during the previous summer. Stephenson already installed iron bridges, the components for which had been manufactured at Bedlington.

The reference to Robert's association with a survey for the London and Brighton Railway is of interest also. The final choice of the route to be adopted lay between Robert's survey, which took in an easily graded

* In 1840 Starbuck was appointed Continental agent to Robert Stephenson & Co.

† Stephenson's nephew (p. 154).

line to the west of the present line, and John (now Sir John) Rennie, the Stephensons' tough old rival, who proposed a more direct way involving considerable earthworks. Rennie's line was adopted, which was a hard blow for Robert (who had employed his friend George Parker Bidder on the survey), because he knew that his route would have saved a great deal of money and labour. It has been suggested that the reason for Robert's undoing in this case was the inclusion of his father as a witness when the Bill went into the Committee stage in the Lords, where the Counsel for the opposition laid every kind of pitfall for the older Stephenson. It is interesting to observe that although George Stephenson did not shine in the cut-and-thrust of smart Parliamentary lawyers, yet Robert soon acquired most formidable powers in that direction, although when it was a question of making speeches in public, he was far less at ease.

George Stephenson's withdrawal from the construction of the Grand Junction Railway, though it must have gone against the grain for him to give up this appointment in favour of Joseph Locke, was probably a blessing in disguise for him at the time, for he had a vast amount of railway business on hand; the necessity of frequent journeys to London—with all their hazards, as the foregoing letter shows—led to the taking of office premises in Westminster (9 Duke Street) for his and Robert's consulting practices.

The 'Great Northern Railway' mentioned in the letter to Longridge was not an early version of the great trunk line of that name which was to run from London to York via Peterborough, Grantham, and Doncaster (that was to come some fifteen years later) but a comprehensive name for the 'Hudson' group of railways which were to link York with the capital. Stephenson was concerned to see construction going ahead; after a fairly lengthy absence from his home he wrote the following letter to a Sheffield firm which clearly wanted to be associated with this work:

Alton Grange. Septr 6th 1835

Dear Sir,

On my arrival at home this morning I found yours of 11th August respecting the projected north line from the London and Birmingham Railway. If the work goes forward and I should want more assistance than those who are concerned with me I shall give you timely notice.

I am

Dear Sir

Yours truly

Geo. Stephenson

4

Rapid Expansion of Railways at Home and their Growth Abroad

For an appreciation of the parallel events, in the 1830s, of the development of a great railway network in Britain, and a great locomotive export industry to countries abroad, it is perhaps simplest to consider these two growths separately, dealing first with railway expansion at home, and George Stephenson's part in it.

We have seen how events led to Stephenson's important meeting with George Hudson, the most influential promoter of railways in those days, and how the profound impression made upon Hudson by Stephenson was leading the latter towards quite exceptional opportunities of participating in new construction, which Stephenson was very willing to take. There was, however, a proviso: Stephenson would not allow his name to be associated with railways unless he was satisfied that they would pay. He had by now become much more convinced that 'his' style of railway (track gauge, dimensions of loading gauge, easy gradients, etc.) was practicable, and that it was desirable to adopt these features in the rising probability that eventually lines would all become connected and that a national network would thus emerge. The comments of his biographer, L. T. C. Rolt, in this connection, are especially interesting:

> The success of his Liverpool and Manchester Railway had brought him a reputation as the foremost railway engineer in the kingdom which neither the efforts of his detractors nor his own mistakes could shake. So much so that when a new railway scheme was launched the appearance of George Stephenson's name on the prospectus as principal or consulting engineer was sufficient to ensure a full subscription list . . . it stands to his everlasting credit that he resisted the bribes and blandishments of railway speculators so effectually as he did.

And again, on Stephenson's achievements:

> In preliminary reconnaissance he was brilliant; that is to say, after one ride or drive through a strange tract of country, he would propose a line for a railway which was not only the best from an engineering point of view but also from the standpoint of traffic potential, grasping as he did the local resources which the new railway might exploit and the part it might play in the future as a link in some through-route. In this last respect George Stephenson had no rival. . . .

Even if we concede to George Stephenson only the minimum responsibility for the railways with which his name is associated as engineer, the work involved must have been prodigious.

Another biographer (Smiles) has recorded that

during the three years ending in 1837—perhaps the busiest years of his life—he travelled by postchaise alone upwards of 20,000 miles, and yet not less than six months out of the three years were spent in London.

In a footnote, Smiles states that

during this period he was engaged on the North Midland, extending from Derby to Leeds; the York and North Midland, from Normanton to York; the Manchester and Leeds; the Birmingham and Derby; and the Sheffield and Rotherham Railway; the whole of these, of which he was the principal engineer, having been authorized in 1836.

The Manchester and Leeds Railway was a very formidable undertaking, away to the north of these other lines; it was the only one of those just mentioned which was outside the control of George Hudson. Stephenson's courtesy in his dealings with property owners affected by his projected railways is shown in the following letter, written in his own hand:

Dear madam,

I beg you and Mr Gaskill will accept my best thanks for the very kind manner in which you received me this morning respecting the diviation of the intended manchester and Leeds Railway through your propiety.

I am your obed ser

Geo. Stephenson

Jany: 7th 1836

By the middle of the 1830s, the scramble to get railways promoted and built was becoming one of the major businesses of the country, and the rise of George Hudson was giving colour to a rapidly growing world of railway politics and finance. Rival groups engaged in bitter contests to thwart one another in fierce attempts to seize control, and to sample the heady exhilaration of successful penetration of each other's preserves. Stephenson himself had come far from the unhappy days when he faced Alderson in March 1825 over the Liverpool and Manchester Railway Bill, and had gained a considerable knowledge of political 'in-fighting' in the railway sphere; allied to his natural caution was a growing astuteness in his weighing-up of new projects and the human factors behind them.

Two letters written in quick succession to Nicholas Wood during this period are worth quoting, because of what is left unsaid (the two letters being taken together). The complicated political background, with its grim accompaniment of sinister and destructive forces at work, has been described with great skill, and no little sense of drama, by L. T. C. Rolt in the chapter entitled 'The Stanhope and Tyne Fiasco' in his biographical work, *George and Robert Stephenson*; at the time of these letters to Nicholas Wood the climax was still some way off. Briefing Wood as a Parliamentary witness, Stephenson writes:

My Dear Sir,

I am anxious that you should join me in giving an opinion as to the North Midland Railway being the best that the country will admit of.

As the proposed Line passes through a good deal of Lord Wharncliffe's property I think he will have no objection to your giving this opinion.

When we get through the Standing orders I can meet you at Leeds, & we can go over the country together having the Plans & Sections with us.

I have written to Mr. Granger of Edinbro' (?) by this post to join us, and I hope to have Mr. Brunel & Robert also to join us in giving evidence.

I hope this arrangement will meet your views, will you inform me by return of post.

Yours Truly
Geo. Stephenson

I have just heard that you have had another increase to your Family my kind regards to Mrs. Wood who I hope is doing well—

16 Duke St Westminster
Feby 3 1836

The Hudson empire was beginning to take shape, although still in quite an early stage of its growth; but it was working its way north with the inexorable progress of an incoming tide; the Pease family were clearly uneasy about the threat to districts where they hoped to develop railways under their own control. Nicholas Wood became, as Warren reminds us, 'an authority in the railway world and his opinion was constantly sought for Parliamentary Committees'. He was a lifelong friend of Stephenson. A further letter sent from Westminster by Stephenson to Wood is appended, in which mention of Brunel's name is of particular interest:

My Dear Sir,

I duly received your letter of the 6th. I cannot see the least possibility of the line on which I wish you to give evidence interfering with Mr. Pease's Line our Line is from Derby to Leeds we also have a Line from Leeds to York. And I am perfectly satisfied that any Line coming south from Darlington must come some where near York.

I am very well aware that an attempt will be made to get a more direct Line

Fig 56. Mahogany desk used by George Stephenson, now at the Institution of Mechanical Engineers.

from the North to Leeds, but this can only be done at an immense cost and bad gradients into the bargain.

The Line I have taken from York to Leeds does not deviate much from a level Line.

I will write you again about the time I think would be most suitable for the Engineers to go over the Line together—I have received a letter from Granger who agrees to come at the time I want him. Brunel will also join us—I will send you some Prospectuses as you wish.

Yours Truly
Geo. Stephenson

16 Duke Str Westminster
Feby 12 1836

Amid all the hurly-burly of railway surveying and construction, it is interesting to find Stephenson continuing to keep up his great interest in steam locomotive designs. He writes, during this period, as follows to Timothy Hackworth:

Newcastle May 3d 1836

Dear Timothy,

Will you have the goodness to send me an account how the new Engine pleases you: and whether we can make any improvements in the one which we are now finishing; and which is in all respects at present the same as the last.—

How do the brass pistons answer? How many miles in a week would this new Engine travel; if it were kept constantly moving and waggons ready to hang on at both ends of the line; so that the Engine should not have to stand at any part; except while taking in Water.—

Could such an experiment be made; without inconveniencing the Company & Trade: it would be very desirable to be done: as it would shew to the Public the correctness of my former statements.

The other Engine will be sent off next week. You will excuse me coming over till that time.

Do you think the Rope would lay better on the Roll at Brusselton if the moving Pulley was shifted 20 feet nearer the Bank-top. This could be easily done, by putting the sheave into the end of a piece of Timber 20 feet long, with its fulcrum in the middle and the other end moved by the Rack. Think on this by the time I come over.

If the Roll should be put across the Road; the Railway would be too low several feet.—I hope to hear from you in the course of a day or two—

I am dear Sir
Your's truly—
Geo. Stephenson

P.S. I wish you could by any means get Brandreth's carriage to work next week, as he is expected to be here at that time.

I suppose it wants a brake put it on and charge me with it—

Could you not use it for carrying lead or anything so as to get it to work.

G.S.

The letter contains references of much interest to students of locomotive history, though it is not clear which of the Stockton and Darlington locomotives is meant. But it belongs to a period when the Forth Street Works were introducing certain new features into their engines. By the end of 1835 the valve gear had been redesigned so that a single lever sufficed for the starting and the reversing of the locomotive. Another modification, about that date concerned the two inner frames (a design feature retained since the days of the 'Planet'); from 1835 these were joined together as a single frame, from a position ahead of the crank axle, continuing thus to the firebox. In the same year, too, the loose eccentrics on the crank axle began to be superseded by two fixed eccentrics. By March 1836, just before the letter to Hackworth, Robert Stephenson and Company had adopted four fixed eccentrics—one for fore gear and one for back gear on each of the two sides of the engine. Things were now heading towards the developments culminating, a few years later, in the 'Stephenson' shifting-link motion, emanating from the Forth Street Works and marking one of the greatest strides forward ever made in locomotive design.

A further point of interest in the letter is its indication of Stephenson's concern for getting the maximum economic use of his machines. Any experimental confirmation of their expected capabilities would be extremely valuable to him personally, as well as to potential customers at Forth Street.

Mr. Brandreth, referred to in the postscript, was presumably the Director of the Liverpool and Manchester Railway who offered his 'Cycloped' locomotive (propelled by a horse) in competition with the other locomotives for the Rainhill Trials, but afterwards withdrew it. The 'carriage', referred to in Stephenson's letter to Hackworth, may have been a steam road-carriage; such vehicles were enjoying a brief popularity which was in the ascendant in 1835.

It is not difficult to imagine the fatherly concern, as well as the profound interest, with which Stephenson regarded the progress of Robert's titanic task in the construction of the London and Birmingham Railway. With the end of the work approaching, a dinner party was held on 23 December 1837 at Dunchurch, attended by Stephenson, which was vividly described in the *Railway Times.* At this notable gathering Robert was presented with a silver soup-tureen, and the celebrations continued almost till daybreak. The *Railway Times* journalist observed how everyone remarked on the great alteration for the better in the appearance of George Stephenson; he

looked at least half-a-dozen years younger. . . . There is the making of a hundred railways in him yet. . . . It would have done any man's heart good to have heard the deafening applause which followed when the healths of the father and son were drunk; everyone felt they came warm from the heart and spoke of feelings that could not be uttered. . . . The youngest man who sat down to dinner on this occasion will never live to see such another day.

In June 1838 a partial service of trains began, the full opening starting on 17 September.

During the year 1838, Stephenson conducted preliminary surveys of alternative routes to connect Edinburgh with Newcastle, one a coastal line, via Dunbar and Berwick, the other an inland one, going by the Gala valley and Carter Fell. Both ideas lay dormant for some years, until the completion of Midland and other main lines as far north as Newcastle-upon-Tyne. As we shall see, the coastal line was eventually adopted. However, for the time being, he expressed his views to Longridge thus:

My dear Sir,

I have received both your letter of 30th July and 3rd Aug—I am making all the preparations I can to visit you and examine the country thoroughly from Newcastle to Edinbro—

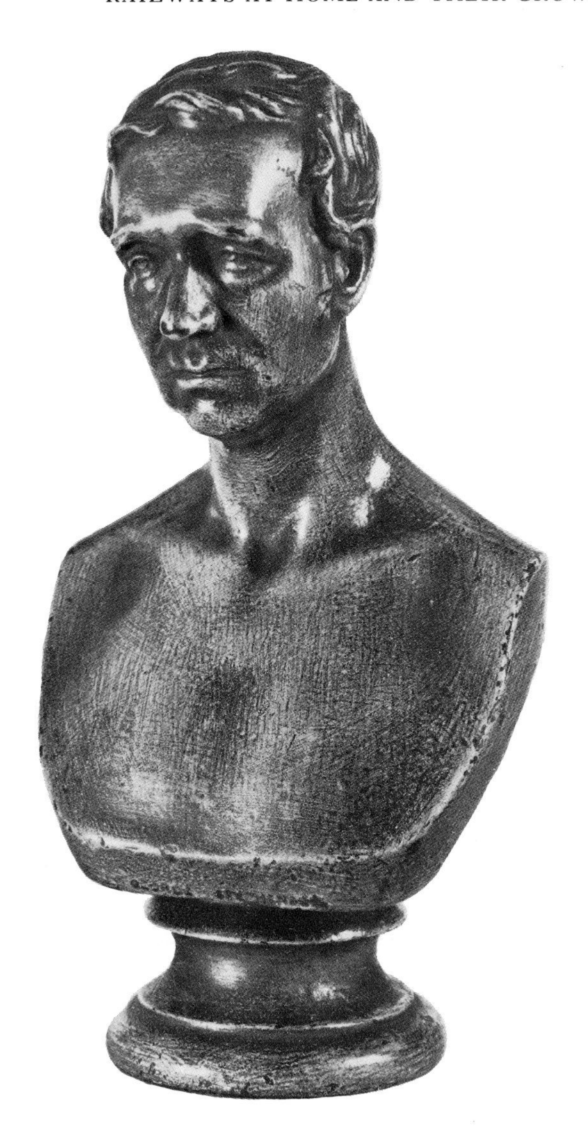

Fig 57. Cast-iron bust of George Stephenson, in the Museum of Science and Industry, Birmingham.

I will take care that my examination of the Country shall be of such a nature as to leave no room for contradiction by any person who may follow me; there does not exist any doubt in my mind as to whether the Coast Line is the best or not, and I believe that the Midland districts will be better accommodated by the Coast than the Inland Line, by taking collateral Branches from the Main Line up the various Rivers into the interior—These Branches must be single and not expensive Lines winding with the Rivers—You know that my system has always been in Main Lines, to keep the Line in a low country, so as to allow of Branches diverging into a high country if such should exist—

I have seen the Section published by Joshua Richardson and it agrees with the Report I made respecting the Inland Line and according to his own showing there must either be six miles of Tunneling at Carter Fell or several powerful

Fig 58. Medal to the Directors of the London and Birmingham Railway, designed by Philip Hardwick, 1838. (Photo: Science Museum, London)

stationary Engines, but it is laid down on so small a scale that it requires a practical man to find out its demerits.

I am my dear Sir
Yours very sincerely
Geo. Stephenson

Alton Grange Aug 7, 1838
(P.S.) I intend being with you about the 20th—When you next write address Tapton House near Chesterfield which is to be my future abode.—

Stephenson wrote on the same date to Mrs. Longridge:

My dear Mrs. Longridge,

You say I am a shabby man in not answering your last letter—I really thought I had answered it, but as I am coming to Bedlington I hope we shall have all these matters quietly arranged and I hope you will have two or three good Crabs for me when I come, but I do hope you won't be crabby.—

I am dear M[rs] Longridge
Yours very sincerely
Geo. Stephenson

Stephenson was now writing his last letters from Alton Grange, for he shortly afterwards moved to Tapton House, Chesterfield, which was to be his address until his death ten years later. He also took a lease on a colliery at Clay Cross, nearby. He clearly attached very great importance to the idea of a railway between Berwick and Newcastle, and evidently visited the North again towards the end of the year, for he writes as follows to his friend Robert Brandling:

Fig 59. Medallion portrait of George Stephenson, and relief representation of bridge at Newton, Liverpool and Manchester Railway. (Courtesy: The Chesterfield Public Library)

Dear Sir,

I have arrived at this place this evening, and have again traversed the Line more particularly than I did before, and I believe you will find when accurate levels have been taken that my report will be found very near the truth as to the merits of the Line between Newcastle and this place.

I called upon Lord Grey and was very kindly received by him. He appeared very desirous to have the Line carried west of his House and he pointed out a Line the levels of which I had taken and I found it to be quite out of the question to take the line in the direction he pointed out, as it would require a Tunnel upwards of a mile long or cuttings so deep that I could not recommend a Company to adopt. I made a full explanation of the nature of the ground to Lord Grey, he stated that he was very anxious that Lord Howick should be there, his Lordship was kind enough to ask me to drive with him, which I did. You may imagine the predicament I was in when all the Ladies seized me at dinner, I wanted your assistance very much to help me through as you have done on former occasions, I have every reason to believe that my explanations

* Lord Grey was father of Lord, Howick mentioned in this letter.

to him and his family were satisfactory. He has not yet consented but I believe he will not stand in the way of a great public good, and I trust when I see Lord Howick I shall be able to get matters put right—Mr. Blackburn dined with us the same evening at Howick and acted a very gentlemanly part on both sides of the question—Mr. Robson who is Lord Greys Steward has been with me for two days. He is quite a gentleman and has given me every information in his power. You were perfectly right as to the drive down to the Sea I certainly had missed it, I apologised to Lord Grey for not mentioning this drive in my report, however since I have carefully examined the country I find I can pass over one drive with an ornamental Arch without in any degree interfering with their comforts, and under the other drive in such a way as to hide the Railway from them and them from the Railway. My explanation to the family was so satisfactory to some of them as to induce one of his sons to say at dinner that my Line was the best and think I was right.

I have had the Levels taken on one of the Routes I proposed near Belford missing Marham Flats, which Line I find much more favourable than I expected and it must be adopted. I had the pleasure of Breakfasting with Mr Clark and his family this morning and I made him also a full explanation. I think we shall have no trouble with him. We pass Miss Craster's residence in such a way that the Railway can be no annoyance to it. I passed the House but did not call as I was informed they would not object to it. There is no other residence where the inhabitants can possibly find fault up to this place.

I have advised Mr. Burn to take the Levels through part of your ground and then thro the Low Land west of Gosforth House, and I believe the line will be found very favourable in that direction. I must meet you on this subject when I return in the meantime Burn will have taken the Levels.—

I am my dear Sir
Yours faithfully,
Geo. Stephenson

Berwick Nov. 10, 1838

Shortly afterwards, Stephenson wrote further about the same project to Robert Brandling; he was now going over the ground in more detail. It is interesting to study his choice of route in relation to other Northumberland railways then extant. Charles E. Lee's superb maps in his *Tyneside Tramroads of Northumberland* are most enlightening. Stephenson wrote:

My dear Sir,

I have examined the route that Bourne levelled by Down Hill, there is very little level to be gained by deviating the Line as you proposed and the more you keep to the West the sooner you get down to the River. I also examined the Line all the way to Netherton very little improvement can be made there, I then examined the country by Plesey Checks and on to the ridge between Down Hill and Cramlington, and I think a better line can be got about half a mile West of

Crumlington village than on the West side of Down Hill—and thence either to the Sheep Wash passing East side of Netherton and leading away to the crossing of the Wansbeck above Bothel—I have ordered Bourne to take three Levels and if practicable to deposit plans of that route as well as the one on the East side of Crumlington.

The Line on the West side of Gosforth as well as the Borrowden Line can be carried into this route very well, it would be too costly to move the Turnpike further West in passing Gosforth so as to let the Railway take the route of the old Turnpike—

I hope you have recovered from your bad cold.—

I am yours
very faithfully
Geo. Stephenson

Newcastle Dec 19th. 1838—

Earlier in this same crowded year (1838) Stephenson had shown a lively interest in the Newcastle meeting of the British Association, then in its very young days, and he acted as one of its Vice Presidents in the section of Mechanical Science; it would be of great interest to know whether recollections of that occasion came to his mind when the first moves were made, eight years later, to found the Institution of Mechanical Engineers. This appointment came at a period when he was especially concerned with surveys for the Chester and Crewe Railway, the Trent Valley Railway, the Birkenhead and Chester Railway, and the Chester and Holyhead Railway! He had reached the peak of his professional life and activities and could meet, on equal terms, people of the highest achievements in many different walks of life. His interest in natural phenomena lasted all through his life and brought him into contact with such diverse persons as Dr. Buckland (Dean of Westminster and an authority on natural history) and Sir Joseph Paxton. Here is a recollection of Stephenson's friend of many years, Thomas Sopwith, F.R.S., relating to the opening of a bridge in 1838:

After walking along the bridge, we found Mr. George Stephenson, the eminent engineer, Mr. William Brandling, Mr. James Walker, the President of the Institution of Civil Engineers, and others, to whom I introduced Mr. Barry. After some conversation, in which Mr. Walker deplored the innovation made on his design by the substitution of three small arches instead of one large arch at each end of the bridge, we proceeded to Pensher Quarry, and after viewing it we returned to Mr. Buddle's house. Here we found Dr. Buckland, Sir Charles Lemon, and Mr. Edward Bigge.

The extremely important part played by the Stephensons in connection with the establishment of railways outside Britain, and in the founding of a prestige export-industry by supplying locomotives to countries abroad, becomes evident from a study of the lives of both father and son. Here, however, we are concerned only with George Stephenson; and, as might be expected, he only took part in the earlier stages of what became a great national enterprise, which did much to expand Britain's commercial achievements in the nineteenth and early twentieth centuries. We may, therefore, to go back now to Stephenson's earlier years, and consider how his railway contacts with oversea countries as a whole grew up until his comparative retirement.

Apart from the visit of the Grand Duke Nicholas, later Tsar of Russia (1825–55), who saw demonstrations of the Blenkinsop rack-rail locomotives, during the period 1811–12, we know of a report made by De Gallois in 1818 on 'the railways used in England, and notably at Newcastle and in Northumberland'. The implication that De Gallois observed Stephenson's early achievements is inescapable. Warren states that De Gallois's report gave an important stimulus to the introduction of railways into France. It is also quite unthinkable that Stephenson, who certainly did not decline to accept credit and acknowledgments, when these were due to him, would stand shyly in the background when foreign observers came to see his steam locomotives in operation.

Then, in 1825, an important visitor, William Strickland, arrived from the United States. He came to gather information on both railways and canals, and his observations were published in the following year under the title *Report on Canals and Rail Roads*; he described his visit to Hetton, where some of Stephenson's locomotives were at work, including the patented design (see p. 33), and remarked on the use of six wheels 'to distribute its great weight more equally on the rails, and perhaps to increase the friction of the wheels on the railway'. Strickland's visit had been sponsored by the Pennsylvania Society for the Promotion of Internal Improvement. An illustration in his report shows the chain-coupling connecting the axles of a four-wheeled Stephenson locomotive.

During 1826 and 1827 a most painstaking and comprehensive series of observations on Stephenson's locomotives was made and was later included in a valuable report by the two Prussian mining engineers, Carl von Oeynhausen and Heinrich von Dechen; their report was published in 1829, in the Berlin technical journal *Archir für Bergbau und Hüttenwesen* (vol. xix). Substantial sections of this treatise, translated into English, were included by Warren in his great history, *A Century of Locomotive Building*, and are all the more useful to the historian because they include details which are no longer traceable within the records of the Forth Street firm. The entire report has now been published by the Newcomen Society. The Stockton and Darlington Railway, then in its early days, was included in this account. There is a revealing passage* which indicates one of the major worries of Timothy Hackworth at that time:

> In practice it is particularly objectionable that many of the moving parts get out of repair, to which the continual rattling during the motion of the engine contributes. This is principally produced by the fact that it is scarcely possible to retain four points of the rails on which the wheels of the locomotive rest continually in one plane, so that the parts of the locomotive must give somewhat in order that they may be able to find their proper bearing.

It is of interest to see that, at the end of their report, Oeynhausen and Dechen give the costs of locomotives and stationary engines built at the Forth Street Works. An 8 h.p. locomotive is quoted at £550; stationary engines of the Watt (high-pressure) type cost £300 to £350 for 8 h.p., rising to £1,200 to £1,350 for 30 h.p.

Railway developments in France, resulting in the adoption of steam locomotives, appear to have had their beginnings due to a group of colliery owners and to M. Beaunier, an engineer associated with them, who had studied reports by De Gallois after his journey to Killingworth. Government permission was secured for the construction of a railway from St. Étienne (a mining town) to Andrézieux. Originally, only the transport of goods and minerals was envisaged, with horses as motive power. A single-line construction was adopted, with sidings as passing places (much as on the Stockton and Darlington Railway in its earlier years).

While these plans were developing, the possibility of another railway, from St. Étienne to Lyon, was exercising the mind of the highly talented engineer Marc Séguin. To him, and to his brothers, the French Government granted the concession in June 1826; and in the following year Marc Séguin visited England, as a member of a group, to study manufacturing industries and railways. During his tour he met George Stephenson and saw the Stockton and Darlington Railway; as a result, he decided on his return to France that his railway should have the easiest practicable gradients and curves. He was also influenced to consider the use of steam locomotives. He must have had every encouragement from Stephenson in the planning of the railway; a report to the shareholders of the Lyon St. Étienne Railway Company in December 1829 refers to 'the illustrious English engineer, who had come to assist his young French confrères with his advice'. The Company were so pleased with the help given by Stephenson that they presented him with an honorarium of 12,500 francs; whilst his praise for the way in which Séguin had laid out his railway must have been praise indeed.

* Quoted by Warren in *A Century of Locomotive Building*, p. 119.

The foundations were thus well laid; Séguin himself stated*:

> The Government granted to the industry leave to introduce into France free of duty two engines from the works of Messrs. Robert Stephenson of Newcastle-on-Tyne, such as were then employed on the Stockton and Darlington Railway. One of these was sent to M. Hallette, a distinguished machine constructor at Arras, for him to study, and the other was taken to Lyon to serve as a model for those which I was to construct for the service of the St Étienne-Lyon Railway.

One could wish that some of the drawings of these locomotives had survived; there are drawings of those built by Séguin himself; and an early illustration (1832) in the *Bulletin de la Société Industrielle de Mulhouse* shows a Séguin design, with a remarkable Stephensonian layout of driving gear for transmitting the power from the cylinders to the wheels. A separate tender was required; it was fitted with a fan for the production of an artificial draught—a result of Séguin's experiments with a stationary boiler. Warren has concluded that the 'Trial' engine of November 1827 (built at Forth Street Works and referred to in that way in the firm's records) may have been one of the two exported to France. Later Séguin abandoned the fan in favour of inducing the draught by the exhaust steam—apparently independently of any English developments in that direction.

One of the most interesting aspects of Séguin's pioneer work in France is his efforts to increase the generation of steam in the single-flue or return-flue boilers used respectively by Stephenson and Hackworth at that time. His account of his work shows that he began to work on the development of a multi-tubular boiler for locomotives nearly eighteen months before the 'Rocket' was built, though its trials were conducted some two months after the Rainhill Trials. It is impossible to prove any exchange of information, at this time, between the Stephensons and Séguin on the two features (exhaust-induced draught, and multi-tubular boiler) which contributed so much to the 'Rocket's' success, though it is tempting to speculate. Once before in Stephenson's life, in the invention of the safety lamp, there had been an extraordinary element of coincidence in the working-out of essentially the same idea in the mind of an unrelated contemporary.

Two other distinguished French visitors to Newcastle, Mm. Coste and Perdonnet, described their observations, during a tour in 1828, in *Annales des Mines*, 2nd Series (1829), vol. VI, when they saw the locomotive sent to Séguin before it was exported, and noted the layout of the cylinders and driving gear. They also saw locomotive working on the Bolton and Leigh Railway by 'the most perfect (locomotive) which had yet been

* See Warren, *A Century of Locomotive Building*, p. 137.

constructed'—the 'Lancashire Witch'. Nearly forty years later, Perdonnet, in a handsome gesture to the twin geniuses of Séguin and Stephenson, caused a fine medal to be designed, bearing the heads of the two engineers, to form an award for research into the resistances of railway trains and into the generation of steam in locomotive boilers.

America must be mentioned next. Warren writes,* with justifiable pride:

The first locomotive sent by Robert Stephenson and Company to America was for the Delaware and Hudson Canal Company;

the locomotive was ordered in 1828 and arrived at New York about the middle of January 1829. The Canal Company had as its agent Horatio Allen, who was then a Resident Engineer on the line of the Delaware and Hudson Canal—in his own words,

the great engineering enterprise of the time, the first of the great works, canal and railroad, that were to bring the anthracite coal of the valley of the Susquehana into the valleys of the Delaware and of the Hudson and to the ocean.

Allen continues:

Such consideration as was within my power led me to a decided conviction as to the future of the locomotive as the tractive motive power on railroads for general freight and passenger transportation, as it had begun to be for mine transportation. . . . Early in the year 1827 I had given all the attention that it was in my power to give, and having come to some conclusions as to the locomotive, that all subsequent experience has confirmed, and believing that the future of the civil engineer lay in a great and most attractive degree in the direction of the coming railroad era, I decided to go to the only place where a locomotive was in daily operation and could be studied in all its practical details.

In the following year (1828) Allen was authorized

to procure one locomotive complete, as a pattern, and that the Chief Engineer (John B. Jervis) is making enquiries to ascertain whether it may not be expedient to authorize the construction of all the locomotive engines in England.

In the event, this development did not take place, as American engineering skills were progressing rapidly. Warren's researches into the first Stephenson engine exported to America (the drawings had vanished) led him to conclude that it resembled the 'Lancashire Witch' of the Bolton and Leigh Railway. One of the actual cylinders of the locomotive, however, has been preserved, and is in the keeping of the Smithsonian Institution, Washington.

* *A Century of Locomotive Building*, p. 150.

A year later, the Forth Street Works built their second locomotive for export to the United States. It is recorded as having been built for a Captain Whistler, presumed to be a member of a party of visiting American engineers who had come to England in 1828 to study the operation of railways and the construction of new lines. Warren believes that this second locomotive generally resembled a new type which was then being built at Forth Street Works, known as 'Darlington Engine A'; it was a six-wheeler, with inclined cylinders at the rear, driving the leading pair of wheels, all of which were coupled. The design was worked out for the Stockton and Darlington Railway, and had an arrangement

for expansive working (Warren states*) by means of a mushroom valve, operated from a cam on the trailing axle; a simplified development of a principle first applied in the 'Lancashire Witch'.

The Darlington A engine had a boiler with a return flue, which was unusual among Stephenson locomotives at the time, though George Stephenson recommended that Stockton and Darlington engines should be altered rather similarly (on the lines of the 'Liverpool Travelling Engine' which had a single flue containing the firegrate, with twin return flues, one on either side of it). But this idea of Stephenson's was before—only just before—the multi-tubular boiler for the 'Rocket'.

Both of these early exports to the United States had bar frames, a point of interest, as that type of construction was to become one of the most characteristically American features among all the components of a locomotive.

After this, there was a curious lull of about two years, suggesting that American engineers were aware of the forthcoming Rainhill Trials and the decisive effect they would have on Liverpool and Manchester motive power. After Captain Whistler's engine, Warren states, 'No more engines of the type followed, the Rainhill trials had rendered them obsolete, and the next locomotive sent by Robert Stephenson and Company to America was of the 'Planet' type, to the order of the Mohawk and Hudson Railroad'. The drawings are dated April and May 1831. Other locomotives, generally resembling those built for the Liverpool and Manchester Railway, followed, and for some years a good export business to the United States was enjoyed by Forth Street Works, declining as American locomotive-building capacity increased. It is interesting to notice that the first bogie locomotive ever built by Robert Stephenson and Company was for an American railroad—the Saratoga and Schenectady—in 1833.

The 'John Bull', built at Forth Street Works in 1831 for a Mr. Stevens,

* *A Century of Locomotive Building*, p. 153.

for use on the Camden and Amboy Railroad, is the oldest complete locomotive in America. It is preserved at the Smithsonian Institution. The early Stephenson locomotives in the United States earned, in several cases, high praise from their users; but the type of track and mode of construction often militated against the English machines, in favour of lighter American types.

Stephenson's railway connections with Belgium were very fruitful. The country was just ripe for railway development. It had become an independent sovereign state in 1831, with Leopold I (uncle of Queen Victoria) as the first King of the Belgians; his reign lasted till 1865. His country had considerable mineral wealth, with important ports having a great deal of trade with northern and western Europe. There was also a concentration of manufacturing potential in its larger towns. In May 1835 Stephenson, accompanied by Robert, had the honour of a royal invitation to visit Belgium, in order to advise on a comprehensive railway system for the whole country. With the King's personal encouragement, a plan for public railways between Brussels and the chief cities was worked out in conjunction with the Belgian engineers. Stephenson's principal biographers emphasize the importance of this new development, and Warren describes it as 'the first of many important Continental engagements, which led to valuable contracts for locomotives but necessarily caused the frequent absence of Robert Stephenson from Newcastle'.

This occasion was not, in fact, the first contact between the two Stephensons and the Belgian railway engineers; Warren records that

> The first studies for this system (the Belgian Railways) were, it appears, entrusted to a Belgian engineer, Albert Simons, but George Stephenson himself was called in later to advise. This . . . led to an order, in 1834, for three locomotives from Robert Stephenson and Company, who transferred the order for one of the engines to Tayleur and Company (the associated firm, in Liverpool) and themselves built the two others. All three engines were of the new standard six-wheeled type. . . . These three engines were employed at the opening of the line from Brussels to Mechlin on 6 May 1835.

One engine was named 'Stephenson'.

Stephenson can hardly have failed to be both impressed and complimented on the events of the day. A Brussels paper's account, republished in *Mechanics Magazine*, states:

> At a quarter past twelve o'clock, the King being at the station, near the Boulevards, to witness the ceremony, the departure of the steam-carriage train was announced by a salute of artillery. Immediately three files of ten carriages, each carrying nearly a thousand persons, began to move, drawn by the 'Flèche', the 'Stephenson', and the 'Éléphant'. The passage from Brussels to Mechlin occu-

pied fifty-three minutes. On their return the 'Éléphant' took in tow all the thirty carriages that had been drawn, by the three locomotives, and would probably have reached Brussels in half an hour, had it not been obliged to stop at Vilvorde for a fresh supply of water. In the evening the Minister of the Interior gave a public dinner to 200 of the principal persons, natives and foreigners, who were present at the ceremony.

Smiles records that several interesting conferences took place between the King Leopold and his ministers, and George Stephenson, and that the King appointed him by royal ordinance a Knight of the Order of Leopold.

As we might infer from his letter of 5 June 1835 to Michael Longridge (already quoted on pp. 160 and 161), Stephenson was highly gratified by the success of his visit. The Belgians evidently took to him, for only two years later he again went to Belgium, with Robert, in response to King Leopold's invitation, and witnessed the public inauguration of the line between Brussels and Ghent. It was a great occasion. Smiles writes:

At Brussels there was a public procession, and another at Ghent on the arrival of the train. Stephenson and his party accompanied it to the Public Hall, there to dine with the chief Ministers of State, the municipal authorities, and about five hundred of the principal inhabitants of the city; the English ambassador being also present. After the King's health and a few others had been drunk, that of Mr. Stephenson was proposed; on which the whole assembly rose up, amidst great excitement and loud applause, and made their way to where he sat, in order to jingle glasses with him, greatly to his own amazement. On the day following, our engineer dined with the King and Queen at their own table at Laeken, by special invitation; afterwards accompanying his Majesty and suite to a public ball given by the municipality of Brussels, in honour of the opening of the line to Ghent, as well as their distinguished English guest. On entering the room, the general and excited inquiry was, 'Which is Stephenson?' The English engineer had not before imagined that he was esteemed to be so great a man.

The participation of the State in the creation of the Belgian railway system was a remarkable feature of that country's industrial development.

While the beginnings of the national system of railways in Belgium were taking place, there were comparable developments in Germany and Russia. In May 1833 the promoters of the Nuremburg and Fürth Railway issued a publication describing their project. They initiated arrangements with Robert Stephenson for the supply of locomotives; then declared that, owing to the difference in the value of money between Germany and England, his prices were too high; turned to German manufacturers, who were eventually unable to fulfil their contract; and then re-entered into arrangements with Robert Stephenson for the purchase of the same engines. An engineman was duly detailed off by the Forth Street manage-

Fig 60. Medal to commemorate centenary of German Railways, 1835 (Presented to the Institution of Mechanical Engineers by Sir Nigel Gresley, C.B.E., D.Sc., M.I.Mech.E., Past President).

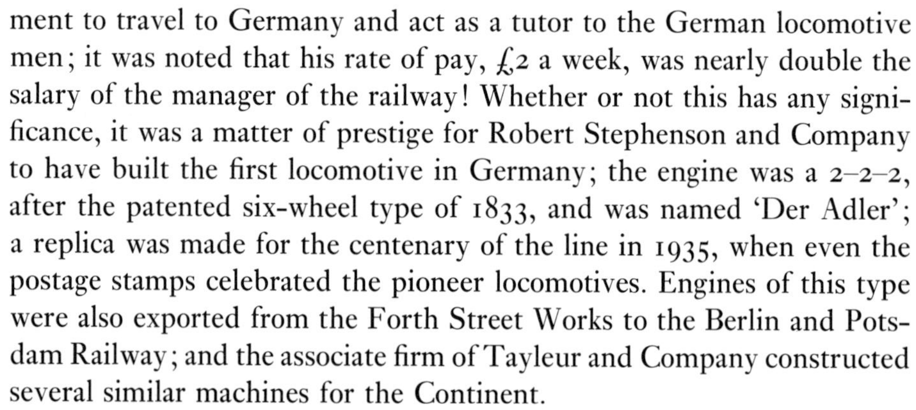

ment to travel to Germany and act as a tutor to the German locomotive men; it was noted that his rate of pay, £2 a week, was nearly double the salary of the manager of the railway! Whether or not this has any significance, it was a matter of prestige for Robert Stephenson and Company to have built the first locomotive in Germany; the engine was a 2–2–2, after the patented six-wheel type of 1833, and was named 'Der Adler'; a replica was made for the centenary of the line in 1935, when even the postage stamps celebrated the pioneer locomotives. Engines of this type were also exported from the Forth Street Works to the Berlin and Potsdam Railway; and the associate firm of Tayleur and Company constructed several similar machines for the Continent.

In regard to Russia, the interest shown by the Grand Duke Nicholas in the Blenkinsop rack-rail locomotives constructed by Matthew Murray around 1811, has already been mentioned. On that occasion, the Grand Duke made a personal visit. But some twelve years later, Joseph Sandars, the moving spirit in the promotion of the Liverpool and Manchester Railway, in *A letter on the Subject of the projected Rail Road between Liverpool and Manchester* (1824) intrigued his readers by stating that the Tsar of Russia actually had, at the time, 'a professional agent investigating the railways of the North', and urging that this example might well be imitated by the British Government.

Warren has related* how

> while the first schemes for railways in England had had to struggle against an opposition which threatened to strangle them, the first railway in Russia may be said to have sprung fully fledged from the decree of an autocrat, who had to consider neither the recommendations of a parliamentary committee, nor the opposition of his ministers. The builder of this first Russian railway was Franz Gerstner, a Czech, who obtained in England the whole of the material required for the railway, the first three locomotives being ordered during 1835–36 from Timothy Hackworth, Robert Stephenson and Company, and Tayleur and Company.

Fig 61. Postage stamp issued in 1935 to commemorate the centenary of the railway from Nuremburg to Fürth. The locomotive is 'Der Adler'.

The Forth Street engine was described as 'a locomotive of a most superior workmanship'; it was built for the St. Petersburg and Pavlovsk Railway, to a gauge of 6 ft., and was of the usual Stephenson six-wheeled type. It is shown on a commemorative medal which was struck for the opening of the line on 30 October 1837. In front of the leading wheels, and both before and behind the driving wheels, brooms were attached, pressing on the rails; one wonders how they behaved during the approaching Russian winter.

By the end of the 1830s, George and Robert Stephenson were being

* *A Century of Locomotive Building*, p. 323.

besieged with requests for advice from Switzerland and Italy, and further valuable contacts with France had come into being. Both father and son had achieved international recognition as the world's leading authorities on railways; their name conferred a 'cachet' upon any lines—and locomotives—with which they were associated; and indeed there never has been, before or after them, any comparable achievements by engineers, affecting the lives of the inhabitants of the whole world, directly or indirectly, yet coming to fruition within a mere fifteen or twenty years.

5

Gradual Establishment of the Stephensonian Railway in the Face of Opposition

Stephenson began as an experimenter, feeling his way carefully and with a great deal of native caution as he passed from one stage to another in his development of locomotives and railways. In his earliest days, as we have seen, he concentrated on locomotives first, making them suit tracks which were already in existence; but from the construction of the Stockton and Darlington Railway onwards (quite apart from the broad aspects of railway construction generally), he was almost entirely concerned with newly laid track, for which he could, within existing limits, decide its carrying capacity. He became more and more caught up in the realization of his dream of a nation-wide network of railways, leaving the work of locomotive development increasingly to Robert and the Forth Street Works staff. Seeing his ideas confirmed by their success in the practical day-to-day operation of railways, his views on railway motive power became more crystallized. The great advances made in locomotive design, in transition from the 'Rocket', via the 'Planet', to the 'Patentee', with suitable variations to adapt such designs to goods traffic, must have given him great satisfaction. Of the 'Planet', one of Stephenson's Directors on the Liverpool and Manchester Railway (Mr. Hardman Earle) in a letter to Dr. Dionysius Lardner dated 16 July 1832* wrote:

> She came nearer to what we consider perfection (relatively of course) than any which had succeeded her.

Lardner was a prolific writer on scientific and technical subjects, on which he sometimes expressed himself without knowledge or discretion, and Earle must have been stung into a forthright defence of his company's locomotive.

But the whole set-up was odd, and in the eyes of some of Stephenson's rivals, quite unethical, in that the Stephenson firm was supplying the locomotives to the requirements of Stephenson, the chief engineer. Not only that, but after the 'Planet' came to be regarded as a standard design by the Railway Company, other firms wishing to tender for the supply of motive power were finding that they would be expected to conform to

* See Warren, *A Century of Locomotive Building*, p. 84.

the 'standard' (inside cylinders below the smokebox, outside frames, and a multi-tubular boiler) layout of the 'Planet'.

Now one of the early locomotive builders was Edward Bury, whose distinctive light-weight machines, with their bar frames and circular fire-boxes, were bought by a number of British railways. Bury was persistent in his requests to the Directors of the Liverpool and Manchester Railway to have one of his engines tried on that line; one can imagine Stephenson's feelings on the subject, especially after the success of the 'Planet'; however, the Directors eventually decided at a meeting on 20 June 1831 (which Stephenson attended) to allow the trial. Stephenson quickly reacted, and in two days produced a report (how one wishes it had survived!) to the Directors which they considered only seven days later; apparently he was critical of Bury's 6 ft. diameter driving wheels which he thought were too big. The Minute Books of the Company recorded that:

> Mr. Stephenson . . . stated he had no objection to the trial as applied for—but he had to state to the Directors that he considered the 6 feet wheels of Mr. Bury's engine injurious to the Road, and less safe than 5 feet wheels, which he was of opinion were as large as ought to be made.

Nevertheless Bury's engine was permitted to try its strength on the line

> taking such loads as Mr. Bury may deem expedient.

But the engine failed in the trials, as Warren states,

> not on account of her 6-foot wheels, but because of accidents, including a broken crank axle, and inability to make steam with her first boiler.*

so she was not bought by the railway company.

In fairness to Bury, it should be said that he was trying to tailor his engines to the permanent way of the period and to keep well within the limits of axle loading. The contrast between Bury's types and the 'Planet' is very great; Warren gives an illustration of the latter's 'chassis' showing its two outside frames and its *four* inside frames, the latter extending from the cylinder casting to the front of the firebox, thus providing a very firm structure which, even in the dreaded event of a crank-axle fracture, would prevent the wheels from leaving the rails. The inside frames had a further function in reducing crank-axle stresses set up by piston loads; they did not carry any of the engine's weight. By comparison, Bury's type of construction was a flimsy affair.

However, Bury was by no means put off, and in August 1831 he attended again a Directors' meeting and said 'he was desirous to make an

* Warren, pp. 256–7.

engine for the railway company if they were in want'. A further Directors' meeting was held on 15 August, when Bury was summoned into their presence to make out a case for his design with inside bearings (he was proposing to build two locomotives for £730 each); after he made his exit George Stephenson was called in, and must have stated *his* views in no uncertain terms for it was recorded in the Minutes 'that Mr. Bury be informed that in any contract for engines the Directors cannot dispence with the stipulation for outside bearings'.

Stephenson was not attracted to Bury's design for a locomotive firebox, which was circular in plan, whereas he himself favoured a rectangular shape. This difference of opinion between Stephenson and Bury came to a head in September 1832, when the Board of Directors engaged an engineering consultant, John Farey, of London, to give his opinion on the point at issue. Joshua Field, later a President of the Institution of Civil Engineers, was also consulted. The consultants reported in favour of the Stephenson type; but the Directors had not heard the last of Edward Bury by any means; and the dispute went on well into 1833. The Directors did buy Bury's locomotive 'Liver' which, as Warren states, was a good engine and, with its larger grate, did slightly better than the 'Planet' during some coke consumption tests in 1832.

To clinch the matter, the Directors resolved, at a Board meeting on 29 October 1832

> That it be a bye law of the Company that in future no Engine shall be allowed to be introduced on the Rail Way with wheels of larger diameter than 5 feet;

and Warren has recorded how the 5 ft. diameter of the 'Planet's wheels

> determined the standard which prevailed for some years on the Liverpool and Manchester Railway.

The respective merits of inside and outside frames for locomotives brought Bury into collision with Stephenson only two months after the pronouncement on driving wheels. Bury, however, was 'allowed his head' in regard to his predilection for fireboxes that were circular (or semi-circular) in plan, as against Stephenson's preference for a rectangular shape. It must have been a bitter blow to the Stephensons when Bury secured the lion's share of the locomotive supplies for the London and Birmingham Railway, and in effect became its locomotive superintendent—the very situation which the London and Birmingham Directors, earlier, had regarded as so unethical that they had ruled out the supply of locomotives from the Forth Street Works for Robert Stephenson's great line. Bury's engines always seemed to excite controversy; and, to vindicate the safety of his designs when their stability and liability to derailment was being questioned in 1842, he devised a truly hair-raising experiment which he described as follows in a letter dated 25 May to the Secretary of the Company*:

I send, for the information of the Board, the particulars of an experiment which was made on Monday and Tuesday last, at this station (Wolverton) on engine No. 18; and as the result proves that a fracture may occur in the fore-axle, without any serious consequence to engines of the description used by the Company, I doubt not that it will be found exceedingly interesting at a time when the public mind is so much excited by the recent accident on the Paris and Versailles Railway.

I must premise, that engine No. 18 was selected for the experiment because she had been sent to Wolverton to undergo a thorough repair; and it was further decided to substitute for her fore-axle one which, having been erroneously made a quarter of an inch less in diameter than the prescribed dimensions, had been long since laid aside.

The axle thus selected was cut circularly through, by a tool three-eighths of an inch wide, close to one of the journals, and to within half an inch of the centre of the diameter, leaving, therefore, an intervening thickness of one inch of metal connecting the partially severed parts.

The engine, in this state, was sent from the station towards Roade; the fore-axle broke in two as intended, at the point where it had been divided, but the occurrence had no apparent effect on the movement of the engine, which continued its course till it reached Roade, when it was crossed from the down to the up line, and returned in safety to Wolverton.

While Bury was doubtless a troublesome rival, from the Stephensons' point of view, a far more formidable challenge to their basic railway engineering principles was taking shape in the mind of Isambard Kingdom Brunel, who had been appointed to make a survey of a railway from London to Bristol, which was to become famous as the Great Western Railway. The lustre of Brunel's achievements is so universally recognized that it is quite needless to comment on it here; his matchless daring and ingenuity earned him undying fame. He was already extremely well known in the engineering world; his most notable achievement before the 1830s was the design of the suspension bridge at Clifton (Bristol). His years of birth and death (1806 and 1859) were so close to Robert Stephenson's (1803 and 1859), so that their careers moved forward in parallel. They were, in the words of Warren, the greatest of personal friends and the greatest of professional opponents.

Brunel's whole attitude to engineering matters was fundamentally different from the Stephensons'; armed with a brilliant and daring originality, he did not tie himself to the findings arrived at by their cautious,

* See Warren, *A Century of Locomotive Building*, p. 328.

plodding methods and their step-by-step progress towards improvements. From the outset, he discarded their principles of railway construction embodying the 4 ft. 8½ in. gauge, with rails carried on stone blocks. He dazzled his Directors into accepting his vision of a splendid high-speed system of transport, far surpassing anything that Stephenson had imagined, and he reinforced his views by his perception of the drawbacks due to difficulties of proper bedding and alignment that had already begun to be noticed in his rival's railway. Stone blocks, in spite of their durability as compared with timber supports for the rails, lacked the flexibility of wooden sleepers; indeed it is rather surprising that Robert Stephenson specified them even as late as the construction of the London and Birmingham Railway, when the better riding of rolling stock on timbered track was beginning to be realized. Brunel's spectacular divergence from George Stephenson's tenets was, however, in his rejection of the idea of a gauge of 4 ft. 8½ in. in favour of 7 ft.

The nuisance value of a break of gauge at various points in the national railway system must have been quite obvious to Brunel, but he saw his super-railway as so much better than the Stephensonian concept that such matters as the transfer of passengers and goods at interchange stations were of only secondary importance. He declared, too, that as the lines with which he was to be concerned were to serve areas devoid of railways, the question of interchangeability of rolling stock did not merit consideration.

The choice of 7 ft. by Brunel seems to have been due to his wish to ensure that coach bodies 6 ft. 6 in. wide should be located between the wheels, not from any desire to have larger locomotives than were possible on the 4 ft. 8½ in. gauge, although advantage was quickly taken of the extra space available. Stephenson himself had grown up with lines carrying colliery chaldrons having bodies between the wheels; these bodies were too narrow for adaptation to passenger traffic, but Stephenson overcame the drawback by the use of outside bearings and by the placing of the wheels below the floors of the carriages; a similar type of construction had been used for the tender of the 'Rocket'.

Regarding locomotives, there was a general desire to keep the centre of gravity as low as possible, the current view being that this would ensure safety and smooth running. To keep the centre line of a boiler low on an inside-cylinder engine, the cranks would need to be spread wide apart if the boiler was large (say, over 4 ft. in diameter), and this could only be done conveniently if the track gauge was greater than that of Stephenson. In fact, the freedom to provide boilers up to the limit that the broad gauge would allow was never fully exploited.

John Hawkshaw, who became engineer on the Manchester and Leeds

Railway, gathered opinions on the question of track gauge from Robert Stephenson and Company, and from Edward Bury, in 1838, and embodied their comments in a report to the Directors of the Great Western Railway.

From Robert Stephenson and Company the following letter came in reply to Mr. Hawkshaw; it was sent from the firm's London office on 1 October 1838*:

Sir,—The extent of inconvenience we experience in the construction of locomotive engines of moderate power (say 14 inch cylinder) for a gauge of 4 feet 8½ inches, is very small indeed. In our early engines an additional width of 3 or 4 inches would have facilitated the arrangement of the working gear and eccentrics; but this has since been simplified, and our latest arrangement of those parts leaves scarcely this small increase of width to be wished for. The construction of engines for Russia for a <u>six feet</u> gauge, leads us to believe that a considerable increase of expense is attendant upon increased width; more especially if the power of the engine is considered to bear any relation to the width of the gauge. If the power or dimensions of the engine be kept the same, the additional expense consequent upon increase of gauge will not be very considerable.

We are, Sir, &C.,
Robert Stephenson & Co.

Edward Bury's observations were as follows†:

Liverpool, Sept. 29th 1838

Dear Sir,—In reply to your letter of the 27th inst. referring to the question of the right gauge which at this time is so much agitated.

I beg to state that though we do not labour absolutely under great difficulties, yet there is no doubt an addition to the present width (4 feet 8½ in.) of a few inches would enable us to make a more perfect engine. The addition of 6 inches would be ample, and I consider anything beyond that would tend to increase the difficulties beyond what we now experience, rather than otherwise.

Yours truly,
Edward Bury

The following terse comment was made by Mr. Hawkshaw‡ on the letter from Edward Bury:

With respect to Mr Bury, it may be observed, that if any manufacturer in England has felt inconvenience from the 4 ft. 8½ in. gauge, he must have done

* *A Century of Locomotive Building*, p. 335.
† Ibid., p. 334.
‡ *A Century of Locomotive Building*, p. 335.

so; for, from the peculiar construction of his engines, it is a principle with him to use inside bearings only, which necessarily leave less room for the working gear than when outside bearings are used.

In passing, it may be remarked that Brunel's 7 ft. gauge was just as arbitrary as Stephenson's 4 ft. 8½ in. gauge, because it was simply related to an assumption of a 6 ft. 6 in. coach-body width, to be accommodated between the wheels. He might just as well have arbitrarily assumed a dimension of 6 ft., or anything else, as 7 ft. About this time a Commission was sitting to decide what to recommend as the gauge to be adopted in Ireland. In their report they favoured 6 ft. 2 in., having based their figure on a type of carriage construction which required the bodies to be between the wheels. Yet for all the force of this argument, only a small proportion of the early Irish railways was ever laid to a 6 ft. 2 in. track gauge. And by quite an early date (1840) the Great Western had abandoned this principle and was building carriages having bodies above the wheels, which were provided with outside bearings, as on Stephenson's railways.

On 15 August 1838 Brunel wrote a highly important memorandum to the Directors of the Great Western Railway, embodying his views on the *desiderata* of railway construction, and justifying his choice of a 7 ft. gauge. To those who wondered whether the extra width would involve greater expenditure on land, and all the additional costs, that wider bridges and tunnels would necessitate, Brunel dismissed objections on the grounds of cost in the following words*:

Yet such is not the case within the limits we are now treating of; a 7 feet rail requires no wider bridge or tunnel than a 5 feet; . . . and on the London and Birmingham Railway with 11 feet, a 7 feet gauge might be placed just as well as a 5 feet, leaving the bridges, tunnels, and viaducts exactly the same.

Brunel continued his memorandum with a long and interesting disquisition on railway speeds, and the better results to be expected from a 7 ft. gauge; his comments were clearly influenced by what was then being achieved on the Stephenson railways. As preparations had to be made well in advance for the opening of the line in 1838, locomotives had already been ordered by this time. The first to be delivered were built by Tayleur and Company and by Robert Stephenson and Company. The famous 'North Star' was supplied by the latter firm. It appears from careful researches which have been recorded by Warren that 'North Star' and a sister engine, 'Morning Star', were a modified version of the usual six-wheel passenger locomotive of Stephensonian pattern, but adapted for a gauge of 5 ft. 6 in., and with driving wheels 6 ft. in diameter, which

* *A Century of Locomotive Building*, p. 337.

had been ordered for the New Orleans Railway of America. However, as a result of a financial panic, the American railway was unable to take delivery of the locomotives, which were left on the builders' hands. Daniel Gooch, who became locomotive superintendent of the Great Western in 1837, had just previously been employed in the drawing office of Robert Stephenson and Company, and Warren considers it possible that Gooch himself made the drawings. By widening the spacing of the frames and by substituting longer axles the two engines were altered to Brunel's gauge, also larger (7 ft.) driving wheels were provided for the 'North Star', but in the case of 'Morning Star' the wheels were unaltered.

It is very interesting to reflect that the earliest Great Western Railway locomotives came from the firm associated with Brunel's greatest rivals. Gooch wrote,* towards the end of his life, about these locomotives:

> The 'North Star' and the six from the Vulcan Foundry (i.e. Tayleur) were the only ones on which I could rely. The 'North Star' was the most powerful one, and in other respects the best. She was my chief reliance.

Beyond all doubt the 'North Star' was a landmark in British locomotive design, and indeed she was recognized as such. After her retirement from active service in 1870, she was preserved at Swindon together with an example of Gooch's ultimate development of the broad-gauge express engines, the 'Lord of the Isles' (1851). In a truly shocking aberration of judgment, an order was given in 1906 for both these veterans to be scrapped; Swindon tried to make amends in 1925 by constructing a replica of the 'North Star', which was sent to the Centenary celebrations of the Stockton and Darlington Railway (and to the British Empire Exhibition at Wembley) in that year; it is now in the Museum at Swindon.

However, the uniqueness of the broad gauge, with its original designs for track with longitudinal sleepers held parallel by iron ties, and with its enormously impressive locomotives, finally resulted in its demise, in 1892.

After the Great Western had been opened, it expanded rapidly into western and south-western countries, and South Wales, at first without producing any formidable problems; but by 1845 broad-gauge and standard-gauge railways met at Gloucester, and the difficulties foreseen by Robert Stephenson then arose. The confusion and delays caused by the transfer of people and goods became, in the words of Warren, 'an evil indeed which could hardly be exaggerated. Supporters of the Stephenson gauge were quick to seize such opportunities of pointing out the general inconvenience of change of gauge, now a fact at Gloucester, which would arise in future wherever the two systems converged.'

* *A Century of Locomotive Building*, p. 339.

It so happened that, at that time, the London and Birmingham Railway and the Great Western Railway were each fighting to gain the traffic from an untapped area between Oxford and Wolverhampton. Both submitted Bills in competition with one another, and by June 1845 they were engaged in what Gooch afterwards described as 'the hardest gauges fight'. In his *Diaries of Sir Daniel Gooch, Bart.* (1892) he wrote:

I had to give evidence on the Bill, and had prepared very elaborate tables showing the speed and economy of the broad gauge. The Committee of the House of Commons sat on it rather over three weeks, and gave us the Bill on the 4th June. We met in a temporary committee room,* and the crowd and heat was excessive. Sitting in this heat all day, and working most of the night preparing evidence for the witnesses, almost broke me down. I will never forget the passion George Stephenson got into when the decision of the Committee was announced. He gave me his mind very freely for fighting the broad gauge against the narrow, in which he said I had been reared. I was not only fighting for my convictions, but also for my employers, who expressed themselves well satisfied with what I had done. The London and North Western and Grand Junction started express trains to Liverpool on 1st May during this fight. I went by the first, so as to be able to make use in my evidence of any facts I could pick up.

In this Parliamentary 'battle of the gauges', the Great Western was successful, and the Oxford, Worcester, and Wolverhampton line was duly constructed. But the publicity which the debate attracted had transformed the rivalry between the 'Great Western' and 'The Rest' into a national issue. In the Commons, Richard Cobden pressed for the appointment of a Royal Commission, and succeeded; the Commissioners (Lieut.-Col. J. M. F. Smith, R.E., former Inspector General of Railways; G. B. Airy, Astronomer Royal; and P. Barlow, Professor of Mathematics, Royal Military Academy, Woolwich) soon got to work, and by 6 August 1845 were hearing the first evidence.

The terms of reference of the Commission were to inquire into: (1) Whether break of gauge could be considered such an inconvenience as to call for preventive legislation; (2) Whether such evils as might result from a break of gauge could be obviated or mitigated by mechanical means; (3) Whether failure to devise such means would make it desirable to establish a uniform gauge throughout the country.

The Commissioners took evidence from a vast number of persons; the managers, engineers, and secretaries of the important railways were examined; in addition, the opinions of locomotive builders, military authorities, and commercial users of railways were obtained—over 6,500 questions and answers altogether.

* The old House had been burnt down in the fire of 1834; the subsequently constructed buildings were not opened till some twenty years later.

Evidence was taken from Robert Stephenson (the first witness to be called), Joseph Locke, Edward Bury, J. E. McConnell (who a year later was to become a key man in the founding of the Institution of Mechanical Engineers), Captain Laws, John Braithwaite, William Fernihough, John Hawkshaw, Major General Pasley (Inspector of Railways), G. P. Bidder, and others. Captain Laws, an ex-Naval officer, who was general manager of the Manchester and Leeds Railway, paid a fine tribute to the Stephensons when he said*:

Mr. Robert Stephenson will tell you there is no difficulty in making an engine as powerful on a 4 feet 8½ inch gauge as can be used with safety upon any other gauge. Now his opinion and that of Mr. George Stephenson I would rather take than any other man's.

He also said:

We owe all our railways to the collieries in the North.

An interesting sidelight on Robert Stephenson, revealed in his evidence, shows the concern for animal welfare which he had inherited from his father; he pointed out that one of the consequences of a change of gauge was that, in transferring beasts they must be allowed to graze in between, to settle their temper.†

Daniel Gooch was, naturally, the chief witness to speak in support of the broad gauge. He was only 29 years old at the time, but he had already had eight years' experience as locomotive chief of the Great Western, and had by 1845 acquired a high reputation for himself. His defence of the broad gauge was founded on the view that steam production was the true basis for comparisons between broad-gauge and narrow-gauge locomotives, and suggested that it was erroneous to compare locomotive capacities on figures for tube heating-surface alone. In regard to spring-gear he stated that the Swindon practice was to use inside and outside bearings, both sprung, because the broad gauge permitted this layout, which made for safety in the event of an axle fracturing. But though Gooch did not say so, on the 4 ft. 8½ in. gauge, both inside and outside bearings had been used for driving axles since the design of the 'Planet' some fifteen years earlier, though the purpose was to ensure safety and not to share the axle loading.

The inquiry went on for more than three months, and took an interesting turn near the end, when Brunel was asked if he had any further points to make. He gave his view that because of the number of varied opinions given by witnesses, it was desirable that further evidence should be gathered as a result of *ad hoc* experiments; he evidently felt sure that the

* *A Century of Locomotive Building*, pp. 378, 383.
† *The Locomotive Magazine*, 1903, vol. 8, p. 151.

broad gauge would then have a chance to show its superiority by incontrovertible facts.

It was difficult to lay down conditions that would be reasonably comparable, since quite different locations had to be used, but Brunel and Bidder were appointed to consider the terms of the experiments, and by December 1845 they had reached general agreement. The Great Western trials were conducted on the broad-gauge locomotive 'Ixion' and the narrow-gauge trials on Robert Stephenson and Company's 'A' engine, which had the 4–2–0 wheel arrangement, and a 2–2–2 locomotive, named 'Stephenson'. The 'A' locomotive was of the 'long-boiler' type developed at Forth Street from 1841 onwards, quite independently of the challenge that came from the broad gauge. The proposal to organize the experiments was sharply criticized in the technical press:

> experiments, ill-contrived, and calculated to embroil inextricably a question which they could not in any event tend to clear up.*

Gooch complained that in the narrow-gauge trials the engine 'jumped the gun', passing the starting post at 15 m.p.h. Other questionable practices, which he thought unfair, were the use of an artificial draught provided by a stationary engine to draw up the fire and hasten steam-raising, and the heating of the water in the tender before a run. But in regard to the feed-water heating, Bidder (as Warren points out) observed that Gooch had set the example in his first experiment! Warren continues†:

> The results show on the whole that the broad gauge engine hauled greater loads at the same speeds, or equal loads at slightly greater speeds, than were obtained with the narrow gauge engine. But there are discrepancies which baffle analysis and justify Bidder's opinion that the unknown factors, among them wind resistance, would make the trials of little practical value.

Bidder did not want to see the trials regarded as a mere contest of speed and power; he went carefully into questions of evaporative capacity and efficient use of steam. All the gauge experiments were, in fact, very valuable records of locomotive performance in the 1840s.

The Commissioners, however, were not required to base their recommendations on the details of the experiments. They took general economic and trade aspects into consideration, and their Report in 1846 stated‡ in its recommendation

> that the gauge of four feet eight inches and a half be declared by the Legislature

* *Railway Chronicle 1845*, vol. II, p. 1993.
† *A Century of Locomotive Building*, p. 387.
‡ Ibid, p. 388.

to be used in all public railways now under construction or hereafter to be constructed in Great Britain.

They avoided the embarrassment of coming out into the open and stating definitely whether narrow-gauge locomotives could be designed as powerful as those on the broad gauge; they considered that, for the track then in use, the broad and the narrow gauges had both reached the limit attainable. For practical purposes, the most important finding of the Commission was simply that there should be a unified gauge.

The main effect of the Commissioners' Report in 1846 was to prevent the general growth of the broad gauge into areas to which it would otherwise have been extended. From about the mid-1860s it began to shrink; moreover 'third rails' (i.e. inner rails spaced 4 ft. $8\frac{1}{2}$ in. from one of the broad-gauge rails) began to be laid down to form a 'mixed gauge'.

Both Ahrons* and Warren† have remarked upon the effect of the Report on locomotive practice; its result was a notable period of rivalry for a sort of 'blue riband' of locomotive performance, for which the principal competitors were Daniel Gooch and Robert Stephenson. For some years after 1846 there was a remarkable number of efforts, on both sides, to excel; and some record performances (for those days) were put up. They have a definite place in the history of locomotive design, but they did nothing to alter the effect of the Gauge Commissioners' pronouncements. Daniel Gooch, who was knighted in later life, and became the Chairman of the Great Western Railway, had a great affection for the broad-gauge; in deference to him it was kept in being until after his death.

Years after the Battle of the Gauges, a President of the Institution of Mechanical Engineers—Samuel Waite Johnson, in whose Presidency the main building at Storey's Gate (1 Birdcage Walk) was completed—said that in his view the ideal gauge was 5 ft. 3 in., which would have avoided the rather cramped assembly on the crank axles of inside cylinder engines and would have been less restricting on firebox dimensions, while at the same time being less expensive than Brunel's gauge. It was, in fact, the gauge eventually adopted for the Irish main lines. Yet the Stephenson 'standard' became the most widely used gauge in the world.

But the gauge question was not the only fundamental issue in the railway world in which George and Robert Stephenson found themselves at variance with Brunel. A completely different system of operation had been proposed, and in the 1840s was beginning to dazzle large numbers of people because it offered quietness in working, absence of smoke, and

* Ahrons, E. L. *The British Steam Railway Locomotive 1825–1925*, Locomotive Publishing Co., p. 68.

† See *A Century of Locomotive Building*, p. 389.

(it was believed) ability to move trains up much steeper gradients than steam locomotives could manage. This was the Atmospheric Railway.

Various desultory attempts had been made, from the early years of the nineteenth century, to harness atmospheric pressure to the propulsion of railway trains. In the period 1810–12 Medhurst had suggested a method of 'conveying letters and goods by air'. Fifteen years later he issued a brochure entitled 'A New System of Inland Conveyance for Goods and Passengers', in which he set out further developments of his ideas, which all depended upon the movement of an airtight piston along a tube or tunnel, using air under pressure to propel it. Four variants had been devised to suit different sets of operating conditions. Subsequently a Brighton inventor named Vallance patented a project for transporting passengers in a train of carriages moving along a tube from which air was being exhausted, the vacuum being created continuously in front of the leading carriage. In 1835, a Mr. H. Pinkus, American by birth but resident in England, was granted a patent for a 'pneumatic railway' embodying a horizontal cast-iron pipe some 3 ft. to 4 ft. in diameter, having a longitudinal slot about 2 in. wide along the top. Along the sides of the slot, the casting was so formed as to provide ribs or 'cheeks', to produce a channel about 5 in. wide and about the same depth, between the sides of which a flexible flap was fitted so as to exclude atmospheric air when a vacuum was produced inside the cast-iron pipe. A piston-carriage was fitted inside the tube, free to move along it, and supplied with a connecting bar attached to an external carriage. There were some tests on the viability of the scheme, which were carried out near the Kensington Canal, but the notion was not exploited further at that time.

However in 1840 the atmospheric railway principle received fresh impetus when it was revived by Messrs. Clegg and Samuda, who obtained a patent for their 'Atmospheric railway' and carried out large-scale tests on it near Wormwood Scrubs, making temporary use of a part of the West London Railway, which was then under construction. A 9 in. diameter tube was used. The tests were remarkably promising; up a gradient of 1 in 120 speeds up to a maximum of 30 m.p.h. were achieved with a load exceeding 5 tons, or 22 m.p.h. with 11 tons.

The project created a considerable stir; even before the trials were concluded, the Directors of the Dublin and Kingstown Railway decided that the atmospheric principle should be used on an extension of their line from Kingstown to Dalkey. Subsequently the London and Croydon Railway successfully applied to Parliament for powers to construct an atmospheric railway alongside their existing tracks to Croydon; they were also empowered to extend the atmospheric line to Epsom. During 1846 the atmospheric railway was completed between New Cross (now New

Cross Gate) and Forest Hill, and it was intended to take it to London Bridge by widening the brick arches of the Greenwich Railway. The chief engineer of the line was William Cubitt, who counselled careful observation of the London and Croydon line before embarking upon the Epsom extension.

The atmospheric principle began to attract increasing attention; it seemed to impress some of the most eminent engineers of the day. In due course a Parliamentary Committee was appointed to consider the merits of the system; Brunel gave evidence in its favour, in which he was associated with Charles Vignoles and William Cubitt. They were convinced that there was no mechanical principle that would invalidate the use of the atmospheric system upon a line of any length. The objectors before the Parliamentary Committee were George Stephenson, Thomas Nicholson, and Joseph Locke. Their objections were largely on (a) economic grounds, and (b) the delays that would occur if one of the lineside exhausting engines were to fail—precisely the old objection to the haulage of trains by ropes and stationary engines.

The Committee, weighing up the evidence, decided that a single line of atmospheric railway was better than a double track worked by locomotives, in regard to regularity as well as safety, because it would render collisions impossible (except at passing places or crossings), and it

> 'excluded all the danger and irregularity arising from casualties to engines or their tenders' (Smiles).

Even G. P. Bidder, who had been so much associated with the Stephensons, was sufficiently impressed to say,

> I consider the mechanical problem as solved, whether the atmospheric could be made an efficient tractive agent. There can be no question about that; and the apparatus worked, so far as I observed it, very well. The only question in my mind was, as to the commercial application of it.

The fact that so great an engineering genius as Brunel was soon won over to it must have helped lesser minds to become enamoured with the atmospheric railway. Such people probably felt that Brunel's experience and judgment were a guarantee; and they doubtless wished to be seen as 'up to the minute' progressives in the field of transport, for there are fashions in engineering practice as surely as there are fashions in ladies' dresses or hats. What appears to us now, with hindsight, as a passing flirtation with a new principle was, in the 1840s, quite a severe challenge, which assailed George and Robert Stephenson from various quarters.

Apart from the London and Croydon Railway, there were serious attempts to change from the principle of haulage by locomotives, and to adopt the fixed-engine atmospheric system on the South Devon Railway, the Chester and Holyhead Railway, and the Newcastle and Berwick Railway. The first of these was particularly a Brunel enterprise, in Brunel country, which was actually constructed, to the everlasting torment of the railway staffs afterwards, for it incorporated some of the heaviest gradients ever planned for a British main-line railway—stretches of 1 in 41 and even 1 in 36—because it was believed that they could be worked satisfactorily on the atmospheric principle. There were gradients which, in those days, were regarded as too steep for convenient operation by ordinary main-line express locomotives; but they have remained, and have always posed formidable problems in locomotive working west of Newton Abbot. Here, as elsewhere, the atmospheric system was a failure in service.

But the Chester and Holyhead line had been surveyed by George Stephenson himself in 1838; and the Newcastle and Berwick Railway had been one especially important to him, as it formed a vital link in his long hoped-for railway communication between London and Edinburgh.

The Chester and Holyhead line was promoted to provide an extremely important link between the English and the Irish capitals. Railways were already in existence on the Irish side; and the appointment of the Irish Railway Commissioners was a Government move which showed official desire to promote a main line of communication and to develop the traffic. The Commissioners at first favoured a railway to Port Dynlaen, on the Welsh coast, centre of a very small community, which they wanted to become the main port for Irish traffic. Stephenson, however, having gone over the route, felt that the gradients that would be involved through the Welsh mountains would make for very costly operation, and recommended strongly that the port to be developed should be Holyhead. So the present line, largely along the North Wales coast, came to be planned.

Although the actual construction of the line was carried out under the direction of Robert, the services of George Stephenson as a consultant appear to have been retained for some years. However the time came when the Company thought that the terms of the appointment could be reduced; Stephenson took it rather hard, and Robert must have felt embarrassed at the situation, which was beyond his control. George Stephenson had written to the Secretary of the Company (G. King) on 22nd November 1844 'expressing his disappointment that the Chester and Holyhead Board had reduced the amount of his account to £500'. In his own words:

'I am much hurt that my services should be looked upon as they are by your present company'.

(The use of the word 'present' is curious; perhaps Stephenson knew of proposals for amalgamation; but the Chester and Holyhead line was not absorbed into the London and North Western till 1858.) On 26 November 1844 Robert Stephenson wrote to King, explaining the circumstances in which he had acquiesced in the suggestion of settling his father's account for £500, a point on which he did not feel he could well express an opinion; and pointing out that his father was not prepared to accept. The surviving letters and memoranda are preserved in the Archives of British Railways.

When the Chester and Holyhead Company were, at an early stage, inclined to commit themselves to atmospheric working, George Stephenson objected to it outright; its inherent drawbacks must have seemed so obvious to him as to make it scarcely necessary to particularize. However, Robert, who was the designated chief engineer of the line, went to a good deal of trouble to defeat the plan on the strength of facts. He gathered information from actual experiments on the Kingstown and Dalkey atmospheric railway, and from observations made on the 'inclined plane' between Euston and Camden Town, then worked by stationary engines; and in 1844 he issued his *Report on the Atmospheric Railway System*, in which he came to the conclusion that the system was definitely unsuitable. Rolt has praised the 'so obviously fair-minded and so carefully considered' character of this Report as being more impressive than George Stephenson's immediate, instinctive dismissal of the atmospheric principle; in Rolt's words:

> Robert foresaw many of the technical difficulties which would later prove insurmountable, but over and above all such criticisms of detail he saw the whole controversy over the atmospheric system as another round in the battle for the steam locomotive against those advocates of fixed-haulage engines whom he and his father had defeated so decisively at Rainhill years before. Except that it used 'a rope of air' he saw no fundamental distinction in the atmospheric system.

Robert's Report was effective, and the Chester and Holyhead Company used steam locomotives. The 'Achilles Heel' of the atmospheric system was the difficulty of keeping it reasonably airtight, owing to the vagaries of the leather or composition flap on the top of the pipe, forming the 'valve'.

But the Newcastle and Berwick Railway proposals were a much more serious matter for Stephenson, and may be regarded as his last great struggle in railway politics. As we have seen, there was the coastal route, which he had surveyed himself in 1838, and which he strongly favoured; and there was an alternative route, inland, which that prominent landowner, Lord Howick, favoured because it kept the railway away from his house. Another supporter of the inland route was the Newcastle and Carlisle Railway, hoping that traffic between England and Scotland would travel over their tracks, at least between Hexham and Blaydon. A further reason given for the inland route was that the bridging of the Tyne could be carried out much more cheaply and simply upstream than by the great bridge that would be needed between Gateshead and Newcastle.

There were considerable delays in getting on with the authorization of the railway, as there were later with its construction. However in the late summer of 1840 Sir Frederick Smith, the Inspecting Officer for Railways, announced his intention of reviewing the situation. Stephenson was unable to meet him, but wrote as follows to Michael Longridge (Stephenson perhaps hoping that Longridge would give a welcome to Sir Frederick):

Tapton House
September 8. 1840

My dear Sir,

I am extremely sorry that I cannot spare time to come to Newcastle to meet Sir Frederick Smith. but having seen him a few days before he set out for the north, I arranged with him that Grainger and Bourne should go with him and point out the Line. I have no doubt they will do it just as well as I should as they know all my views on the subject.

I am dear Sir
Yours truly
Geo. Stephenson

M. Longridge Esqr.

Plans were now proceeding for railways both north of the Border (named, at this stage, the Great North British Railway) and south of it (the Great North of England Railway, between York and Darlington) which were to join up with the Newcastle and Berwick line to form a trunk route.* Stephenson could not believe that Sir Frederick Smith's eagerly awaited report would be otherwise than favourable to the coastal route; indeed he looked forward confidently to the formation of the railway company, as the following letter to R. W. Brandling shows:

Tapton House
Novr 18—1840

My dear Sir,

On my arrival here I found your letter of the 9th I have not heard whether

* The Great North of England Railway amalgamated later with the Newcastle and Darlington Railway to form the York and Newcastle Railway; later still, the combined line fused with the Newcastle and Berwick, to become the York, Newcastle and Berwick Railway, one of the main constituents of the North Eastern Railway, formed in 1854.

Sir Fredk. Smith's report has come out, but I have no doubt but the Eastern (i.e. the coastal) line will be recommended by him. I think the route through Newcastle will depend very much on the proceedings of the great North of England that is on which side of Gateshead the approach to Newcastle will come, whenever the Great North British Line commences it can only be brought to Newcastle, in the first instance we shall not be able to get money to go through the Town at first but it is highly desirable that it should be brought to that part of the Town, where it can be carried forward to Gateshead on the best possible plans, if Sir Frederick's report comes out very favourable to my line I have no doubt of getting the Company up next year, I think your plans will be best canvassed when the Com is formed, but if you wish either my son or I will lay them before Sir Frederick and explain the same, I shall be in London the early part of next week, I shall be glad to attend to any commands you have,

I am yours truly
Geo. Stephenson

R. W. Brandling Esq.
Low Gosforth
Newcastle on Tyne

Like the early London and Birmingham scheme, the Newcastle and Berwick Railway project went into retreat for a lengthy period, but was galvanized into activity in the autumn of 1843, when George Hudson was urging forward the completion of the Newcastle and Darlington Junction Railway over which he had secured control (to the intense chagrin of the Pease family, who had hoped to preside over it).

Michael Longridge, who had taken a great interest in Stephenson's coastal route, as it was planned to go near his iron works at Bedlington, was in correspondence with Stephenson on the subject. Lord Howick had intensified his objections to the project, about which Stephenson wrote feelingly to Michael Longridge:

Tapton House November 30th 1843

My Dear Sir,

I have received your letter of the 27th inst. I am rather astonished at Lord Hawick's observations about the line passing Hawick. It does not go through any of their pleasure grounds. it passes over one of their drives which runs down a dingle to the coast: it passes under the other road without at all injuring the level and strange to say there is a high way, I mean a turnpike road betwixt the house and the intended Railway; and the same roads are crossed, one over the dingle and the other on the level; and the land the line passes over is tillage land. My senses are puzzled in judging how these people can set about making such paltry objections! It is compensation they want, nothing else. The line cannot be moved to the place Lord Hawick alludes to, west of the house. it would require a tunnel a mile long. it would be very well for Lord Hawick as it would pass through their Limestone Quarries. I understood from Mr. Grey that the line was to be put nearer the Sea, this might have been done well enough: This species of objection is a genteel way of picking the subscribers' pockets there cannot be a doubt but it is meant to do so—I proposed to Lord Grey's family when I was there that if they wished we would cover the road in altogether; in passing the objectionable ground. It may however be better to keep these observations quiet until we come before Parliament. I have never taken any part in politics but I think I now will and become a Tory; and I shall buy a piece of land in Northumberland to oppose Lord Hawick—I do not like this double dealing work—We shall not fear Lord Hawick's opposition. Is the great thoroughfare through England and Scotland to be turned aside injuriously, for the frivalous remarks made by Lord Hawick? no! the times are changed. the legislators must look to the comforts and conveniences of the Public. are hundreds and thousands of people to be turned through a tunnel merely to please two or three individuals? I wonder their pulse does not cease to beat when such imaginations enter their brains! these failings are not becoming human beings. I can have no patience with them. However I suppose we must bend and keep our tempers until we get what we want.

Mr. James Locke is a sensible man; I am sure he will do what he thinks to be right without making any attempts to job.

When I was last in Newcastle I saw some of the parties connected with the private Coal Line from the north; and I think they are quite disposed to keep it back until they see if the public line can be got.

I should like to meet Mr. Grey on the subject of the line when I come to Newcastle next.

I am My Dear Sir,
Yours truly
Geo. Stephenson

Michl. Longridge Esqr.

Now I'll you that you have been living high by getting the gout into your hand. I dare say you have had some Turtle soup lately? you must have a poultice put on to every nail and you will find it will do you good, but it must be so arranged that it does not come in contact with the adjoining skin—if it does it will prevent the oil having its proper passage to the growth of the nail which I dare say is flat, looks red and inflamed underneath, and cuts brittle, for want of the liquid I have just mentioned.

G.S.

But Lord Howick, in his desire to ensure the defeat of the scheme for the coastal line, decided to mount the most formidable opposition obtainable against it. So he engaged the professional help of the most powerful personality available to him in the world of railway engineering: Isambard Kingdom Brunel.

Nothing could have constituted a greater challenge to George and Robert Stephenson than the appearance of Brunel in Newcastle to meet Lord Howick and to gather together all the evidence to support the inland route to Berwick. The situation was, to them, all the more monstrous because here was Brunel, not only turning up to promote a railway in a county which was particularly Stephenson's territory—but arriving also as a leading supporter of the atmospheric principle! In the words of Samuel Smiles:

When Stephenson first met Brunel in Newcastle he good-naturedly shook him by the collar, and asked 'What business had he north of the Tyne?' George gave him to understand that they were to have a fair stand-up fight for the ground, and shaking hands before the battle like Englishmen, they parted in good humour. A public meeting was held in Newcastle in the following December, when, after a full discussion of the merits of the respective plans, Stephenson's line was almost unanimously adopted as the best.

The rival projects went before Parliament in 1845, and a severe contest ensued. The display of ability and tactics on both sides was great. Robert Stephenson was examined at great length on the merits of the locomotive line, and Brunel at equally great length on the merits of the atmospheric system. Mr. Brunel, in his evidence, said that after numerous experiments, he had arrived at the conclusion that the mechanical contrivance of the atmospheric system was perfectly applicable, and he believed that it would likewise be more economical in most cases than locomotive power. 'In short', said he, 'rapidity, comfort, safety, and economy, are its chief recommendations.'

But the locomotive again triumphed. The Stephenson Coast Line secured the approval of Parliament; and the shareholders in the Atmospheric Company were happily prevented investing their capital in what would unquestionably have proved a gigantic blunder. For, less than three years later, the whole of the atmospheric tubes which had been laid down on other lines were pulled up and the materials sold—including Mr. Brunel's immense tube on the South Devon Railway—to make room for the working of the locomotive engine. George Stephenson's first verdict of 'It won't do', was thus conclusively confirmed.

Robert Stephenson used afterwards to describe with great gusto an interview which took place between Lord Howick and his father, at his office in Great George Street (Westminster) during the progress of the bill in Parliament. His father was in the outer office, where he used to spend a good deal of his spare time; occasionally taking a quiet wrestle with a friend when nothing else was stirring.* On the day in question, George was standing with his back to the fire

* 'When my father came about the office,' 'said Robert', 'he sometimes did not well know what to do with himself. So he used to invite Bidder to have a wrestle with him, for old acquaintance' sake. And the two wrestled together so often, and had so many 'falls' (sometimes I thought they would bring the house down between them), that they broke half the chairs in my outer office. I remember once sending my father a joiner's bill of about £2 10s. for mending broken chairs.'

when Lord Howick came to see Robert. Oh! thought George, he has come to try and talk Robert over about that atmospheric gimcrack; but I'll tackle his Lordship. 'Come in, my Lord,' said he, 'Robert's busy; but I'll answer your purpose quite as well; sit down here, if you please.' George began, 'Now, my Lord, I know very well what you have come about: it's that atmospheric line in the north; I will show you in less than five minutes that it can never answer.' 'If Mr. Robert Stephenson is not at liberty, I can call again,' said his Lordship. 'He's certainly occupied on important business just at present,' was George's answer; 'but I can tell you far better than he can what nonsense that atmospheric system is: Robert's good-natured, you see, and if your Lordship were to get alongside of him you might talk him over; so you have been quite lucky in meeting with me. Now just look at the question of expense,'—and then he proceeded in his strong Doric to explain his views in detail, until Lord Howick could stand it no longer, and he rose and walked towards the door. George followed him downstairs, to finish his demolition of the atmospheric system, and his parting words were, 'You may take my word for it, my Lord, it will never answer.' George afterwards told his son with glee of 'the settler' he had given Lord Howick.

But Lord Howick did not give up then, as Stephenson got to know very well, for on 19 June 1845 he wrote, from Westminster, to Michael Longridge:

My dear Sir,

Lord Howick still intends to follow us into the Lords with his opposition & we want you to assist in getting a Petition from the village of Bedlington, the Bedlington Iron Works. & another from Blyth.

I hope every individual in those places will sign the Petition & you will oblige me by giving your best assistance to this.

I am

Yours truly

Geo. Stephenson

The intensity of feeling in Northumberland about the conflict was remarkable. Smiles has recorded how

So closely were the Stephensons identified with this measure, and so great was the personal interest which they were known to take in its success, that on the news of the triumph of the Bill reaching Newcastle, a sort of general holiday took place, and the workmen belonging to the Stephenson Locomotive Factory, upwards of 800 in number, walked in procession through the principal streets of the town, accompanied with music and banners.

The formal incorporation of the Newcastle and Berwick Railway, embodying the route surveyed by Stephenson, took place on 31 July 1845, and no other challenge of such magnitude assailed George Stephenson during the rest of his life. The success of the Bill was a new triumph for him, and must have given him the greatest satisfaction.

6

Latter Years: Life at Tapton House, Chesterfield

Stephenson's restless and exhausting life, while he lived at Alton Grange, Ashby-de-la-Zouch, had left him little time for relaxation; even when in the locality, his attention was given to the Snibston colliery developments, which were proving a lucrative investment. But the time came when he began to long for a more leisured life, which he was now well able to afford. He wrote to Michael Longridge the significant letter given below:

My dear Sir,

I am sorry that I was from home when you were at my house. I shall be glad to see you and Mrs. Longridge on your return and I will endeavour to be at home the last day of this month.—

I intend giving up business in the course of two or three years when I shall be able to devote more time to my Friends. I have had a most delightful trip amongst the Cumberland Lakes, I should like to have remained a month to fish, I intend going again next year if I have time & have a large party with me— I hope you will accompany us.

I want to take in 30 or 40,000 acres of land on the West Coast of England I think it will be a good scheme.

I am Dr Sir
yours Truly—
Geo. Stephenson

Alton Grange Aug 13, 1837—

I will talk to you about the Belgian Trip when you come here

M. Longridge Esq

The West Coast retreat was a dream never realized; one would imagine that, even if railway communication were not far distant, Stephenson would have felt rather isolated; and his whole life was evidence that he relished being in the centre of scenes of action in the railway world.

It was recorded earlier that he moved to Tapton House in 1838; he had noticed the house at a time when he was carrying out some tunnelling work on the Clay Cross Tunnel and other railway construction in the neighbourhood of Chesterfield for the North Midland Railway. He had also, while in the vicinity, observed the potential of the district for

Fig 62. Tapton House School, Chesterfield (formerly George Stephenson's home). (Photo: W. Pearson)

industrial exploitation—limestone at Ambergate and coal at Clay Cross, revealed during tunnelling—rather as he had sensed the possibilities of Snibston in the early 1830s. The original agreement, dated 25 March 1838, included both house and lands for a period of 10 years, at a rent of £280 a year; it was between G. Y. Wilkinson Esq. and George Stephenson Esq. Parsonage has recorded* how Stephenson

> was the leading spirit in establishing the Clay Cross Coal and Iron Company, the limestone quarries at Crich, and the lime kilns at Ambergate. He personally opened pits at Tapton, Birmingham, and Newbold. Tapton House was included in one of the (colliery) leases and as it was conveniently situated to many of his activities he made it his home.

Stephenson, having now settled himself at Tapton House, and having begun his Clay Cross and Ambergate developments, made arrangements for the transport of their products, and for the further exploitation of the territory, as the following five letters will show; they cover the period 1840–46. The first of them has been made available by Clay Cross (Land and Minerals) Ltd., through the kindness of Mr. R. F. Childs; the others are in the possession of the Institution of Mechanical Engineers. Another document, dated July 1840 and preserved by the Clay Cross Company,

* *Proc. I. Mech. E., 1937*, vol. 136, p. 381.

relates to the provision of transport for the lime works. Mr. Morris was the Warwick solicitor engaged by Stephenson for these transactions.

Crich.
Octr 29th 1840.

To:

Mr. William Cartledge.

Sir,

If you are disposed to let your limestone quarries at Crich to Mr. George Stephenson & Co, they will pay you the same price per Ton, that they have tendered to the Earl of Thanet. viz, $1\frac{1}{4}^{d}$ per Ton, for stone, or 2^{d} for the Lime: and any damage done to the surface, to be settled by competent judges, that is each choosing their own valuer to select an umpire.

I have seen Mr. Chambers, Lord Scarsdale's agent, and he was, I believe, perfectly satisfied with the same tender that l formerly made to Lord Scarsdale as I am now making you: I am quite sure, that if we come to terms, your property will be four to five times increased in value. If you assent to my terms you will signify it by signing on the other side:—

I William Cartledge as . . . . . for James William Mary Ann Cartlidge do hereby agree to agree to the terms offered by Mr. George Stephenson, for the Limestone quarries held under my trust (situated in the parish of Crich) viz $1\frac{1}{4}^{d}$ per ton for the stone, or 2^{d} per ton for the Lime (when burnt).

(signed) Geo: Stephenson
Wm Cartlidge

Original document, signed by George Stephenson, in the Archives of the Clay Cross Company, Ltd.

Clay Cross July 1840

I the undersigned George Stephenson on behalf of myself and my partners [in] the Clay Cross Colliery, do undertake to make and maintain a Railway from Crich Cliff to the Cromford Canal and my Limekilns near Amber Gate and to commence the formation of the Railway as soon as the consents of the Landowners are obtained.

(Signed) Geo: Stephenson

Tapton House
Augt 3 – 1841

Dear Sir,

Are you doing anything with the Lease between Mr. Wilkinson and myself, I wish to have a wall built round part of the Land this Summer and I do not think it is prudent of me to begin until the Lease is settled.

I am yours Truly
Geo: Stephenson

T. Morris Esq.r
Solicitor
Warwick

Tapton House
Decr 19 – 1841

Dear Sir,

When I had the pleasure of having you to Dine with me here I had not then read over the draft of the Lease of Mr. Wilkinson's Coal, which was sent to me by Mr. Charge, in reading it over there are several omissions of clauses that I wanted in, one of the clauses, thus. That in case I commenced the opening in Mr Slaters ground, I was not to be bound to take any of Mr. Wilkinson's land until I really wanted it, for sinking Pits in, and when I did take it, not to pay more than a Farming Rent for the Land until I brot other Coals than Mr. Wilkinson's thro' the property, when I should then pay Four Pounds per acre per annum.

These observations I made to you when we first met about the Lease –

You said you would leave them entirely to Mr. Bailey, I saw Mr Bailey after that on the subject and he agreed to insert in the agreement the clauses I have just stated, I wish you would instruct Mr Bailey to come here and go over the agreement with me; there are some other little points requiring altering in the wording. It is impossible for a Lawyer to go through the different clauses required in the Lease of a Colliery, without having the assistance of some one conversant with the working of a Colliery, by his side.

Yours truly
Geo: Stephenson

After Bailey and I finally settle we could meet you at Derby.

T. Morris Esq
Solicitor
Warwick

Tapton House May 8th 1843

My Dear Sir

I quite forgot to add the rent for the four acres which I occupy for sinking my pits; I now send you a post office order for the sum.

I am
My Dear Sir
Yours truly
Geo: Stephenson

Thomas Morris Esqr
Warwick

Tapton House
April 9. 1846

My Dear Sir,

I received your note the other day stating you would be here on the 20th inst – I hope I may be at home when you come – if I am you must come to dinner – you will learn at the station if I am at home.

About a week ago I wrote a note to Charge stating that as he was the Attorney for Mr. Slater I wished him to send some one to meet me to divide the disused Turnpike road – he gave the young man I sent a very ungentlemanly reception – no reply to my note in writing; but 'all he had to say to Mr. Stephenson was that the Railway Company sold the land to Mr. Slater'. The young man asked him who sold it – his reply was 'you have got your answer'. Now as I told you before Parker told me the Railway Co could not sell the land; that the lane by law was to be divided betwixt the two adjoining Land-owners – I believe Charge knows he has done wrong but did not expect it would have been noticed – I should think Mr. Wilkinson's share is worth £40 or £50 – Should I be at home when you come I will endeavour to have Slater to meet us – I think it would only be right to knock down the fence, but I shall put that off until you come.

I expected I had a capital tenant for part of the land that Cowley farmed, but on examining the land he found it in such a bad state he durst not take to it. After telling me of this I went over the ground with him, and it is indeed in a shocking state. I now learn that Barber has taken part of it from you and Turner the other part. I have examined Limb's pits to see if he was coming near Mr. Wilkinson's coal, but find he is not near it.

I hope you have kept clear of the mania of wild Railway schemes – thousands of people will be ruined: as I have learned that many have mortgaged their little properties to get money; of course their property will be lost up to the amount of money they have got.

I have not yet seen any thing to suit your friend W.

I am Dear Sir
Yours truly
Geo: Stephenson

Thomas Morris Esqr

In the Clay Cross development he had William Claxton, Sir Joshua Walmsley, Joseph Sandars, of Liverpool, and George Hudson, 'the Railway King' as partners in a new company, first known as 'George Stephenson and Company'; Stephenson, the first chairman, was succeded in 1848 by Robert who, however, sold his interest in 1852, whereupon the firm was renamed 'The Clay Cross Company'.

Tapton House was in a neglected state when Stephenson acquired the Clay Cross concession; it would appear that he rented it for some years before he obtained the lease. The actual document is in the Library of the

Institution of Mechanical Engineers, and bears the date 25 May 1843. The house stands in extensive grounds on the top of a hill from which magnificent views of the surrounding countryside could be seen. It is now a grammar school. The garden was in a sorry condition, but in the course of time Stephenson cultivated it very successfully and it became one of the great joys of his old age. But in his first years at Tapton House, Stephenson was too much occupied with railway surveying and construction to devote much of his time to the garden. He was, in addition to his new enterprises in the Chesterfield area, heavily involved in surveys for various projected railways, mainly in the Midlands and in the North. In addition to those with which he was already concerned in 1838, he took on a survey for the Preston and Wyre Railway in Lancashire, which is of some interest as showing the workings of his mind on railway planning.

There were at the time two railways under consideration which, it was hoped, would join and then be extended so as to form a trunk route to Scotland. These were the Liverpool and Preston line, and the Preston and Wyre. Stephenson was consulted about the extension of the latter route through Cumberland, to form a west coastal line to the Border, giving direct access from Liverpool to Carlisle. He surveyed a line along the coast, by Whitehaven and Maryport, which he regarded as the only feasible route; he ruled out a railway across Shap Fell as quite impracticable. Stephenson's conclusions reveal his predilections for undemanding gradients. He based his view on the argument that, from a commercial viewpoint, a locomotive was a revenue-earner, better employed in moving the greatest practicable loads than in lifting carriages and wagons against gravity. Though the coastal line through Lancashire and Cumberland did get built eventually, it was left to Joseph Locke to plan the Shap Fell route which became the main line to Scotland, while the Whitehaven to Carlisle section only achieved secondary status. Nevertheless Stephenson's instincts had strong justification, for the Shap route, which includes a 4-mile stretch of 1 in 75, always made the most fearful demands upon locomotives.

Notwithstanding heavy responsibilities for the construction, at this time (1839) of the Manchester and Leeds Railway, the North Midland Railway (Derby to Leeds), and the York and North Midland (Normanton to York)—the first section of the last-mentioned line was opened on 29 April—Stephenson took pains with his Preston and Wyre report, which he signed on 5 June 1839 and dispatched to the Directors of the Company. After describing the state of the works at that juncture, and pointing out 'unworkmanlike brickwork' by a contractor, he continues:

> I feel it my duty to call attention to the measures which I conceive should be adopted in order to completely develope the resources of the undertaking.

With respect to the Harbour of Wyre I need say but little, as it must be obvious to everyone that the fact of its possessing a safe entrance at all times of tide combined with its extremely favourable situation with reference to the Ports of Belfast, Drogheda, the Isle of Man, and other adjacent places must render it a desirable station for the steam vessels which now start from Liverpool and I do not doubt that on the completion of the Railway the owners of these vessels will find it in their interest to use it.

In the next place, a Railway being in a rapid progress from Glasgow to Ayr which will have the effect of materially shortening the sea voyage from Glasgow to Lancashire, your harbour will evidently offer much superior advantages to steam vessels from Ayr than the Port of Liverpool.

The subject to which I would, however, more particularly direct your attention is the great benefit which your line will derive from the formation of a Coast Line from Liverpool to Preston, a distance of about thirty miles, and which line would be extremely inexpensive in its construction. It needs little more than a reference to a map of that part of the country to convince you how materially this line will assist the Preston and Wyre Railway and I cannot urge upon you too strongly the propriety of taking measures to get this line forwarded.

All that I shall want from your Company will be to procure the consent of the owners of the land between Liverpool and Preston, as I feel confident that I shall be able to raise the money required to make the line. As many of the Landowners as possible should be induced to take a sufficient number of shares to qualify them for seats in the Direction.

Supposing this line to be made from Liverpool to join your line near Preston, it will then be necessary for you to endeavour to get the Cumberland people to form a Harbour on the north side of the Duddon Sands, from which place to Whitehaven the line will be almost a dead level, and from Whitehaven to Maryport is also nearly a dead level. The country from Maryport to Carlisle is also extremely favourable and an Act has been obtained for the line, part of which is in course of execution.

The route which I have now described appears to be the only practicable line from Liverpool to Carlisle, as the enormous sum required for making a Railway across Morecambe Bay is too great and the scheme too hazardous to be attempted unless it should be taken up by Government, and the making of a Railway across Shap Fell is out of the question. It is therefore clear that the line I have described is the practicable line for a Railway Communication with the West of Scotland.

Keeping in view all these circumstances, I have no doubt that the Preston and Wyre Railway and Harbour will ultimately become a profitable concern.

I am, Gentleman,
Your Most Obedient Servant
Geo. Stephenson

The price of the land at the Preston end of the line which the Company have power to purchase should in my opinion be obtained.

During the year 1840, an astonishing amount of new railway mileage was brought into use: the whole of the York and North Midland Railway was opened; and the North Midland, the Chester and Crewe, the Chester and Birkenhead, the Manchester and Birmingham, and the Maryport and Carlisle were also opened to traffic—321 miles in all. In addition, the Manchester and Leeds line was well advanced. These lines were built under Stephenson's supervision. The North Midland Railway (Derby to Leeds) was a line for which the Railway King, George Hudson, seems to have had a particular affection, probably because of its vital importance in the railway politics of the time; with characteristic showmanship, he caused the opening ceremony, on 30 June 1840, to be marked by noteworthy celebrations, the event of the day being the running of a special train, in which he travelled, from York to Derby, and then back to Leeds. Thus York was brought into communication with London for the first time, the route mileage being 217. The direct line from King's Cross (188 miles) did not materialize until a decade later.

This remarkable period of railway expansion was also being mirrored in many other countries; it meant good business for the locomotive and railway equipment manufacturers, and new firms sprang up in considerable numbers to meet the demand, both in the home and in the export trades. In some countries, engines were customarily imported from England—generally recognized as the fountain-head for locomotive expertise—until railway industries could be established in the countries concerned; others relied a good deal more on British-built material. In Belgium, Cockerill had built his first locomotive at Séraing by 1835, modelling it on Stephenson's 'Patentee' type of two years earlier. By about 1840 other countries had established their own railway industries, including France, Austria, and Germany. The welcome given by George Stephenson to Paulin Talabot, a French railway engineer who had visited England as a young man in order to study its railways, and the friendship extended to Talabot by Robert Stephenson over many years proved to be very fruitful. George Stephenson continued, naturally, to be a partner in the Forth Street Works, which he visited whenever opportunity offered, though matters of locomotive design were now usually delegated by him, through Robert, to the works staff.

In the latter part of 1840, Stephenson was much concerned with some structural trouble which had developed on the Manchester and Leeds line, opened earlier in the year. Originally proposed in 1824, construction plans were shelved till 1837, when Stephenson, who was the responsible engineer, appointed Tom Gooch to take charge of the works. The line, which rises on the western slopes of the Pennines, reaches the summit at Littleborough, where a tremendous tunnel, 2,885 yd. long, had to be driven through the great range of hills. Reports of unsafe conditions, and fears of a collapse of a portion of the tunnel, in December 1840, brought Stephenson to the scene, to carry out a personal inspection, in company with Tom Gooch, after which they both signed the following report, dated 21 December 1840, to the Directors of the Manchester and Leeds Railway*:

We beg to inform you that we have closely inspected the fractured part of the Invert in the Summit Tunnel between Nos. 2 and 3 shafts, which has been referred to in Mr. Dickinson's last reports—

About 80 yards in length shows symptoms of weakness, but the defect has been discovered before any movement has taken place to affect the stability of the Arching and Side Walls, which are in a sound and perfect state, and we see no reason whatever to apprehend that any future derangement in them will occur.

The tunnel at this part passes through an extensive fault in the strata commencing near to the No. 3 shaft and extending about 120 yards towards No. 2. The material is very much dislocated, of an uncertain and variable character, and the bottom being soft has a strong tendency to rise, from the superincumbent weight on the (indecipherable) this has thrown a greater weight upon the invert than we expected which however will be sufficiently strengthened by being constructed of stone and increased in thickness, and there is no doubt but that by the adoption of this plan the Tunnel will be made perfectly secure.

This operation cannot be effected in less than six weeks but may possibly occupy two months—we should recommend therefore that the line be opened up to the East end of the Tunnel as early as practicable, and as we expect to have both lines of Rails from Hebden Bridge to this point laid by the middle of this week it may be opened during the present year.

You may rest assured that no time will be lost in making the Tunnel complete.

We are, Gentlemen,
Your Obedient Servants
Geo. Stephenson
Thos. L. Gooch

The note of optimism must have cheered the Directors. It is remarkable how they were told that the eastern part of the line 'may be opened during the present year'—by the time they had received Stephenson's and Gooch's report, and considered it, there can have been hardly a week left of 'the present year'. But in those times a Christmas 'break', such as we now know it, if indeed it was a matter for a holiday, was a brief affair. The beginning of 1841 saw the opening of the line. On 28 February, Stephenson wrote to Tom Gooch:

* The Archivist to the British Railways Board states: 'This Report probably came from Mr. Fielden, deputy chairman, L.M. & S.R. (previously Lancashire and Yorkshire Railway)'. The Report remains in B.R. Archives.

Tapton House
February 24th, 1841

My dear Sir,

I have drawn up a few observations about the Tunnel. Look it over and see if it will do to be attached to your report, let Mr. Gill see it and if he can put in any better words about you let him interline it. I should advise you to cause the Locomotive Engines to go slower certainly not exceeding 26 to 28 Miles per hour until the Road gets consolidated, at the speed you are now running you will destroy both Rails & Engines, I believe I came along the other day at the rate of 50 Miles per hour—

I am my dear Sir
yours Truly
Geo. Stephenson

T. Gooch Esq.

The original letter was presented to the Institution of Mechanical Engineers by Dr. Austin Wright in April 1956.

When Stephenson had discharged his obligations as responsible engineer to the railways with which he was associated at the time of his removal to Tapton House, he really did begin to retire—only partially, at first, for he was very much in demand, and there were tremendous developments within the railway world, both at home and abroad, in which he was deeply interested. But the latter part of the year 1841, likewise the years 1842 and 1843, if one can judge by such letters as have survived, suggest an increasing interest in the Chesterfield area, in the lands he had had leased to him, and in the development locally of the coal and lime industries. Except for the year 1845, which was something of an *annus mirabilis* for him, with just about all life's major experiences thrown into it, he slowly and gradually withdrew, as he said he would, and began to enjoy the leisure he had so far denied himself. Many of his old friends and associates came to see him, and were made welcome, for he was a sociable man by nature, and his house at Chesterfield was an attractive home for entertaining his visitors. The neglected grounds and gardens were gradually re-cultivated, and he took an enthusiastic interest in horticulture. A friendship grew up between him and Joseph Paxton, the head gardener to the Duke of Devonshire, who had charge of the gardens at nearby Chatsworth (Paxton earned lasting fame for his work on the design of the first Crystal Palace, in Hyde Park, for the Great Exhibition of 1851, his *magnum opus*, which gained him his knighthood). Stephenson was in keen competition with Paxton at many agricultural gatherings where prizes were offered for fruit and vegetables. He enlarged his greenhouses, extending them until he had ten in all, and he was a pioneer in introducing hot-water pipes for heating them. This great interest in the cultivation of fruit and vegetables re-echoed his early efforts in the same direction when he was at Killingworth. Smiles writes:

All his early affection for birds and animals revived. He had favourite dogs, and cows, and horses; and again he began to keep rabbits and to pride himself on the beauty of his breed. There was not a bird's nest upon the grounds that he did not know of; and from day to day he went round watching the progress which the birds made with their building, carefully guarding them from injury. No one was more closely acquainted with the habits of British birds, the result of a long, loving, and close observation of nature.

Parsonage states:

He made Tapton Park a bird sanctuary*

Stephenson used his considerable powers of deduction, too, in the cultivation of his property. A most interesting sidelight on this aspect of his vigorous mind has been recorded about his bee-keeping efforts. His wife had noticed that the bees did not seem to thrive at Tapton House, which stands on the top of a fairly steep hill. The hives were then at the summit. Stephenson one day noticed the bees at the foot of the hill, laden with honey, trying to make the ascent up to the hives. They appeared to be exhausted from long periods on the wing, and could hardly struggle to their home. When he mentioned this matter to a naturalist, the latter was impressed by the acute powers of observation which Stephenson possessed.

In between his days at his home, he frequently visited his coal-mining and lime-burning enterprises, which became flourishing concerns, and he found employment for a considerable number of his former assistants, some of them coming from the north, and others being transferred from the Snibston collieries. His colliery interests were now considerable. In a letter (now in the possession of the Institution of Civil Engineers) dated 18 October 1841, he writes to his solicitor, Mr. T. Morris, of Warwick, about a proposal to transport coal won at Clay Cross, to the West Midlands for sale in the vicinity of Warwick; the letter is interesting as it shows how, in general, the bother and expense of transporting coal before the general extension of railways, had tended to restrict and localize the areas within which it was normally sold. Warwick was near a coal area, anyway, which made Stephenson doubtful about the scheme contemplated by Morris's friend, Nelson:

Tapton House
Oct. 18—1841

Dear Sir,

Yours of the 13th I duly rec^{d}—I shall endeavour to be at Home on the

* *Proc. I. Mech. E., 1937*, vol. 136, p. 382.

25th of this month, and shall be happy to see you & your friend Nelson, to dine with me at 6 oclock on that day, I will write to Mr. Charge to join us. It is rather uncertain whether I can make any arrangements with your friend about my Clay Cross Coal, as there are person's already engaged selling Coals in your district, but this we can discus fully when your friend comes over—

The rent for Mr. Wilkinson's house will be ready for you, when you come.

I am anxious to have some conversation with you respecting the projected R Way from Hampton to Warwick, as I wish to go to Parliament next Session with it. if we can raise the Capital—

I am yours very truly
Geo. Stephenson

P.S. Will you give me a line by return saying whether you can dine with me.

The 'projected R Way' was in an area which had been a very early scene of railway promotion; William James, who had championed the cause of railways when George Stephenson was only locally known, became an estate agent and colliery owner in Warwick, and was later the Vice-Chairman of the Stratford and Moreton Railway, part of an ambitious idea for a line for coal traffic from Warwickshire to London. In neighbouring Staffordshire, too, over the boundary with Warwickshire, was the redoubtable J. U. Rastrick, who, with his partner, Foster, had built the 'Stourbridge Lion' for America in 1829, and the 'Agenoria' (the latter gave about 3 years' service on the Earl of Dudley's Colliery Railway at Shutt End). Incidentally, both these engines have been preserved, the former in the U.S.A. and the latter in Britain.

At this time, George Hudson was approaching the zenith of his powers in the railway sphere; he controlled many railways in the Midlands, in the North, and in East Anglia; an appeal to him by Stephenson to place a man on a railway was likely to be successful, for Hudson had a great respect for Stephenson's unrivalled experience and sagacity. So it was natural, when Joseph Paxton wanted to introduce an acquaintance to the Railway King, for him to approach Stephenson first. A letter on such a matter, from Stephenson to Paxton, is still treasured among the Stephenson relics at Tapton House. The letter, kindly transcribed for the purposes of this book by Mr. Pearson, the present Headmaster of Tapton House School, reads:

Tapton House
January 20 1843

My dear Sir,

On my arrival here I found yours of the 21st.

I have forwarded your letter respecting Ward to Mr. Hudson with my own remarks upon him as I believe him to be a good man.

I think it is likely that Hudson will be Chairman but this is rather uncertain from the accident that has taken place, however if the Railway goes on well between now and the next meeting the bad feelings that have taken place with respect to the accident might blow over.

I am sorry the Duke and his friends have been frightened from the Railway I believe there is no occasion to be alarmed now as the work appears to be going on smoothly.

I am yours very truly
Geo. Stephenson

J. Paxton Esq.

A proposal to link Shrewsbury with Birmingham by rail, via Wolverhampton, was taking up Stephenson's attention during 1844. There must have been some rivalry with Brunel over this, as Shrewsbury later became an important point on the Great Western trunk line from London to Birkenhead, via Chester. But the London and Birmingham Railway appeared at that time to have hopes of securing Shrewsbury traffic, for Stephenson wrote, on 3 July 1844, a letter, concerning the route to be followed, to Richard Creed, their Secretary, as follows:

Referring to the Line which is proposed from Shrewsbury by Wolverhampton to Birmingham, you are aware that I had my attention particularly directed to this District of Country in 1836 and after a thorough examination of it and duly weighing the circumstances which are likely to affect the cost of construction I was decidedly of opinion that a junction with the Grand Junction near Wolverhampton was the only course which I could recommend for adoption.

I was in some degree influenced in this decision by the very large and uncertain expense which would be incurred in purchasing the property between Wolverhampton and Birmingham not only the surface but the minerals underneath the line of railway. Compensations of this kind are always large but in Staffordshire my experience leads me to believe that it would be excessively heavy, not to say enormous.

I cannot avoid calling your attention to this circumstance before the proposed Birmingham and Shrewsbury Railway is finally decided upon as I am confident the cost of construction and compensation has not been sufficiently considered. I shall be glad if it be thought desirable to go over the country with the Engineer of the Birmingham and Shrewsbury Line. I do not know that I shall ever then be more competent than I am now to speak decisively although I might be able to give my opinion more in detail as to the prudence of stopping short and joining the Grand Junction Railway at Wolverhampton thus securing an easy and by far the most eligible entrance into Birmingham.

There are certain points of interest in this letter, reminding us once again of Stephenson's great caution before throwing his weight into any scheme for new railways and of his habit of taking into consideration, when making a report, the many factors that might arise not only during construction, but afterwards. In the world of railways, a rich field for future harvest was being sown at this time for the legal profession; one can easily picture protracted and expensive wrangles over the exploitation of mineral wealth under a line of railway. Stephenson himself, while always a man of the very highest principles, certainly believed in taking advantage of developing certain industrial projects (as at Snibston and Clay Cross) which had suggested themselves to him while he was engaged on the construction of new railways; and while those collieries of his were new developments, the returns on which could not be foreseen, the mineral wealth beneath the Staffordshire countryside was known of old, was already profitable for mining, and might be expected to rank very high in claims for compensation.

The phenomenal rise in the number of projected railways at this time, culminating in the 'Railway Mania' of 1845, with its ruinous aftermath, is a matter of history. Many of the lines that were proposed would have simply linked two towns, and the capital in such cases would in all probability have had to be provided from local sources, while—in the cold light of day—no great returns could have resulted. It has been stated by L. T. C. Rolt that:

> The practical expression of George Stephenson's foresight was his insistence upon uniformity of gauge, but his mind could never grasp the implications of his vision in terms of administration and finance. Just as he favoured the small contractor, so he believed that railways should be sponsored, financed, and administered locally by those immediately concerned.

To drive home his point, Rolt reminds us that

> In the year of his death George Stephenson wrote to T. R. Cobb of Warwick urging him to ensure that money for the proposed Leamington and Banbury Railway was raised locally so that none of the great companies could secure control of the project.

In this passage, an interesting comparison is made between the viewpoint of Stephenson and that held by George Hudson and Joseph Locke:

> George Hudson, like Joseph Locke, saw that the future lay with the big battalions. In construction, Locke favoured the large contractor; in operation, Hudson favoured the big company and did not believe that a national railway system could be effectively worked by a multiplicity of small undertakings. Hence he directed all his energies towards unification with such effect that at the height of his power he controlled 1,450 route miles of line out of the total of 5,000 miles then built.

These influences, then beginning to have effect, had been gradually paving the way for the great amalgamations which took place among the country's railways during the period 1844–54. A good summary of what went into the formation of the Midland Railway, a particularly widespread amalgamation, as well as being one of the most important, is given in an excellent historical work by Rixon Bucknall*:

In 1844 a number of companies . . . agreed to amalgamate under the title of The Midland Railway. These constituent companies were The Midland Counties, which connected Nottingham, Derby, and Leicester, and which gave access to The London and Birmingham by means of a branch to Rugby; The North Midland, which ran from Leeds to Derby; and The Birmingham and Derby Junction, which again gave access to the London and Birmingham at the terminal city, as well as at Hampton-in-Arden on the London–Birmingham main line, and which, in 1839, had given Derby its first rail connection with the capital. Then in 1846 The Leicester and Swannington joined The Midland, as did also The Birmingham and Gloucester. . . . Another acquisition, and also in 1846, was The Bristol and Gloucester broad gauge line; and then in 1851 The Leeds and Bradford; and in 1852 'the little' North Western, which ran from Skipton to Morecambe. . . .

Another feature of railway promotion of the 1840s was the urge to build 'direct lines' between places already linked by railway; this was to some extent the result of the Stephensonian policy of gentle gradients, which made for ease of operation but at the expense of a greater mileage. Sometimes the 'undulating railway' principle (p. 50) would also be urged as an attraction! But there certainly was some case for co-ordination, at least, amongst the railways in 1844, when, on 21 November, Stephenson wrote to Richard Creed as follows:

I beg to acknowledge the receipt of your letter of 9th instant enclosing a minute of the London and Birmingham Board, expressive of their satisfaction at an arrangement about to be made for me and my son to arrange various points of difference between your Company and the Grand Junction as proposed by Mr. Moss, but stating it to be the conviction of your Board that no permanent arrangement could be secured without the concurrence of the Manchester and Birmingham Board and the Committees of the Shrewsbury Company, the Chester and Holyhead Company, the Chester and Shropshire Company, together with the Manchester and Birkenhead Company, of the Trent Valley Company and Churnet Valley Company. At the time when I communicated with Mr. Glyn (George Carr Glyn, the banker, who was a Director of the London and Birmingham Railway and first Chairman of the London and North Western Railway) I considered myself fully authorised by Mr. Moss to make the proposal of reference which I did, but from a letter which I have since received from him it appears to be doubtful if he intended to go so far and at all events there is a

* Bucknall, R. *Our Railway History*, 3rd ed., 1972, (London: George Allen and Unwin).

decided objection on his part to include the Churnet Valley and Birkenhead parties in the reference and I am therefore afraid that the negotiation must be considered at an end.

There must have been many instances when deadlock ensued in such negotiations between railways when there were 'too many cooks'. The formation of the Midland, which was Stephenson's favourite railway, must have done much to simplify agreements with other lines; another amalgamation of the highest importance followed in 1846, when the London and North Western Railway was constituted out of the London and Birmingham, the Liverpool and Manchester, the Manchester and Birmingham, and the Grand Junction Railways. The Lancaster and Preston, and the Lancaster and Carlisle Railways were also included in working arrangements (and were amalgamated later), so that rail access by the West Coast route to the Scottish Border was finally achieved.

Both George and Robert Stephenson were concerned with the promotion of some of the early railways in East Anglia in the 1840s. This was a very difficult area to develop; the whole district was almost entirely rural, and there was the usual opposition from landowners. The first of the lines—the Eastern Counties Railway—got as far as Colchester by 1843, but, for financial reasons, languished; and construction in the direction of Norwich was long delayed. Meanwhile another company, the Northern and Eastern, had done rather better in striking north, from London through Broxbourne and Bishop's Stortford to Cambridge and Ely, some 70 miles, and was opened in July 1845. Another line—the Norfolk Railway—from Norwich had opened its first section from Norwich to Brandon, in the direction of Ely; later in the same year, through running from London to Norwich was established by completing the link between Ely and Brandon.

The delays in the construction of the line north from Colchester to Norwich led to an agitation for a connection from Norwich to the sea at Yarmouth to be promoted independently. Powers for construction of such a line had been obtained some years earlier, but had lapsed owing to the delays in construction. Finally, to bring matters to a head, a Yarmouth and Norwich Bill was piloted through Parliament and received the Royal Assent on 18 June 1842. Stephenson was elected Chairman of Directors, and Robert was appointed Chief Engineer. The line was opened to traffic on 30 April 1844.

As pointed out by C. J. Allen in his book, *The Great Eastern Railway*,*

In those days Yarmouth was quite a fashionable watering-place, and because it also served as the port for Norwich, though with very indifferent facilities for

* Published by Ian Allan Ltd., Shepperton, Middlesex.

transport between the two towns, the provisional estimate of traffic valued at £40,000 per annum was regarded as justified.

The towns were 20½ miles apart by the new railway, which enabled the journey to be done in 40–45 minutes. It is interesting to note that this was the first railway to install, even if in a primitive form, block signalling; Allen records that the Cooke and Wheatstone electric telegraph was used for the purpose.

Stephenson was always quick to appreciate the possibilities of developing trade in conjunction with the opening of new railways, and he reacted enthusiastically to a letter sent to him by a Mr. Charles Palmer, in the following reply, which he sent from London:

24, Great George Street,
Westminster,
3rd October 1844

Dear Sir,

I have received your Letter of the 1st instant, which I have carefully read over, and have to state that my views quite coincide with your own. It is my opinion that the Merchants and Inhabitants of Yarmouth ought to bestir themselves immediately. I shall be happy to give you any assistance I can in carrying out your plan. If the entrance to your Port could be improved, so as to admit of first-rate Steamers entering at all times, there could be little doubt of Yarmouth becoming one of the great Ports for London. The subject appears to me to be a National one, and worthy of the attention of the Government. You are at liberty to make use of my name in any way that may promote the views just stated. The situation of Yarmouth is not only such as to form the best communication to London from the Continent, but to almost all the Manufacturing Districts in England, by the Chain of Railway Communication that will be shortly formed.

I am, my dear Sir,
Yours truly
Geo. Stephenson

To Charles J. Palmer Esq.,
Great Yarmouth

It would be interesting to know whether Stephenson, in writing this letter, cast his mind back twenty years to the situation at Stockton where, through the failure of the Tees Navigation Company to keep a satisfactory waterway for navigation, with full port facilities, led to the decline of the town as a port, and to the resignation of Mr. Meynell, Chairman of the Stockton and Darlington Railway, and to the extraordinary rapid developments at Middlesbrough.

The fact that Mr. Palmer wrote on 1st October, and that Stephenson was able to reply only two days later, speaks well for the postal services in East Anglia at the time; the line to Norwich was open, but trains did not start running between Norwich and London until several months later.

It will be noticed that Stephenson still had to visit London for business; during the next year (1845) his journeys were frequent, and he was particularly pleased when the London and Birmingham Railway allowed him a free pass over their line. Of this privilege he wrote to Richard Creed, the Company's Secretary, on 15th February 1845, as follows:

> I beg to acknowledge the receipt of your letter of yesterday enclosing the very handsome and gratifying minute of the London and Birmingham Railway Board in tendering me a free pass over their line.
>
> I have to request you will offer them by best thanks for the complement (*sic*) they have paid me which I shall be proud to accept as a proof of their kindly feeling towards me. Permit me to thank you also for the flattering manner in which you have expressed yourself in communicating the resolution of the Board.

Honours from various directions were now being accorded to Stephenson; he was at the height of his fame, and he was one of the comparatively few people to have a statue commissioned while still living. Late in December 1844, his statue, in marble, was ordered by the Liverpool and Manchester Railway Directors; it was not, however, until after his death that it was placed in St. George's Hall, Liverpool.

The year 1845 was an extraordinarily crowded one in Stephenson's life. It was the year of the Railway Mania, against which Stephenson had uttered a warning during the previous October, when he addressed the Directors of the Leeds and Bradford Railway at Ben Rydding. He foresaw quite clearly the dangers of speculation in railway shares, in which the lay public were indulging so recklessly.

It was impossible for the Stephensons to escape being importuned throughout this period, by people who were hoping to acquire fortunes in this way. Smiles has described their offices in Great George Street, Westminster

> . . . crowded with persons in various conditions seeking interviews, presenting very much the appearance of a levee of a minister of state. George Hudson was often there; but a still more interesting person, in the estimation of many, was George Stephenson, dressed in black, his coat of somewhat old-fashioned cut, with square pockets in the tails. He wore a white neckcloth, and a large bunch of seals was suspended from his watch-ribbon. Altogether he presented an appearance of intelligence, health, and good humour that rejoiced one to look upon in that sordid, selfish, and eventually ruinous saturnalia of railway speculation.

The ominous look of the situation may have prompted the final sentence in the following letter which Stephenson wrote to Joseph Pease, Jun.:

Tapton House Feby 6th 1845

My Dear Sir,

On my arrival here I found your note of Jany 27. together with the plans of part of the Redcar Railway.

I trust I may have an opportunity of being with you on Saturday morning, and hope this will be in time for Mr. Harris to meet me. I suppose there will be no difficulty in going over the line on Saturday and back to Darlington at night in time for the last train? I presume this will depend on the state of the tide?

What a Railway World this is! when is the bustle to be over?

I am

Yours truly

Geo. Stephenson

Joseph Pease Junr, Esq.

In the spring of 1845, Stephenson paid another visit to Belgium. He had been requested on several occasions to go abroad to advise railway promoters; this, however, was an especially important event for him. His visit was primarily to go over the whole length of the proposed Sambre et Meuse line, but while abroad he visited coal mines near Jemeppe, noted methods for draining them, and inspected colliery winding engines and their braking devices.

On 4 April 1845 he was invited to a magnificent banquet. The chair was taken by M. Massui, Chief Director of the Belgian National Railways. A marble bust of Stephenson, crowned with laurels, was on view to the guests. The railway administration surpassed itself to show every possible honour to him. A model locomotive, under a triumphal arch, was placed on the table. Stephenson examined it. It was the 'Rocket'. Could any compliment have been more beautifully conveyed? Stephenson's geologist friend, Tom Sopwith, a Fellow of the Royal Society, was with him, and remembered the occasion long afterwards.

On the day, Stephenson was invited to a private interview with the King of the Belgians at the royal palace at Laeken. Sopwith was also invited; his geological knowledge was especially advantageous, as the King wanted to discuss the coalfields in Belgium and their structure. Stephenson was also highly knowledgeable on the subject; and Smiles has described how he discussed the formation of the coal-bearing strata to the King, 'using his hat as a sort of model to illustrate his meaning'. Stephenson also told the King how industry and commerce tended to follow the exploitation of coal measures. After they had left the palace, Stephenson said to Sopwith

By the bye, Sopwith, I was afraid the King would see the inside of my hat; it's a shocking bad one!

Later in the same year, Stephenson made a further journey to Belgium, this time to advise on the West Flanders Railway.

He was also caught up with the several sessions of the Gauge Commission during that year, and (as we have seen) with the tremendous battle for the coastal route for the projected Newcastle and Berwick Railway, which was incorporated on 31 July.

Fig 63. The 'Rocket' shown on a matchbox of Spanish origin (in author's possession).

While all these engagements were pressing on him, Stephenson suffered the worst blow that can befall a man: the death on 3 August of his wife Elizabeth, whom he had married twenty-five years earlier; her name appears above his own on the memorial tablet in Holy Trinity Church, Chesterfield.

In the latter part of this most eventful year of joys and sorrows Stephenson embarked upon an adventure which nearly cost him his life. He was invited to travel to Spain in order to report on the possibility of constructing a railway from Madrid to the Bay of Biscay. The project had already gained some support and the Spanish Government had agreed, in principle, to grant a concession for the construction of it; in fact some of the surveying work had already begun. However, it was felt that George Stephenson's advice would be valuable, and he generously agreed to give it without any financial reward, and only claimed the payment of his travelling expenses. The project was to be called the Royal North of Spain Railway; and there appear to have been some British interests involved in its promotion; a company had been formed, but progress had been delayed while its Directors were trying to get better terms for their concession. Until a better basis for negotiations had been obtained, the Directors were holding back from depositing the money required by the Government. In the hope of striking a better bargain for British interests, Sir Joshua Walmsley had agreed to visit Spain on behalf of the Directors, in order to make an approach to the Spanish Government. Stephenson was much interested; in fact, Smiles has recorded that he himself offered to accompany Sir Joshua. A full description of the expedition has been chronicled by Smiles, and is well worth reading. On the way to Spain, the party was joined by Mr. Mackenzie, who had been engaged on the construction of a railway from Orléans to Tours and who showed them the works in progress and accompanied them as far as Tours.

Stephenson and Sir Joshua, having crossed the Pyrenees, began their preliminary survey, Stephenson becoming much impressed by the mountainous character of the terrain, and concluding that heavy tunnelling would be needed. He worked extremely hard, from daybreak to dusk, sleeping in his day-clothes wherever he could get shelter. It was too much for a man of his age (he was 64) to put up with such rigours and to emerge without impairment of health. Toiling through ravines and over mountain passes, he rested in a hovel one wet night; rain leaked through the roof and, though his determination to finish the job succeeded, he was held up in Madrid for several days while he and his colleagues awaited the decision of the Spanish Government. No reply was forthcoming. To entertain Stephenson and his companions while they waited in Madrid, an invitation was conveyed to them to a bullfight, but Stephenson had no wish to see such revolting barbarities, and with icy politeness made it clear that the purpose of his visit to Spain was to survey a railway. There being no further point in waiting for the Spanish Government to make a move, Stephenson gave his advice, namely, that the financial deposits demanded by the Government should not be made, and that the project should not be proceeded with; Smiles records Stephenson's opinion that the traffic would not amount to one-eighth of the estimate.

Returning from Madrid, Stephenson was obviously ill and probably feverish as a result of his soaking night in the hovel. Reaction set in, and his thoughts frequently strayed to his own home and his friends in England. He knew he had to be in London for important business by 30 November 1845. By the time he had reached Paris, he was so ill that it seemed most inadvisable to go on, but he insisted on travelling to Havre, for the boat to Southampton, by which time it was seen that he was suffering from pleurisy. Once back at home, he recovered, even to the extent of imagining he was quite fit again; but this was not the case and he had to go more warily—in fact, he had less than three years to live.

During convalescence he wrote thus to Michael Longridge:

Tapton House
22nd Novr 1845

My Dear Sir,

I have your letter of the 17th ins^t^ before me.

I am now at home and quite well, my recovery has been most extraordinary, the attack I had was pleurisy: I think it was first occasioned by taking unwholesome food at Bordeaux from that place I travelled night and day to Paris: I took very ill there, but still persevered in getting to England; on arriving at Havre I was obliged to have a Doctor who took 20 oz blood from me on board the Steam boat; I was then very weak but still wished to get on to England; the boat sailed at 5 o'clock P.M. I got to London the next day about half past 2 o'clock & there got the best advise; they got two Physicians to me; they put me to bed and cupped me on the right side; how much blood they took by cupping I cannot tell, they then put a blister on my side and gave me Calomel every four hours from Saturday night to tuesday night: I then became so weak that they durst not give me any more—on the wednesday morning I was considerably relieved from pain and could then eat a little—my rapid recovery since that time has been astonishing. I am now as well as I ever was in my life, but I am advised to keep quite (quiet) for a while. I do not know when I be in Newcastle. Hudson has become too great a man for me now. I am not at all satisfied at the way the Newcastle and Berwick line has been carried on, and I do not intend to take any more active part in it—I have made Hudson a rich man but he will very soon care for no body, except he can get money by them. I make these observations in confidence to you.

My best regards to Mrs. Longridge and all your family.

I intend going to London on tuesday. I shall be back here the end of the week.

I am
Yours truly
Geo. Stephenson

Mich[l] Longridge Esq.

P.S. I have had a most extraordinary journey in Spain. I crossed the Pyrenees 5 times; and rode on horse back 50 miles amongst the mountains seeking out the lowest pass—we had our carriage drawn up by bullocks on to the mountain passes where a carriage had never been before—we passed just under the snow range. I shall give you an account of my travels when I see you: we travelled 3000 miles in 33 days: stopped 4 days in Madrid, 2 days at the summits of the mountain passes—I was kindly received in every Town where I was known.

A fortnight later Stephenson wrote further to Longridge:

Tapton House Dec[r] 5th 1845

My Dear Sir,

I have your letter of Nov[r] 24th before me.

I am now quite recovered from my illness—

I should like to visit you at Bedlington but I am afraid I shall not be able to come down at the time you state; I want to stop as much at home as I can for the next two months; I have frequently to be in London but this I can do in a few hours.

I shall be at home the latter end of next week should you be disposed to travel to this place I should be extremely glad to see you.

I am
yours truly
Geo. Stephenson

Mich[l] Longridge Esq.

When the Spring arrived in 1846, Stephenson learned of an illness which had laid low Michael Longridge, to whom he wrote as follows:

Tapton House
March 31st 1846

My dear Sir,

On my arrival here I found your letter of March 28th—I am extremely sorry to learn of your illness; when you go to London make *this* your resting place, and if I can go with you I will;

There is no doubt of the North Midland paying the £500. I will tell them about it.

I have the Manchester people in capital case about the North British Railway, as as (sic) soon as the Commissioners make their report, which must be favorable to our Line, we must then get a company up ready for next year; you must be sure to let Bourne go with the Commissioners when they come down, if you see Sir Frederick Smith, who is the leading Commissioner you will find him quite a gentleman I think him above taking any bribe from any person.

I am, My dear Sir
Your's very sincerely
Geo: Stephenson

M. Longridge Esqre
Westgate Street
Newcastle—

The £500 mentioned in the letter does not seem to have been explained; it may have been a debt owed to the Forth Street Works, of which Longridge was a Director, for the supply of locomotives to the North Midland Railway.

During 1846, which necessarily had to be much less strenuous for Stephenson than 1845, we find him taking out patents, jointly with William Howe, for a design for a three-cylinder locomotive which was duly built and which distinguished itself in taking a special train from Wolverton to Birmingham on 7 May 1847, during which it covered a section of 41 miles in 42 minutes, with a maximum of 64 m.p.h., despite the effects of a side wind. The Locomotive Superintendent of the railway (the Southern Division of the London and North Western Railway), Mr. J. E. McConnell, was on the footplate. We shall find McConnell in another—and most portentous—context towards the end of 1846, to be mentioned in the next chapter. Howe was a patternmaker at the Forth Street Works, a man of considerable attainments, who at this time left the North to become engineer at Stephenson's Clay Cross collieries. A further claim to distinction is due to Howe: he perfected the 'Stephenson' link motion for working steam locomotives expansively, having developed this form of valve gear from the original idea which had been first thought of by a young draughtsman named William Williams at the Forth Street Works. The importance of the Williams–Howe valve gear as an improvement in locomotive operation and performance can hardly be over-estimated. In 1846, too, Stephenson was much concerned with the 'undulating railways' faction (pp. 50, 218); and when the Prime Minister (Sir Robert Peel) made reference to them in one of his speeches, Stephenson thought it time to impart a little education; not feeling that he could express himself so well as his son, George Stephenson persuaded Robert to write a letter to the Prime Minister which he (George) would sign, embodying his views on the necessity for gentle gradients. The Prime Minister gave indication, in a subsequent speech, that he had taken note of the letter, although he did not refer to Stephenson's conclusions.

In the same year Sir Robert Peel showed his approval of the Trent Valley Railway, a line in which Stephenson had taken a very great interest. It put Tamworth into direct communication with London.* As regards his appearance in support of new Bills for railways, Stephenson in 1846 appeared for only one—the Buxton, Macclesfield, Congleton, and Crewe Railway in which, as a coal owner, he was personally interested. He had become by now almost entirely withdrawn from the active promotion and construction of railways, even though the public frenzy for railway speculation continued: in 1846, Parliament conceded powers for the construction of 4,790 miles of new railways in Britain which, it was stated, would need £120,000,000 of capital to get them started.

Stephenson can have seen little of his son at this time; Robert was heavily engaged on the building of the Britannia tubular bridge over the Menai Strait as the crowning achievement in the construction of the Chester and Holyhead Railway. The Conway tubular bridge was ready for assembly about the same time: the foundation stone of the Britannia Bridge was laid on 10 April 1846 and that of the Conway Bridge on 12 May. Robert was also pushing ahead on Tyneside with the construction of the great High-level Bridge between Newcastle and Gateshead, closing the last gap in the rail link from the Thames to the Tyne. Both father and son were now widowers, Robert's adored wife having died of cancer in 1842.

Tapton House was now a great solace to George Stephenson. He enjoyed receiving callers, among whom were young men seeking advice on their careers. Whenever possible, he tried to help them on their way. In a characteristic letter he wrote to William Ellis, of Bingley (the letter was misdirected by the Post Office to *Bingham*, Notts, and forwarded thence to Yorkshire); he had met Ellis's nephew at Bayonne during his visit to Spain the previous year:

Tapton House 30th May 1846

Dear Sir,

On my arrival here I found your letter of the 25 inst wherein you state that

* Sir Robert Peel lived at Drayton Manor, near Tamworth.

you want a situation for a young friend of yours. It would give me great pleasure if I could be the means of assisting you in your application—I have now almost entirely given up my profession as Civil Engineer, and am therefore not in the way of placing people in situations. If the young man is clever you must get Fairbairn to recommend him to my Son as they have a great deal of business together. When I see Fairbairn and my Son I will talk to them about the young man: the former will be the best judge of the young man's talents—if he is clever he will be sure to get on; but if not clever he cannot do much as there are far too many coming into the profession.

I am Dear Sir
Yours truly
Geo. Stephenson

William Ellis Esqr

P.S. I do assure you I was quite surprised to see your nephew Mr. Ellis at Bayonne: it gave me much pleasure to see him as I had spent many pleasing hours with his Father.

Many of the surviving letters belonging to the period of his life after his return from Spain are primarily concerned with local matters, but they throw some light on his interests and are included for that reason. Some letters to Frederick Swanwick, by now an officer of the Midland Railway, have been kindly lent (for transcription) by Mr. Michael R. E. Swanwick, M.B.E., of Chesterfield, the great-grandson of Frederick Swanwick:

Tapton House April 10th 1847

Dear Swanwick,

I have had a long conversation with Richardson about Mr. Hall's coal and the crossing of the railway at Long Eaton. I find there is too much coal yet to be worked on the west side of the Railway so as to prevent any attempts to buy the road off—he says there are 10 or 15 acres and the rent that Hall pays is £200 per acre

You will therefore be good enough to make the level crossing immediately—and make the road to the place I pointed out to you on the map. Richardson informs me that one horse can not get the carts across the present crossing that is made on account of the sharp ascent for the loaded carts and on this account Hall has stopped the Colliery. I will now write to Hall on the decision I have come to on the crossing: I will also request him to give me a detail of the damages he has sustained—Now let me advise you to alter the road immediately.

I am
Yours truly
Geo. Stephenson

Fr Swanwick Esq.

Tapton House April 18 1847

Dear Sir,

I received yours of the 12th inst together with the sketch of the railway and land in Hall's property.

I think the point of crossing marked on the sketch meets my views, my opinion is you have nothing to do with crossing the train road besides there is no difficulty in crossing it—my advise is therefore to make the road as I proposed —if you can agree with Hall to do it for you do so, but it appears to me to be so trifling a thing that you ought to make it at once—

I shall be at home tomorrow if you have anything more to say to me about it.

Yours truly
Geo. Stephenson

Fr Swanwick Esq.

Tapton House Oct 10th 1847

Dear Swanwick,

I send you the damages sent to me of Hall's property—there must be something very wrong in the statement made out—Let me see you here—I shall have to give it up, it is too complicated a case. Sandars (? Sanders) should see it.

Yours truly
Geo. Stephenson

Fr Swanwick Esq

There was also an exchange of letters between Stephenson and a Mr. J. Cocking, of Tapton, evidently a near neighbour, relating to the sale of coal. Stephenson wanted to help Cocking to get a fair price, and Cocking did not seem quite sure how to set about it, so Stephenson wrote him the letter (undated) appended below, sending at the same time the draft letter (also appended) for Cocking to use if he so wished:

Tapton House

Dear Sir,

On the other side I send you such a letter as I think you ought to write to me about your coal: If we make a charge with Miss Lord's coal for Sir Henry Hunlocke, it will bring you in a good price for yours almost immediately, that is supposing your coal to be combined with Miss Lord's which I think it ought to be—I am

Yours truly
Geo. Stephenson

—Cocking Esq.

Copy of letter to be sent by Cocking to Geo. Stephenson

Dear Sir,

You will recollect that you stated to me, that if you bought Miss Lords coal you would take mine at the same price. We certainly did not draw up any agreement for the sale of my coal: but as men of honour do not want agreements I leave it to yourself whether in common justice, my coal ought not to be taken along with Miss Lords in the exchange you are now making. Could you favour me with an answer to this. I am

Yours truly
(signed) Cocking

Geo. Stephenson Esq.

The letter to Cocking, and the draft, are now in Chesterfield Public Library. In the safe keeping of the same Library is a letter written by Stephenson to his Clay Cross engineer, William Howe, about a man seeking employment at one of Stephenson's collieries:

Tapton House
April 29: 1847

Dear Sir,

Binns tells me to day that you stated to him that you had got an answer from the person who I thought would suit Snibston & that he was willing to engage for 36^{s}/. per week house rent & fire with a suit of flannels every year—Now I am willing to comply with his request, that is to give him what he wants, but it must be understood that he will have to work himself as well as take the charge of those who may have to work with him as the Colliery is not large enough to keep a person to overlook only. He will have to attend to the Sinking pits, putting in pumps, erecting engines & all other work required on the Colliery in his capacity—If he conducts himself properly he will be well treated—there is a house ready for him and the sooner he comes the better—Will you correspond with him immediately.

I am
yours truly
Geo. Stephenson

Mr, William Howe

One of the last of Stephenson's letters to have survived was written between four and five months before his death; it is addressed to his former assistant, John Dixon, by that time fifty years of age. Dixon had been a junior engineer under Stephenson for the construction of the Stockton and Darlington Railway, to which he returned after working for some years on the notorious Chat Moss section of the Liverpool and Manchester Railway. In 1844 Dixon was appointed chief engineer to the Stockton and Darlington Company. Stephenson had a very high regard for him; in fact, he had written to Dixon on 11 January 1846:

You have no occasion to fret about a situation as long as I am in the land of the living.

Dixon was evidently concerned about the passage of Stockton and Darlington trains over colliery workings for on 16 March 1848 he wrote to his old chief, who sent a prompt reply as follows:

Tapton House
March 18, 1848

My Dear Sir,

I have received yours of the 16th inst respecting the coal under the Railway at Etherley Colliery.

I have duly considered the situation of the railway with respect to the coal under it and my opinion is to let the Coal owners take away the coal in any way they like—I have in several cases given the same advise my advice would be different if there were tunnels or heavy viaducts, I have a case before me now where £22,000 are claimed as damages, but this is under a Canal tunnel and damages must be paid in such a case. In your case you have little to fear by using longitudinal sleepers and keeping a good watch as you propose. The trains might be ordered to go at a moderate speed over such ground. I have been working the coal from under the railway at one of my own Collieries without saying one word to the Directors about it as I know there would be no danger although the coal is thicker than yours, but at a greater depth. I think it is likely the surface of the ground may go down 18 inches or two feet, but it will not go suddenly down unless there is a great thickness of rock, which from your letter does not appear to be the case.

You are at liberty to make what use of this letter you think proper.

I am
Yours truly
Geo. Stephenson

John Dixon Esqre

Stephenson's suggestion to order the trains 'to go at a moderate speed over such ground' certainly came home to roost in later years, as particularly tiresome railway-speed restrictions had to be introduced in the Chesterfield area for the very reason that colliery workings below the tracks did not make normal running speeds advisable.

A few months before his death Stephenson married again. He had lost his second wife nearly three years previously. In February 1848 he married Ellen Gregory, daughter of a farmer at Bakewell, Derbyshire, and sister of a doctor practising at Youlgreave; she had been his housekeeper for some time. Stephenson shows his concern for her during an illness which she contracted in 1847 while he was in London; it is intriguing to note the practical way in which he wanted to know how ill she was before deciding to leave his business in London and return to her (the exact date is not given). The letter, written in his own hand, is preserved in the Science Museum.

Fig 64. Small medallion for coat lapel, with George Stephenson's profile. (Courtesy: The Institution of Mechanical Engineers)

24 Great George Street,
Westminster, 1847

My dear Glen,

I have just got Mr. Marks (?) letter which gave me much pain to hear of your illness I do hope you are better. I shall not leave here until Tuesday morning so that I can have a letter before (leaving?) London to say how you are if you cannot write in time for me here I shall hear from you at Tapton if you are no better I will come down to to (sic) you but do not let me come unless you feel very ill.

I shall be home to be with you by the end of the week.

I am my dear Glen
Your loving friend
Geo. Stephenson

The last three or four years of Stephenson's life were (except for 1845) not so strenuously occupied as the years preceding them. He now had more opportunities to follow one of his great interests, the education and training of engineers. In these matters he gave a great lead, for, although the needs of civil engineers had begun to be better understood and provided for, there was not, in the 1840s, any proper, general recognition given to mechanical engineering as such. His contributions to these aspects of his profession are a lasting memorial to him.

7

George Stephenson and the Engineering Profession: the Establishment of the Institution of Mechanical Engineers

In all his major railway achievements, Stephenson was essentially the practical man, the empiricist; he had to be, for, despite the corpus of civil engineering knowledge of his day, he was doing things which nobody had done before. The works of the Liverpool and Manchester Railway were, at the time of their completion, unparalleled in their magnitude and in their clear demonstration of difficulties triumphantly surmounted. In these enterprises he was sustained not only by a unique blend of high personal courage and natural caution but also by an unshakable belief in railways as a system of transport and in steam locomotives for their operation. So courage did not exaggerate itself into foolhardiness, neither did caution act as a damper on innovations.

As Stephenson's own railway activities increased, and with the growth of railways generally, he realized that he must provide for their future construction and operation by ensuring that trained young engineers should be forthcoming, well versed in his principles, who would be able to influence railway engineering in the future in directions which he would have approved. He therefore took under his care indentured apprentices, who were formally bound to him for an agreed number of years, with the written consent of a parent or a guardian; some of these indentures have survived to this day. When he conveniently could do so, Stephenson took the young man into his own home during part of the apprenticeship, where he lived as one of the family. Some of these young men greatly distinguished themselves in their subsequent careers. Taking the country as a whole, there was little formal engineering education available in those days; those who intended to live that life were 'thrown in at the deep end', which has always been an effective way—within limits—of ensuring the effective survival of some, at least, of the candidates.

But while training under the supervision of Stephenson was probably the best practical instruction in the new profession of railway engineering, Stephenson himself was, deep down, conscious of his own educational shortcomings, and he must early have realized that, if the profession were to flourish in the future, it would have to embrace also an accompanying knowledge of the basic technical principles. So, quite apart from his concern for a grounding for Robert in the theoretical aspects of engineering, he had a sincere desire to see provision made for the needs of those who would follow him. Smiles has recorded Stephenson's interest in Mechanics' Institutes:

From an early period in his history, he had taken an active interest in these institutions. While residing at Newcastle in 1824, shortly after his locomotive foundry had been started in Forth Street, he presided at a public meeting held in that town for the purpose of establishing a Mechanics' Institute. The meeting was held; but as George Stephenson was a man comparatively unknown even in Newcastle at that time, his name failed to secure 'an influential attendance'. Among those who addressed the meeting on the occasion was Joseph Locke, then his pupil, and afterwards his rival as an engineer. The local papers scarcely noticed the proceedings; yet the Mechanics' Institute was founded, and struggled into existence. Years passed, and it was now felt to be an honour to secure Mr. Stephenson's presence at any public meetings held for the promotion of popular education. Among the Mechanics' Institutes in his immediate neighbourhood at Tapton, were those of Belper and Chesterfield; and at their soirées he was a frequent and a welcome visitor. . . .

Smiles states, too, that Stephenson was 'an immense favourite with his audiences' at the Leeds Mechanics' Institute. We have seen, moreover, his interest in the British Association for the Advancement of Science, which he assisted in their Mechanical Section in connection with the Association's meeting in Newcastle in 1838. Some twenty years previously, he had appeared before the members of the Literary and Philosophical Society in Newcastle to explain the working of his safety lamp. It is good to know that the 'Lit. & Phil.' is to this day an important and flourishing institution in Newcastle.

R. H. Parsons, in his Centenary History of the Institution of Mechanical Engineers states:

The spread of education was always one of his great desires . . .

He knew from his own experience how hard is the path of the ambitious man who has had no introduction to the stores of accumulated knowledge in his youth. When working as an engine wright he had laboured early and late to gain the means of giving a good education to his own son. His conviction of the benefits of education made him give influential support to the Mechanics' Institutes that began to spring up in industrial centres to provide for the needs of working people, and he frequently visited them and addressed words of advice to their members. It was in keeping with his desire to promote the spread of engineering knowledge, and to encourage the spirit of invention, that he accepted

Fig 65. Statue of George Stephenson in Neville Street, Newcastle upon Tyne. (Photo: L. G. Charlton)

the Presidency of the Institution when it was founded to render to the profession generally just those services that he had so much at heart.

But Stephenson's belief in the value of technical education for young engineers was far more than paying tribute to it as a guiding principle. He translated it into a notable willingness to help the individual, as has been shown in his letter to William Ellis (p. 227). Parsonage, too, has recorded* how—

* *Proc. I. Mech. E. 1937*, vol. 136, p. 383.

Young men often called upon George Stephenson for advice or assistance in commencing a professional career. When he had assured himself of their good sense and ability he was always ready to give help. He hated foppery and would always reprove any sign of it. To one youth who called upon him flourishing a gold-headed cane he exclaimed: 'Put that stick by and then I will talk to you.' Stephenson was an excellent judge of character and engineering ability, and surrounded himself with a number of most able young men to carry out his projects. An attribute of genius is to inspire others with its fire. This was particularly true of Stephenson and his pupils. His pupils became the eminent engineers of the world. He was fond of questioning them and quick to detect an evasive answer. . . . His object was to stimulate his pupils to educate themselves, to induce them to develop their own mental powers and gain self-reliance. He was against any form of cramming and disapproved of competitive examinations, saying, 'You should never judge a goose by its stuffing.'

Stephenson was always on the look-out for talent in young men, whoever and wherever they might be, and to give that talent encouragement. One youth, a carpenter working on the Liverpool and Manchester Railway, excited his attention; before many years he was, through Stephenson's aid, recognized as an engineer of distinction. . . . Nothing gave Stephenson more pleasure than to help an able youth and in his own phrase to 'make a man of him'.

An example of Stephenson's desire to assist a youth at the outset of his career has remained to us in a letter which he wrote, less than a year before his death, to William Hutchinson, who for many years had been the extremely able and active Works Manager at the Forth Street Works, Newcastle (Robert Stephenson used to refer to Hutchinson as 'The Oracle'):

Tapton House
Septr 15th 1847

My Dear Sir,

This will be handed to you by Mr. Beasley and his Son who he wishes to go into the Manufactory, the matter must be left entirely in your own hands: Mr. Beasley is a highly respectable man, he has been introduced to me by one of the Clergymen of this neighbourhood.

Yours truly
Geo. Stephenson

W. Hutchinson Esqre

Looking back to the times when Stephenson was gaining his reputation, one cannot help being struck by the rapid advance of steam engineering from the days of Boulton and Watt to the middle of the nineteenth century. But the advances were largely based upon empiricism—upon practical experiments, guided by that peculiar unfathomable intuition which led to such vital steps forward as (in the world of steam locomotives) resulted in the design of the 'Rocket' and, soon after, the 'Planet', or in the development of the Stephenson link-motion. Seldom were such improvements due to theoretical studies, though they would be explainable by them—afterwards. In the case of Stephenson, himself a great empiricist, one senses that he joined whole-heartedly in developments such as higher railway speeds, greater boiler-pressure, and heavier locomotives, *but only up to a point*; when he felt instinctively that a reasonable limit had been reached, he would disapprove of fresh endeavours to go beyond it. A better theoretical training would have assisted him enormously. It is all the more to his credit, therefore, that he sought to make good facilities available for the technical education of engineers.

What was the state of theoretical knowledge of engineering subjects in Stephenson's time? The great principle established by Sadi Carnot, in 1824, was little known. There was no engine designed *intentionally* to embody the theory that work can only be extracted from an engine by providing for a drop in heat from a higher to a lower temperature. There were no steam tables. The vital work published by J. P. Joule on the mechanical equivalent of heat first appeared in 1843, and then only (initially) in the Proceedings of the Manchester Literary and Philosophical Society. It was generally believed that heat was a substance contained in the 'pores' or molecules of materials; it was referred to by the learned as 'caloric'. The only practical use of electricity in Stephenson's lifetime was the electric telegraph; he was always much interested in the subject, and saw the introduction of telegraphic communication on railways in 1837.

With hindsight, we can now see how well the stage was set for the establishment of the Institution of Mechanical Engineers, and how greatly Stephenson was attracted to the idea. The real events leading to its foundation were the rapid industrial developments in the life of the nation, especially those resulting from the spread of the railway network. The particular influences to which the Institution owes its existence have been recounted in different ways by various people; it is unlikely that we shall ever know the whole story.

The oft-told tale of the Institution of Mechanical Engineers being 'founded' by George Stephenson as a sort of counter-blast to the Institution of Civil Engineers, who rejected his application for election unless he submitted to an educational test, received very wide credence, and doubtless there are many people today who believe it. It gained an added piquancy by being represented as a sort of David and Goliath situation. Only in comparatively recent years have endeavours been made to see it in a different light. In 1956 the Institution of Civil Engineers published a review of the situation in a duplicated document headed *A Study of an Alleged Slight*, which, in addition to marshalling a number of factors concerning Stephenson's career and his position in the professional engineering world, gives a number of anecdotes about him as a person. It is a very interesting survey, and deserves to be better known; it contains a fine tribute to his character:

> George Stephenson emerges from this cursory study of his own and his contemporaries' lives as a great National figure, who had the good fortune to be acclaimed during the span of his own life-time by his fellow countrymen.

It refutes anecdotes about 'the great engineer's thwarted desire to become a member of the Institution of Civil Engineers', and claims that in the face of Stephenson's stature in the nation the story 'loses all pathos and becomes little more than a tax on the reader's powers of credulity'.

Four years later, L. T. C. Rolt's *George and Robert Stephenson* was published; in it the author sums up the whole situation in terms of human relationships. Stephenson, during the course of his career, had run into conflict with established civil engineers on many occasions, especially with such men as the Rennies, Palmer, Giles, and Walker, who were at the centre of things within the Institution of Civil Engineers. He had also had the disagreeable experience of his survey of the Liverpool and Manchester Railway being checked—and criticized—by Thomas Telford, the first President of that Institution. These men had made their name in the construction of roads and canals, not railways; and Stephenson must have felt affronted by their sitting in judgment upon him. He was very sure of himself in matters of railway engineering; and to witness the most reputable civil engineers of their day pronouncing in favour of fixed engines instead of locomotives for the haulage of trains must have been particularly exasperating. In the broad practical canons of railway construction and operating he had had far more experience than any other man in the land; *he knew it*, and this fact alone cannot have made him a sympathetic figure to them. From *their* point of view he was lacking in education, opinionated, and obstinate; he would never have fitted comfortably into the 'Civils' hierarchy, so it was perhaps as well that this did not come about. It was left to Robert to receive, and later to give, lustre through election to the Institution of Civil Engineers.

A look at the earliest records of the Institution of Mechanical Engineers leaves no doubt that J. E. McConnell was the driving force behind the foundation of the Institution. It may well be that the matter was discussed one afternoon in 1846 when certain railway engineers were witnessing locomotive tests on the formidable Lickey Incline between Birmingham and Bristol, when, during heavy rain, the party had sheltered in a plate-

Fig 66. Curzon Street Goods Station, Birmingham (early offices of The Institution of Mechanical Engineers), by Claude Buckle (Photo: British Railways Board)

layer's hut. The upshot of the discussion in which they engaged while sheltering was that mechanical engineers ought to have their own Institution; and McConnell subsequently arranged a meeting at his own house, when some half-dozen interested engineers foregathered. The early events in the Institution's existence have been carefully chronicled by R. H. Parsons in his *Centenary History of the Institution* (1947); the exploratory meeting was held at the Queen's Hotel, Birmingham, on Wednesday, 7 October 1846; a committee was appointed to approve the rules on 18 November; and on 27 January 1847 the Institution was formally launched at a general meeting, convened for that purpose, at the Queen's Hotel. The Chairman on that historic occasion was J. E. McConnell. Stephenson was present, and proposed the adoption of the provisional rules, after which, amid applause, he was formally elected President.

Stephenson then took the chair, and addressed his audience on the subject of his early life at Killingworth as an engine-wright. It is a great pity that his observations have not been preserved. He would have needed no prompting; he often dwelt on his early days, and was not in the least embarrassed by the circumstances of his birth and childhood. There is no doubt that Stephenson was proud of the new Institution and took a great deal of interest in it. The Headquarters remained in Birmingham for thirty years before the move to London took place; it was a good central location, with rail links in various directions, and attendance at meetings was not unduly difficult. Expense, however, was another matter; on 21 April 1847 the Secretary was instructed 'to write to George Stephenson Esq., President of the Institution, requesting his co-operation in procuring free passes from the different Railway Companies to their Quarterly Meetings'.

Additional Council meetings, apart from regular quarterly ones, were held from time to time; thus on 1 May 1847 there is a Minute recording 'the excellent example given by the President in his handsome donation of £100'; the President was regarded as an example to follow for, at the same meeting, it was resolved 'that the Treasurer be authorized to receive donations'. It was also agreed, on the same date, that the President was to receive a copy of the Minutes of each Council Meeting.

Later in the year, on 16 October 1847, the Council actually held their meeting at Tapton House. Stephenson may well have proposed the venue himself, for he had a fine house in a grand situation, and he enjoyed entertaining his guests. Ellen Gregory must have had to meet the occasion as a special challenge. It appears that it was at this meeting that the subject for discussion at the next General Meeting of the members was to be decided; Stephenson proposed railway brakes and safety measures, a subject in which he was greatly interested. The title agreed upon was 'The Safety Break for Railway Carriages, *by the President*—and, in connection with it, the desirableness of some means of communication between the Guards and Engine Drivers'. Fortunately a record of the occasion has been preserved in the archives of the Institution, beautifully written in copper-plate script:

Fig 67. Diagram to illustrate system of railway brakes invented by George Stephenson. (Photo: Science Museum, London)

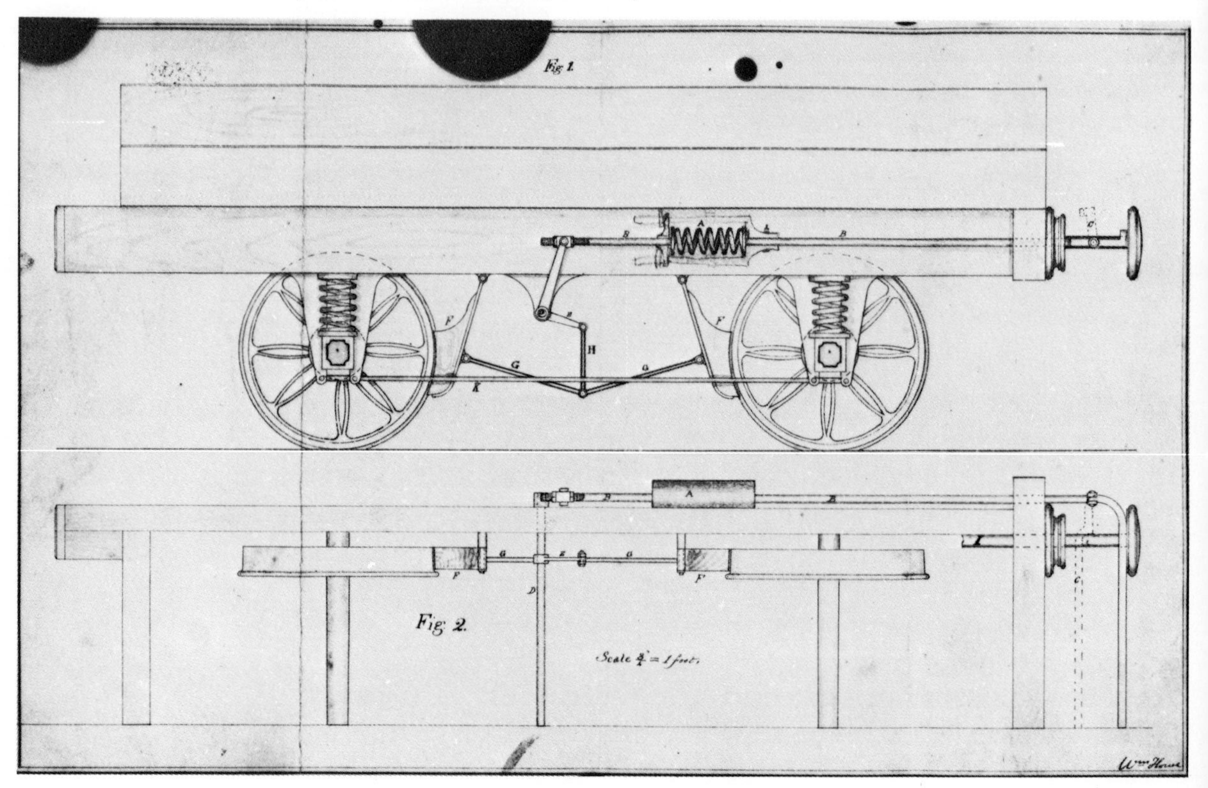

STEPHENSON'S SELF-ACTING RAILWAY BREAK

At the quarterly meeting of the Institute (sic) of Mechanical Engineers, lately held in the theatre of the Philosophical Institute, Cannon Street, Birmingham, J. G. (sic) McConnell Esq of the London and North Western Railway Company, in the Chair, the following communication was received from George Stephenson, Esq, President of the Institute, on a new selfacting break, a beautiful model of which accompanied the paper:

The various accidents on railways arising from concussions and collisions (and especially the late accident at Wolverton), have induced me to draw my attention to the construction of a self-acting break, which I have for several years had in view, a plan and model of which I have made, and now lay before the society with my description of its action and effects.

When a railway train is moving at the rate of from 40 to 60 miles an hour the momentum is so great that it cannot be stopped in any reasonable distance by the breaks at present in use, or if an axle-tree break or any accident happen to the Engine so as to prevent its progressing the sudden check causes the Carriages to overrun each other, and those next the Engine are almost certain to be crushed. In an accident of this kind neither the engine-driver, stoker or guard can be prepared, and before there is time for any of them to put on the break at present in use, so as to be in the least degree effective, the collision or concussion has taken place.

When the engine-driver shuts off the steam or applies this break on the tender, the self-acting break is immediately brought to bear upon every wheel attached to every carriage in the train so powerfully, if necessary, as to bring every wheel into the condition of a sledge. I think the train will be brought to a stand by this break in one tenth of the space in which it can be by the breaks at present used.

My plan is as follows:—I attach a couple of spiral springs to the levers of the break of every carriage, and also connect them with the buffers, and if the carriage requires gentle breaking (which will always be the case when a train approaches a station) the engine-driver, by shutting off a portion of the steam, or applying the break gently will have complete command over the train, without any of those violent uneasy motions which are very frequent and excessively disagreeable to passengers, and as the guard is frequently compelled to apply his break so powerfully as to make the wheels slide on the rails and cause a considerable amount of wear and tear on the tire of the wheel, by which it becomes flat-sided and makes the carriages uneasy and creates a jumbling motion on the rail.

Suppose a train of carriages moving at the rate of from thirty to forty miles an hour and a signal is held out for the engine driver to stop the moment he shuts off the steam the whole of the breaks are brought into instant application of sledging the wheels which will be more effectual than fifty men applying the common breaks, as the mischief is frequently done before the guard can be apprised of the approach of danger.

It is frequently necessary for the trains to be backed into a siding. When this is required the train will first have to be stopped, and in one minute the whole of the breaks can be disengaged from the buffers, as is shown in the model, and when the train proceeds they are again dropped into gear.

The plan altogether appears so simple that any ordinary mind can easily understand the whole of it; and I think the cost of putting the breaks on each carriage would not exceed more than from £5 to £10.

Any effectual plan for increasing the safety of railway travelling is, in my mind, of such vital importance, that I prefer laying my scheme open to the world, to taking out a patent for it, and it will be a source of the greatest pleasure to me to know that it has been the means of saving one human life from destruction, or that it has prevented one serious concussion.

Signed

George Stephenson

There was evidently a lively discussion, as an adjourned meeting was arranged. Stephenson's observations on communication between guards and drivers were as follows:

TO THE MEMBERS OF THE INSTITUTION OF MECHANICAL ENGINEERS

Gentlemen,

As I promised to make some observations on the practicability of effecting a mechanical communication between the Guards and Engine Drivers of Railway Trains I shall now lay before you some of the various schemes that have been submitted to me as well as what I consider the most feasible plan. You will all have observed a Paragraph going the round of the Newspapers suggesting the use of a speaking tube from every Carriage to the guard or engine-driver this scheme is almost too absurd to comment upon, I will therefore only say that it is impossible for the sound of the human voice to reach the guard so as to be intelligible, the tremulous motion of the Carriages and the atmosphere around them would effectually prevent it; but supposing this could be done, there would be always some timid person alarmed at mere trifles who would be causing stoppages and delays innumerable.

Another plan has been suggested that is, to have a looking glass on each side of the Engine, and at such an angle that the whole of the train can be seen, by the driver on one side, and the stoker on the other, so that if any of the Carriages get off the rail it may be observed. I can imagine a case where this might be of use the accident upon the Manchester & Leeds line for instance.

Numerous other plans have been suggested to me, but they are too ridiculous to be noticed: I will however mention one

The guard is to ride on the last carriage and if he saw any thing wrong in the preceding carriages he is to throw out an anchor as though he were at sea—only imagine what a smash this would make!! I might mention others that are more ridiculous still, but which were mentioned to me in confidence; and for which, I have no doubt patents will be taken out.

My own view of the subject is this—that two guards should be placed on each train, one on the carriage next the engine driver and the other on the last carriage but one facing each other and having a red flag to hold up by day; and a red lamp by night; if any thing goes wrong the signal could be immediately given, and by having a bell placed upon the engine-tender with a cord carried to the first guard he could alarm the driver by ringing the bell without taking his eye from the other guard. This plan combined with the self-acting break is, in my opinion, the simplest, and most effectual for ensuring the safety of the travelling public.

(signed) Geo Stephenson

It is extremely interesting to study the paper which follows the President's on this ancient document. It was written by Edward Ellis Allen, of 14 Argyle Street, Regent Street, London, and was presented on 27 October 1847; it described a make-and-break electrical circuit under the control of the guard, to operate the whistle on the engine. The circuit was to incorporate a battery on the engine; the principle of the scheme was that of soft iron 'becoming magnetic, whenever a current passes through it. The whistle would continue blowing until stopped by the engine-driver himself, as the electricity merely serves to set free a spring fastened to it'. The circuit was to be 'completed by insulated wires passing underneath or along the tops of the carriages'.

The next part of the proceedings is in the form of a report by Stephenson upon a new design of pressure gauge, which he introduces thus:

TO THE MEMBERS OF THE INSTITUTION OF MECHANICAL ENGINEERS

Gentlemen

I have to inform you that a most important invention Patented by a Mr Sydney Smith of Nottingham, has been submitted to me for approval: it is intended to indicate the strength of steam in steam engine boilers.

It is particularly adapted for steam boats as it can be placed on deck, in the cabin or any other part of the vessel where it may be seen by every passenger on board.

It may also be fixed in the office of every every (sic) Manufactory where a Steam engine is used, and at a considerable distance from the boilers. I am so satisfied with it as to its utility that I have had one put up at one of my own Collieries: it is in the engine house a distance from the boilers and works beautifully shewing the rise and fall of the steam in the most delicate manner. It is quite from under the control of the engineer or any other person, so that its indications may be strictly relied upon; and the construction is so simple that it is scarcely possible for it to get out of order. The indicator is like the face of a clock with a pointer making one revolution in measuring from 1 lb. to 100 lbs upon the square inch of the pressure of steam in the boiler. The pointer is worked from a piston rod with a small flexible band of whalebone which works upon the same principle as a rack but much more smoothly: the bottom end of the piston rods rests upon an india rubber cap in a small cylinder; to this is attached a small pipe, say $\frac{1}{2}$ inch in diameter which descends 16 or 18 inches, it then turns up the same length, and is carried forward to form a connection with the steam pipe or boiler. The bent part of the pipe is filled with cold water, the steam coming from the boiler acts upon the surface of the cold water on the top of the descending tube, which acts upon the elastic india-rubber on which the piston rod rests; and as I have before stated puts the piston rod in motion to work the balance weight which is connected with it; and works upon the same principle as a very delicate scale beam.

I think it is our duty to examine this machine minutely and give our opinion as to its utility to the public. As I before stated (and I think you will agree with me) I think it was most adapted to steam boat boilers when it is applied for this purpose it must be suspended so as to accommodate itself to the undulations of the vessel—this may be easily effected by having a small india-rubber tube connected with the cold water pipe.

(Signed)
Geo. Stephenson

Read on
27th Octr 1847

The distressing number of boiler explosions in the first half of the nineteenth century must have been in Stephenson's mind when he gave the foregoing comments on the new pressure-gauge; and it must have been most gratifying to the man who devised it to learn of the high praise it received from the President of the Institution. Safety on railways was an extremely live and sensitive subject at the time; the President was therefore 'right on the ball' with his suggestion of this topic. Railway brakes had been exercising his mind for some years; as early as 1841 he had written to Henry Labouchere, President of the Board of Trade, on that and on associated matters of public safety. The credit which he arrogated to himself in the first paragraph of the letter (p. 245) would appear unseemly today; but doubtless Stephenson believed it, and it is true that if he had not made his tremendous stand for the steam locomotive in the period 1825–30, the development of railways could have been held up for a generation. There is another point of interest in the letter: Stephenson's mind was evidently considering the usefulness to the nation of an organized consortium of engineers, to be called together when appropriate, so that inventions and improvements would not be submitted to the Board of Trade in a half-baked state, but only after a representative body of engineers had duly weighed up their merits. When the Institution was formed, he clearly wished this to be one of its functions. The letter is addressed thus:

To the:
Right Honble. H. Labouchere,
President of the Board of Trade.
Sir,

Since my examination before the select committee on Railways I see the difficulties you have to contend with from the opposing members to your Bill in bringing forward a measure for the management and better regulation of Railways. I am quite sure that some interference on the part of Government is much wanted. Perhaps I ought to be the last man to admit this (the whole system of Railways, and Locomotive Engines having been brought out by my exertions) but when I see so many young engineers, and such a variety of notions, I am convinced that some system should be laid down, to prevent wild, and visionary schemes, being tried, at the great danger of injury or loss of life to the public. I consider it right that every talented man should be at liberty to make improvements, but that the supposed improvements should be duly considered by proper judges. Then the question follows, from the opponents to the Bill, who are those judges to be? I beg to lay before you my views on this point.

Suppose any engineer has any improved plan for the better working of Railways to propose, he should submit his plan to the Engineer belonging to the Board of Trade, but before that Engineer should give his decision as to the utility of the scheme, he should have full power to call together the chief Engineers of the principal Railways of the Kingdom, and after the subject has been fully discussed, votes should be taken for and against the measure: the discussion should be laid before the Board of Trade, accompanied with the observations of the government Engineer, and if approved of should then be placed into his hands to carry out.

I should propose for the consideration of the different Engineers that the speed of Locomotives should not exceed forty miles per hour on the most favourable Lines, excepting on special occasions: curved Lines to diminish in velocity according to the radius. I am quite aware that this cannot be carried out to any great nicety, but still it would be a check upon the Drivers. Collateral Lines require government consideration is a very strong point of view.

Uniformity of signals is another desirable point.

As several persons are now turning their attention to self-acting breaks, it will soon appear that great benefit and safety to travelling will be found by their adoption. In the meantime no train should be allowed to travel which has not two breaksmen, and four coaches in each train should be provided with breaks to allow for contingencies. It is my opinion that no contrivance can be found out by which the breaks can be dispensed with.

Six-wheeled Engines and carriages are much safer and more comfortable to the travellers than four; any person riding one hundred yards upon an engine or coach constructed upon this plan would discover the difference. The rim of all Railway wheels ought to be made the same width, and the axle trees of all coaches of a strength approved of by the Engineers, both wheels, springs, and axles should bear the government stamp, to be made of the best materials, as every practicable means ought to be made use of in order to have these made of the best iron.

All disputes between Railway Companies should be decided by the Board of Trade.

It appears to me that the above suggestions might be carried out with success, without interfering injuriously with Railway property. I hope that you will consider that I am [?not] intruding by sending you these observations.

I am, Sir,
Your Most Obt. Servant,
Geo Stephenson

Tapton House,
Nr. Chesterfield,
March 31st, 1841.

Bearing in mind Stephenson's own estimation of his part in the development of railways, expressed so weightily in the foregoing letter, one can imagine the feeling of disgust which must have assailed him after reading, in the *Stockton and Darlington Times*, of 8 April 1848, a sickeningly fulsome letter by 'Nemo' which the paper saw fit to publish. 'Nemo's' letter is too long to publish here; moreover one cannot escape a feeling of revulsion at its nauseating style, but from the viewpoint of Stephenson, its reference to Edward Pease as

> . . . the man who first conceived the idea, and so successfully carried out the completion of the first railway for the conveyance of goods and passengers. That man is Edward Pease, Esq., and that Railway is the Stockton and Darlington Railway . . .

was outrageous to Stephenson who, unlike his son Robert, certainly did not believe in hiding his own light under a bushel; he wrote in a fury to Michael Longridge to enlist his support in putting the record right, at the same time enclosing the offending newspaper-cutting.

Tapton House
April 20th 1848

My Dear Sir,

I am going to give you a little work to do if you like to, but if you don't then send back the enclosed observations.

I am disgusted with a letter which has been published in the Stockton & Darlington Times of April 8th which I enclose you.

You are the only man living except myself who knows the origin of Locomotive engines on the Stockton & Darlington Railway. I shall be obliged if you will take the matter up and shew that Edward Pease is not the man of Science who has done so much for the country.

I am My Dear Sir
Yours faithfully
Geo. Stephenson

To revert to the Institution of Mechanical Engineers, as being undoubtedly Stephenson's *magnum opus* for the benefit of his professional colleagues and for the interests of the future education of mechanical engineers, it was envisaged by him as a kind of higher development of the Mechanics' Institutes in which he had taken much interest, and it was from the start regarded as being of national, instead of local, importance. A month after the inaugural meeting of the Institution, Stephenson wrote to Mr. J. T. W. Bell, from Tapton House:

Dear Sir,

I have received yours of the 23rd inst. In reply to it I have to state that I have no flourishes to my name, either before it or after, and I think it will be as well if you merely say Geo. Stephenson. It is true that I am a Belgian Knight, but I do not wish to have any use made of it.

I have had the honour of Knighthood of my own country made (? offered) to me several times, but would not have it; I have been invited to become a Fellow of the Royal Society; and also of the Civil Engineers Society, but I objected to these empty additions to my name. I have however now consented to become President to I believe a highly respectable mechanics' Institute at Birmingham.

I am, Dear Sir,
Yours very truly,
Geo. Stephenson

Speculation as to Stephenson's precise meaning in this letter has gone on for years, and no doubt will continue. The Institution of Civil Engineers, in their document *A Study of an Alleged Slight*, observe:

To many people's minds there will be as little doubt that Stephenson was referring to the Institution of Civil Engineers as that he was referring to the Institution of Mechanical Engineers.

However, it does seem clear that Stephenson did not wish to accept an honour from any authority or organization unless he was particularly involved in it. There is no reason to suppose that it was 'daggers drawn' between the older Institution and the new one; indeed, at the dinner held on the evening after the original committee was appointed, 'The Institution of Civil Engineers' was one of eleven toasts drunk; other toasts included George Stephenson, referred to as 'the Father of Railways', and *Mr* Robert Stephenson 'the worthy son of a worthy sire'. The omission of 'Mr' before Stephenson's name is perhaps an indication of how universally he was known. The President of the 'Civils', in 1849, paid a fine tribute to Stephenson and added that 'he was well known to us all and not infrequently joined in our discussions'.

A General Meeting was held in the Theatre of the Philosophical Institution, Birmingham, on Wednesday, 26 April 1848, at 5 p.m., with Stephenson in the Chair. He

congratulated the members on the prosperous state of the Institution, and expressed the pleasure he felt in meeting so many of the eminent mechanical engineers of England. He would come amongst them as often as he possibly could, for it gave him sincere pleasure to do so.

This was evidently a highly successful meeting. The following papers were presented for discussion:

'On Boring and Fitting up Cylinders for Locomotive Engines', by Mr. Charles F. Beyer.

'On the Formation of the Teeth of the Drivers of Pin Wheels', by Mr. F. Bashforth.

'On a Boiler and Condenser suitable for extending the Cornish Economy, and for preventing Boiler Explosions', by Mr. T. Craddock. (A small working model was placed before the members.)

'On a Hydraulic Starting Apparatus', by Mr. P. R. Jackson.

'On Chesshire's Safety Buffer', by Mr. E. Chesshire.

In connection with the last papers,

a series of experiments were made on a model railway erected at the back of the theatre. A train of carriages with the safety buffers was started from one end of the line, and another without them was set in motion from the opposite end. A collision took place in the centre of the line, and the carriages to which the safety rods were fixed remained upon the rails, with the exception of the luggage van behind, while those without the rods were scattered about in all directions. The shock was received by the van which . . . was intended to be loaded with heavy luggage.

At this point Stephenson remarked:

I think one of the points must be to take the mass and the momentum, to see what the velocity is. It will surprise some of you who have not paid attention to these matters, to know, that supposing a train starts with sixty waggons, the last waggon receives the greatest shock upon starting. The question is, therefore, whether, without these safety buffers, the last carriage does not get the shock.

The momentum, or force, has to be stopped somewhere and can't be got rid of.

Fig 68. Member's card issued by The Institution of Mechanical Engineers to Edward Fletcher (Locomotive Superintendent, North Eastern Railway, 1854–1883). (Photo: British Railways Archives, York)

A very animated discussion followed. After the reading of a statement on 'Banks's Patent Steel Tyres' for railway wheels, which was briefly discussed, the President closed the meeting, expressing himself well pleased with that evening's discussions; he hoped the next meeting would prove as interesting. He also promised to present a paper 'on the Fallacies of the Rotary Engine', a type of engine which, he said,

> never had been, and never could be, used with advantage, 'and his paper would shew the reason. It had been tried in Birmingham, and, of course, without success. Mechanics ought to know the reason of that. Very erroneous notions existed on the subject of the 'crank'. The crank, he considered, was the most beautiful and efficient motion, and the idea that power was lost by it was a great mistake. It was in vain to attempt to evade the great law of mechanics,—a pound for a pound, a pound of weight for a pound of power,—and no person who knew the law would think of opposing it. At the next meeting he would endeavour to explain the crank to the members, and to make them understand it, although many members of the Institution no doubt understood it well.

The closing time of the meeting was not stated but it must have been a marathon session, and exhausting for Stephenson. The members asked that the next meeting might start an hour earlier. The intention was to take Stephenson's paper at the next meeting, on 13 June 1848, but he was unavoidably absent, so Mr. McConnell read a paper on the balancing of wheels instead; two other subjects were also discussed. Stephenson presented his paper at a meeting held at the same venue in Birmingham on Wednesday, 26 July 1848. It was his last appearance before the members. Earlier in the day a Council Meeting had been held in the

Institution offices in Birmingham; Stephenson was present. But comparatively little formal business was transacted.

The rotary engine which was discussed had been developed by a Mr. Onion, who was present at the meeting and who had made a model of it, which was on view. The President's short dissertation was based entirely on an explanation of a diagram, and it is impossible to follow his paper without it; unfortunately, the diagram presented by Stephenson only refers to the relationship of a piston and a crank throughout a revolution and includes nothing on the basic components of the rotary engine, so the reader is at a great disadvantage. Mr. Onion was under heavy fire in the ensuing discussion, which did, however, reveal that a number of rotary engines had been made, including one installed at Derby station, by permission of the Midland Railway's Locomotive Superintendent, Mr. Matthew Kirtley; this engine was reported as having been at work 'for some weeks', and 'during that trial, experiments with his (Mr. Onion's) and another engine had proved that his effected a material saving in fuel'.

Mr. Kirtley was stated to have authenticated the test results by issuing Mr. Onion with a certificate on the fuel saving effected by the rotary engine. The rotary engine devised by Lord Dundonald was said to have been working in Portsmouth Dockyard for the last seven years. The general upshot of the discussion was that rotary engines could be made to work, but were an almighty nuisance to keep steam-tight. Apparently a locomotive had been fitted with such an engine; it was painted black and commonly known as the 'Jim Crow Engine'. The members mostly seemed to be sceptical about rotary engines; they may well have been swayed by Stephenson's weighty condemnations of them; the discussion was inconclusive, and Stephenson called on the author of the next paper to hold forth 'On a Machine for Preparing Bone Manure, &C.'.

The President's last recorded remark to the assembled members was that several meetings of the Committee of Council, appointed to alter and amend the Rules and Bye-laws, had been held; and that the result of their labours would, in a short time, be submitted to the members for their approval. Stephenson's own paper is appended:

ON THE FALLACIES OF THE ROTARY ENGINE

As all levers give out their powers at right angles to their fulcrums, it will be seen that the right angle line I, (referring to the accompanying diagram) from the connecting rod to the centre of the beam, will be the true measure of the length of the beam, when the crank is at half stroke; therefore, $\frac{1}{20}$ of half the length of the beam will be gained by the piston end of the beam. The crank being 3 feet long, the up and down stroke of the piston will be 12 feet; the crank pin will, of course, have passed through a space of nearly 19 feet.

Now, a weight hanging upon the drum, which is nearly 4 feet in diameter,

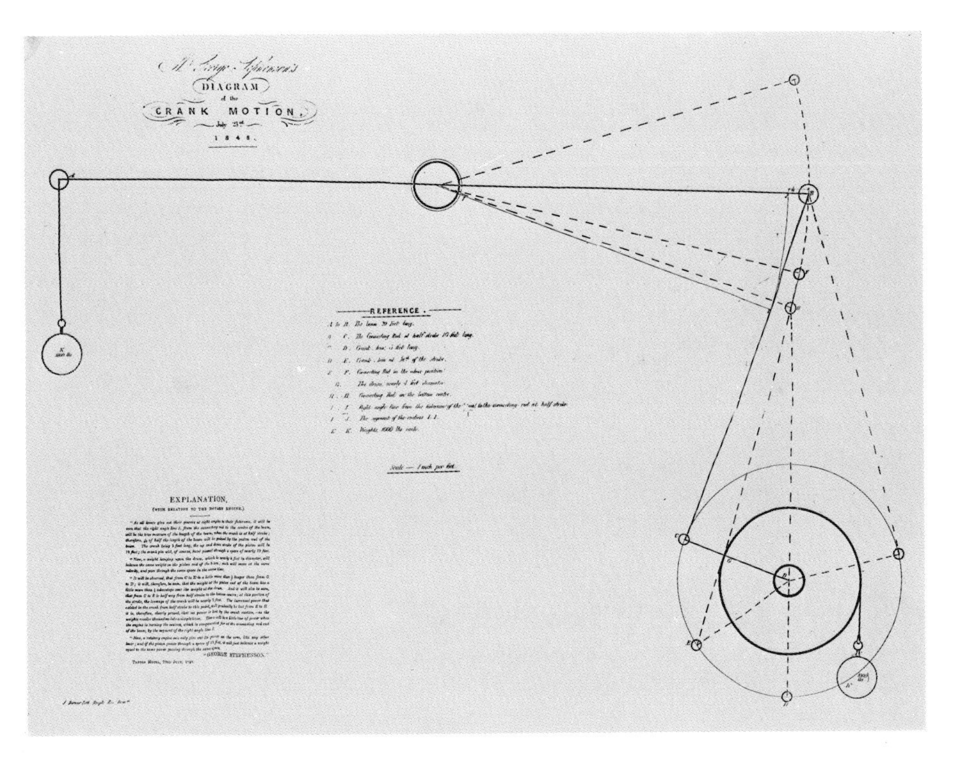

Fig 69. Diagram (reduced to small size) illustrating paper by George Stephenson on 'Fallocies of the Rotary Engine'.

will balance the same weight upon the piston end of the beam; each will move at the same velocity, and pass through the same space in the same time.

It will be observed, that from C to D is a little more than $\frac{1}{3}$ longer than from G to D; it will, therefore, be seen, that the weight at the piston end of the beam has a little more than $\frac{1}{3}$ advantage over the weight at the drum. And it will also be seen, that from C to E is half way from half stroke to the bottom centre; at this portion of the stroke, the leverage of the crank will be nearly 2 feet. The increased power that existed in the crank from half stroke to this point, will gradually be lost from E to H: it is, therefore, clearly proved, that no power is lost by the crank motion,—as the weights resolve themselves into a simple lever. There will be a little loss of power when the engine is turning the centres, which is compensated for at the connecting rod end of the beam, by the segment of the right angle line I.

Now, a rotary engine can only give out its power on the arm, like any other lever; and if the piston passes through a space of 19 feet, it will just balance a weight equal to the same power passing through the same space.

GEORGE STEPHENSON

Tapton House, 23rd July, 1848

About a week after this historic meeting of the Institution, Stephenson fell ill; a serious attack of pleurisy developed, and it was soon realized that his condition was critical. He made a last valiant attempt to rally his strength on 11 August, but in spite of devoted attentions by his wife and the care of Dr. Condell, of Baslow, he died on the following day, in his sixty-eighth year. He was interred with full Masonic honours, on 17 August in Holy Trinity Church, Chesterfield, where his resting-place is marked by a plain stone slab bearing only his initials and the year of his death. It forms part of the floor under the Holy Table at the East end of the church, so is not normally on view to visitors. However, a memorial tablet, which was placed on the south wall of the chancel after his second wife's death, now had his own name added. Later, Robert gave a large memorial window, which replaced the original plain glass at the East end of the church.

With the approach of the year 1938, which would be the centenary of Holy Trinity Church, a move was made to raise funds for the building of a George Stephenson Chancel in the church. To promote interest in this proposal, and to remind members of the Institution of their indebtedness to their greatest President, Mr. W. R. Parsonage, then Principal of Chesterfield Technical College, contributed to the Proceedings the excellent *Short Biography of George Stephenson* which was published in vol. 136, from which several passages have been quoted in the present work. This praiseworthy project never reached completion; it deserved to be launched on a wider basis, but the Second World War killed any chance of success, and apart from the stained-glass window, the memorial tablet, and the stone slab (invisible to visitors) the chancel remained as it was. However, in 1948, the town of Chesterfield made amends by special commemorative events during the centenary year of Stephenson's death, and an additional memorial slab was inserted in the floor of the church where it could be seen, in memory of the Institution's First President.

A Civic Commemoration Service was held in Holy Trinity Church at 3 p.m. on Sunday, 15 August 1948, conducted by the Rector (the Rev. E. Garston Smith) and the Archdeacon and Vicar of Chesterfield (the Ven. T. Dilworth Harrison). Because of the size of the attendance, arrangements were made for the service to be relayed to the church grounds. The following Prayer of Commemoration was written for the occasion:

Almighty God, our Heavenly Father, from whom cometh every good and perfect gift, we give thee hearty thanks for the life of George Stephenson, and for the benefits which his labour and skill have conferred upon mankind. We humbly beseech thee, so to give us grace, that with a like perseverence in the face of difficulties, and putting aside all selfish and unworthy aims, we may serve thee faithfully in our generation, and finally by thy mercy obtain everlasting life, through Jesus Christ our Lord.

Amen.

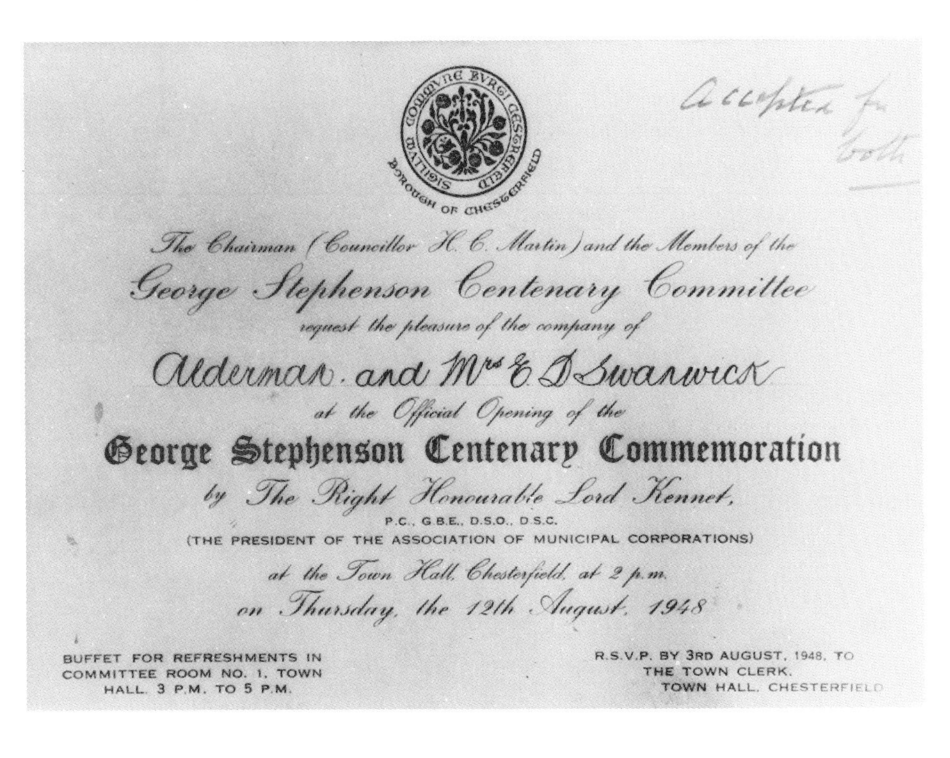

BOROUGH OF CHESTERFIELD

Accepted for both

The Chairman (Councillor H. C. Martin) and the Members of the
George Stephenson Centenary Committee
request the pleasure of the company of
Alderman and Mrs E. D. Swanwick
at the Official Opening of the
George Stephenson Centenary Commemoration
by The Right Honourable Lord Kennet,
P.C., G.B.E., D.S.O., D.S.C.
(THE PRESIDENT OF THE ASSOCIATION OF MUNICIPAL CORPORATIONS)
at the Town Hall, Chesterfield, at 2 p.m.
on Thursday, the 12th August, 1948

BUFFET FOR REFRESHMENTS IN COMMITTEE ROOM NO. 1, TOWN HALL, 3 P.M. TO 5 P.M.

R.S.V.P. BY 3RD AUGUST, 1948, TO THE TOWN CLERK, TOWN HALL, CHESTERFIELD

Fig 70. Card of admission to George Stephenson Centenary Commemoration, Chesterfield, 1948. (Courtesy: M. R. E. Swanwick)

The death of Stephenson was an occasion for genuine sorrow throughout the whole country. Family, friends—including Edward Pease, then in his 81st year—old workmates and employees made their various ways to Chesterfield to pay their last respects, in company with many people from the great world of railways which he had so wonderfully nursed through its uncertain early days into a vigorous, flourishing maturity.

Tributes innumerable, expressed at gatherings or printed in the press, poured in, to honour Stephenson's name and his unparalleled achievements. They have continued to be made over the intervening years, down to the present day. Even when making full allowances for the Victorian custom of *De mortuis nil nisi bonum*, and for the fashion for flowery writing, there remains, even in the mind of a late twentieth-century reader, an overwhelming impression of Stephenson's indomitable character and almost superhuman energy. There is something awe-inspiring about the man and the way he surmounted the obstacles in his path. As has happened in other great chapters of our history, the hour produced the man; Stephenson was *necessary* for railways to succeed just as they did, and just at that period. He must certainly have had an inner awareness of this, and so must his contemporaries. It is heart-warming to reflect that he lived to receive great acclaim during his lifetime; many events, in the last ten or twelve years of his life especially, show the public estimation of his work. Most satisfying of all, perhaps, is the way in which the

Fig 71. Commemorative brass plaque from Argentina expressing 'Homage to George Stephenson' at the centenary of the Stockton and Darlington Railway, 1925.

whole engineering profession gradually recognized his worth, and his place in the life of the nation.

On a more domestic level, to give just a small sample of this high regard for him, it must have been gratifying to him when, on 15 February 1848, the Council of the Institution of Mechanical Engineers resolved to convey their best thanks to Mr. Henry Dubs, of Warrington, for presenting an iron bust of the President, to the Institution. The 'Mechanicals' is now one of the great treasure-houses of Stephenson relics, which are perhaps not so well known as they deserve to be. They cover many aspects of his life, from his struggles over the safety lamp down to the granting of probate for his estate.

The universality of his interests was astonishing. He must have been one of the most stimulating of companions. It would be a great mistake to imagine that he could think of nothing but coal mines and railways, although the majority of his surviving letters may have given that impression. One of the treasures of the Institution of Civil Engineers is a scrap

Fig 72. The Presidential Chair at The Institution of Mechanical Engineers. The heads of George and Robert Stephenson are a prominent feature of the design of the chair, which was presented by Sir John A. F. Aspinall, D.Eng., M.I.Mech.E. (Past President) in 1929.

book compiled by Stephenson, containing newspaper cuttings gathered over many years; anything that caught his interest, and was worth saving, seems to have found its way into this album. The range is as wide as humanity itself.

Fig 73. George Stephenson Research Medal. (Courtesy: The Institution of Mechanical Engineers)

This scrap album was purchased by a Mr. William Home from the furniture and effects of the late Mrs. Stephenson (Ellen Gregory), of Beauchamp, Shrewsbury, on 11 June 1900. It remained in his possession for more than thirty years before it came into the possession of the Institution of Civil Engineers. A note inside the cover states that Mrs. Stephenson was a sister to Mrs. Thorp, wife of the Rev. William Thorp, then Minister of Swan Hill Independent Church, Shrewsbury (Ellen Stephenson went to live in Shrewsbury after her husband's death).

Here is a sample of the subjects of the entries, taken at random: W. Hawkes's Newly Invented Portable Cockle for Hot-air Beds (a portable stove for conveying hot air into beds). Royal Personages. Military News. Swindling. Note on Liverpool and Manchester Railway Shares. Ponies. Fogs. Thames Tunnel. Painters and Paintings. Witchcraft. Purity of Flour. Divorce in France. London University. Hoar Frost. Sir Walter Scott. American Tariff. Stockport Fancy Dress Ball. Turkish System of Warfare. Irish Poor Laws. Wings of Insects. Commemoration of Shakespeare. Explosion on a Steam Packet. Interesting Anecdote of a Cat. Piracy. Brazilian Diamonds. Advice to Young Ladies. The Jewish New Year. Statue of Peter the Great. Curious Musical Instrument. Temperance in America. Daring Burglary. Windsor Castle. The Bible Society. The Game of Chess. Goat's Milk at Lisbon. Paganini's Departure from Dublin. Gretna Green Marriages. Instinct of the Horse. Qualifications for the Greek Priesthood. Duels of Bees. Method of Warming Cottages. Opening a Mummy. A Volcanic Island. Anecdotes of Bruce. City Birds. Mr. Abernethy. Yorkshire Musical Festival. Life of Lord Byron. Importance of Heraldry.

The variety is amazing; it would be difficult to tell, from the subjects covered by these extracts, what did *not* interest Stephenson, at least as matters for thought, discussion, and philosophizing. W. R. Parsonage, in his *Short Biography of George Stephenson*, relates how the great American writer, Emerson, met him in Chesterfield early in 1848, at Whittington House, the home of Frederick Swanwick. Emerson remarked later that 'it was worth while crossing the Atlantic were it only to have seen Stephenson—he had such force of character and vigour of intellect'. 'He seems to have the life of many men in him.' And this impression was not long before the end. To have encountered the towering personality of Stephenson in his prime must have been an enduring experience.

Parsonage, in his admirable *Short Biography*, has reminded us of the

Fig 74. Member's badge, The Institution of Locomotive Engineers, Jubilee Year, 1961.

remarkable number of ways in which Stephenson's name lives on in his great Institution of Mechanical Engineers; on official occasions the members wear a badge on which is embossed Stephenson's head; it appears, too, on the President's Chair in the Meeting Hall; the building contains the large bronze plaque given by Argentinian railwaymen, embodying Stephenson's head and bearing the words 'To the Honour and Everlasting Memory of George Stephenson'. There is, too, the George Stephenson Research Fund and Prizes. There is a plaque on the staircase, a replica of that which graces the outside wall of Stephenson's home at Wylam. There is the George Stephenson Room, with its souvenirs and relics of Stephenson; and there are several paintings, busts, and engravings of him. The book-plate used in the Library incorporates his likeness. The Railway Division (now incorporating the former Institution of Locomotive Engineers) has on the distinctive tie for its members a side view of the 'Rocket'.

Readers who may care to trace the history of the Institution will find three volumes of Proceedings which are of particular interest (in addition, of course, to the comprehensive *Centenary History* published in 1947). These are: 1847–9, one small volume containing the records of the earliest meetings, including Stephenson's participation in discussions; 1897, parts 3 and 4, describing the Jubilee meeting, held appropriately in Birmingham, the Institution's birthplace, and including a précis of its early history and subsequent growth, by E. Windsor Richards, the then President; and 1899, parts 1 and 2, which contain a review of the origins of the Institution and trace the steps leading to its move to Westminster, first to Victoria Street, and later to the building it now occupies.

The 1847–9 volume contains the magnificent Stephenson memorial oration by Mr. J. Scott Russell, which is so important that Parsonage appended lengthy extracts from it to his *Short Biography*; the gem of the 1897 volume is the speech (p. 276) made by Mr. Richard Williams, last survivor of the members elected in 1847, with personal recollections of the Stephensons; and the 1899 Proceedings gives many names of engineers supporting the foundation and early running of the Institution. Even then, more than 70 years ago, this anonymous but very useful survey states (p. 255), concerning the genesis of the Institution, 'No one is now living who can state with certainty the precise way in which it originated.' This, in the absence of any discoveries of old documents, would seem to put to silence later speculations on the subject.

Fig 75. The Institution of Mechanical Engineers' Library book-plate, designed by J. R. G. Exley.

Behind all these delvings into the past and the endeavours to sketch their background, the massive genius of Stephenson still occupies a dominant place. Probably it always will. Biographers have surpassed one another in their praises of Stephenson's achievements; one could fill pages

Fig 76. Large memorial plaque from Argentina to commemorate the centenary of the opening of the Stockton and Darlington Railway, 27 September 1825–1925. The English inscription reads: 'Homage from railwaymen of the Argentine Republic to whose great locomotive invention has so largely contributed to the progress of the country'.

with their tributes, and the temptation to do so is hard to resist. But two very brief ones which particularly impressed the author were, first, one by R. H. Parsons in his *Centenary History*: 'Among the first officers of the Institution, Stephenson has so long become a part of English history that any reference to his achievements would be superfluous'; and second, L.T.C. Rolt's tremendous assertion in the first sentence of the Preface to his book on George and Robert Stephenson: 'George Stephenson is the most famous engineer who ever lived'. As a most able biographer of the

Fig 77. George Stephenson's likeness on a commemorative envelope issued for the Diamond Jubilee of the Stephenson Locomotive Society (in author's possession).

Stephensons, and as a Vice President of the Newcomen Society, which makes the study of engineering history its prime activity and is linked with the 'Mechanicals' in the publication of the present volume, he is in a position to know.

APPENDIX 1

Conditions for the Rainhill Trials

The engine must effectually consume its own smoke. If of six tons weight, it must be able to draw, day by day, twenty tons weight (including the tender and water tank) at ten miles an hour, with a pressure of steam on the boiler not exceeding fifty pounds to the square inch. The boiler must have two safety-valves, neither of which must be fastened down, and one of them be completely out of the control of the engineman. The engine and boiler must be supported on springs, and rest on six wheels; the height of the whole not exceeding fifteen feet to the top of the chimney. The engine, with water, must not weigh more than six tons; but one of less weight would be preferred, on its drawing a proportionate load behind it; if only four-and-a-half tons, then it might be put on only four wheels. The company to be at liberty to test the boiler, etc., by a pressure of one hundred and fifty pounds to the square inch. A mercurial gauge must be affixed to the machine, showing the steam pressure above forty-five pounds per square inch. The engine must be delivered, complete, and ready for trial, at the Liverpool end of the railway, not later than the 1st of October 1829. The price of the engine must not exceed £550.

APPENDIX 2

New, Previously Undiscovered Letter

(PRIVATE) Newcastle December 12th 1824

Dear Sir,

I have just received a letter from Mr. Hartley, complaining of my neglect in not returning thanks for the use of his level; and also of its being injured by me. I am sure Mr. Hartley would excuse me if he had only known the many things I had on my mind and the great bustle I was in to get off to Newcastle. If any part of the level is injured, let him get it repaired to his own wish and I will pay the expense. A pair of legs belonging to his old level it appears have not been returned. I think Oliver has them. Will you be so good as (to) enquire of him for them and send them to Mr. Hartley, with my thanks for the use of them and the others, and I am sorry I have given him any reason for complaint.

I hope you will not keep Oliver and Blackett longer than is actually necessary.

After leaving Liverpool and on my way to Bolton, and whilst at Bolton I collected a great deal of useful information respecting the coal field in that neighbourhood, viz. St Helens and Bolton. It is my opinion that coal will be found under Chat Moss. I think there will be none under Kirkby Moss; but immediately on the southeast point of Mossbro Road from when the Railroad crosses I think it will be found: and I believe the coalfield will pass up even under Knowsley Hall and continue through the whole of that high country by Prescott. But I should not advise any purchase to be made of coal fields until a closer investigation is made, even though you were certain of the Act passing.

I have just learned that a Mr. Straker from this neighbourhood has been called up to Liverpool, to give his opinion on Railroads. It struck me it could be no other but yourself and if so, he must be sent for by Mr. Ewart and the founders in this county. I will not state my opinion of Mr. Straker's principle as I will leave that to your own enquiring when you come to the north.

The few days I was engaged for Lord Carlisle at Brampton (on my way home) I had an opportunity of examining a Railway of both *cast* and *wrought* iron, some of the latter had been laid 16 years, and apparently very little worse although much too narrow in its bearance and laid on a bad principle. The cast iron had been down about 12 or 14 years and was considerably more worn than the wrought besides perhaps there is not half of it now in use, from the continual breakage to which it has been subject. Lord Carlisle's Agent's remarks on this Railway will appear in the Newcastle Courant of next week.

I have just learned that a project of a Railway is going on from Manchester to London by a London Company. I think this rage for Railroads is so great that many will be laid in parts where they will not pay.

I am, Dear Sir,
Yours very sincerely,
Geo. Stephenson

Index

List of Authorities Consulted

ABRONS, E L *The British Steam Railway Locomotive 1825–1925*; The Locomotive Publishing Co.; London. 1927.

ANON *Northumberland Railways from 1700*; North Gosforth: Northumberland County Council Record Office. 1969.

BREES, S C *Railway Practice*; London: John Williams and Co.; 1847.

BUCKNALL, RIXON *Our Railway History*; 3rd ed. London: George Allen and Unwin; 1971.

CLARK, D K *Railway Machinery, vols I and II*; London and Edinburgh: Blackie and Son; 1855.

ELLIS, C HAMILTON *British Railway History*; *1830–1876*; 3rd imp. London: George Allen and Unwin; 1960.

INSTITUTION OF CIVIL ENGINEERS *A study of an Alleged Slight*; London: The Institution of Civil Engineers; 1957.

INSTITUTION OF MECHANICAL ENGINEERS *Proceedings*; especially 1847–49; 1890; 1897; 1899 and 1937.

LEE, CHARLES E *Tyneside Tramroads at Northumberland*; Trans. Newcomen Society 1948–49, vol. XXVI, p. 199.

The Evolution of Railways; 2nd ed. London: The Railway Gazette; 1943.

The Steam Locomotive in 1852; London: The Railway Magazine.

MARSHALL, C F DENBY *Centenary History of the Liverpool and Manchester Railway*; London: The Locomotive Publishing Co.; 1930.

Early British Locomotives; London: The Locomotive Publishing Co.; 1939.

Acknowledgment is also made to E L Abrons' *The British Steam Locomotive 1825–1928* (The Locomotive Publishing Co. Ltd); to C F Deny Marshall's *Centenary History of the Liverpool and Manchester Railway* (The Locomotive Publishing Co. Ltd); and to J G H Warren's *A Century of Locomotive Building* by Robert Stephenson and Co. 1823–1923 (Newcastle upon Tyne: Andrew Reid and Co. Ltd). 1923.